An Organic Chemistry Monograph
Consultant Editor: M. F. Grundon, The Queen's University Belfast

RADICALS IN
ORGANIC CHEMISTRY

Oldbourne Chemistry Series

Radicals in Organic Chemistry

C. J. M. STIRLING, B.Sc., Ph.D.

The Queen's University of Belfast

This book is published and distributed
in the United States by
AMERICAN ELSEVIER PUBLISHING COMPANY, INC.
52 Vanderbilt Avenue, New York, N.Y. 10017

OLDBOURNE BOOK CO. LTD.

1–5 Portpool Lane, London, E.C.1

© *Oldbourne Book Co. Ltd.* *1965*

Printed in Great Britain
by Spottiswoode, Ballantyne & Co. Ltd.
London and Colchester

PREFACE

SIXTY years have elapsed since the discovery of radicals, and it is thirty years since the existence of reactive radicals in solution was recognized and the study of their reactions started. This branch of chemistry has expanded enormously in the intervening period, but in spite of attaining immense technical and theoretical importance, radical chemistry has often been rather sketchily treated in courses for advanced students, and many practising chemists have a poor knowledge of this field.

The aim of this book is to provide not only an introduction to the field but also to deal, even if only briefly, with some of the latest developments in it. Emphasis has been placed particularly upon radical behaviour, and the material is arranged, broadly speaking, according to reaction types. Inevitably, much important work on radicals has had to be left out. Gas-phase reactions are hardly mentioned and the chapter on polymerization is only a very superficial treatment of this important area. It is hoped that the many references given for further reading may go some way towards making good the deficiencies that a volume of this size imposes. Problems have been included at the end of Chapters 2 to 10. These have deliberately been made fairly difficult but 'answers' may be found by a sufficiently diligent search of the literature.

The author has drawn heavily from Professor Cheves Walling's book, *Free Radicals in Solution* (Wiley, 1957) which is an invaluable source of information and enlightenment. In addition he acknowledges his indebtedness to Professor J. I. G. Cadogan who read the entire MS., to Dr. R. G. R. Bacon who read Chapter 7, to Dr. B. D. Flockhart who gave valuable advice on the sections dealing with ESR spectroscopy, and to Dr. M. F. Grundon whose many editorial comments and suggestions have greatly improved the original version. Finally, he thanks his wife who has helped so constantly and made this task, like so many others we have shared, a pleasurable one.

Belfast, January 1965.   C. J. M. STIRLING.

CONTENTS

Chapter 1

INTRODUCTION: FORMATION, DETECTION, AND REACTION TYPES

Throughout this book the term 'radical' will be taken to refer to an atom or molecule which contains one or more *unpaired* electrons, and this definition will exclude atoms, e.g. of transition metals, which have an unpaired electron in an inner shell. We shall be chiefly concerned with reactions of these species in solution and only passing reference will be made to the important information about radicals that has been collected from studies of their reactions in the gas phase.

There were a number of false alarms before the discovery of the first authentic radical. Frankland in 1849, for example, had claimed the isolation of ethyl which later turned out to be butane. In 1900 Gomberg, who was investigating the synthesis of polyarylalkanes reported that hexaphenylethane, a colourless solid, gave *coloured* solutions which on treatment with a variety of reagents gave *triphenylmethyl* derivatives. Gomberg postulated dissociation into triphenylmethyl radicals (containing *tri*valent carbon) and although this was a shock to the pundits who had been reared on Kekulé's doctrine of the constant quadrivalency of carbon, his conclusions were amply justified by subsequent work. Triphenylmethyl and certain related radicals differ from most others in being remarkably 'long-lived' in solutions at ordinary temperatures and for this reason are dealt with separately in the following Chapter.

The next important discovery was that by Paneth and Hofeditz (1929), who demonstrated the existence of reactive alkyl radicals in the gas phase. When a tube, along which was passed a steam of lead tetramethyl in an inert carrier gas, was heated at point (*a*) (Fig. 1.1), a film of lead was deposited. When the tube was subsequently heated a short distance upstream, point (*b*), a second film was deposited and that at (*a*) *was removed*. Clearly some highly reactive species, capable of reacting with a free metal, was being produced in the thermal decomposition of the lead alkyl, and the product of the reaction, collected in the cold trap at (*c*), was found to be lead tetramethyl.

Paneth and Hofeditz suggested that the reactive species produced were methyl radicals, and by varying the distance *a–b*, deduced their mean lifetime to be 10^{-3} sec at 2 mm.

Substantial evidence for the formation of reactive ('short-life') radicals in solution was obtained by Hey (1934), who found that a number of reactions, such as the Gomberg reaction of diazonium salts, used for aromatic phenylation, always gave some *p*-isomer irrespective of whether the substituent group present was *o*-,/*p*- or *m*-directing in electrophilic substitution. Evidently the reactive species were insensitive to the electronic effects which dominated heterolytic aromatic substitution and it was suggested that these were *phenyl radicals*. Later confirmation of these conclusions was provided by Waters, who showed that species from diazonium salts were capable of attacking metals suspended in solution, recalling the Paneth-Hofeditz experiment.

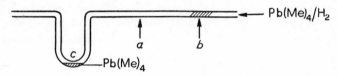

Fig. 1.1

In the same year (1934) Backström suggested a *radical chain* mechanism for the autoxidation of benzaldehyde (Chapter 5). The important feature of this mechanism was that once started, the reaction was, in principle, self-sustaining. Kharasch and Mayo (1937) suggested a similar mechanism for the hitherto puzzling 'abnormal' addition of hydrogen bromide to allyl bromide.

$$HBr + CH_2{=}CHCH_2Br$$

dark   *slow*   *fast*   light and/or presence of peroxides

$CH_3CHBrCH_2Br$ $BrCH_2CH_2CH_2Br$
'normal product'

Reaction under illumination or in the presence of peroxides was considered to involve the production of bromine atoms which initiated a chain sequence:

$$HBr \longrightarrow Br\cdot$$

$$Br\cdot + CH_2{=}CHCH_2Br \longrightarrow BrCH_2\overset{\cdot}{C}HCH_2Br$$

$$HBr + BrCH_2\overset{\cdot}{C}HCH_2Br \longrightarrow BrCH_2CH_2CH_2Br + Br\cdot$$

This is the prototype of a wide range of radical additions to unsaturated compounds (Chapter 6). At this time Flory also proposed a radical chain mechanism for the polymerization of olefins initiated by catalysts such as benzoyl peroxide. These reactions are dealt with in Chapter 7.

Since 1937 a large number of reactions have been investigated for which the most satisfactory mechanisms are those involving radical intermediates. As chemical reaction involves bond making and breaking it is appropriate to differentiate between *heterolytic* bond fission [reaction 1.1 (a) and (b)], in which unequal division of the electrons of the bond occurs, and *homolytic* fission [reaction (1.2)], in which the electrons are equally divided between the fragments produced

$$A:B \nearrow \overset{\ominus}{A:} + \overset{\oplus}{B} \qquad\qquad\qquad (a)$$
$$\text{HETEROLYSIS} \qquad \ldots(1.1)$$
$$\searrow \overset{\oplus}{A} + \overset{\ominus}{B:} \qquad\qquad\qquad (b)$$

$$A:B \longrightarrow A\cdot + B\cdot \quad \text{HOMOLYSIS} \qquad \ldots(1.2)$$

FORMATION OF RADICALS

This section will deal only with the generation of radicals from non-radical precursors; many radicals are produced from other radicals, particularly in olefin addition and in abstraction (pp. 12–13).

(a) Thermal Cleavage of Covalent Bonds. Pyrolysis of all organic compounds at temperatures above 800° yields radicals capable of removing metallic mirrors. In solution, molecules containing weak bonds with dissociation energies (p. 167) of 40 kcal/mole or less, dissociate at a useful rate at temperatures below 150°. This is a widely used method of generating radicals but the types of compound suitable are inevitably rather restricted.

Diacyl Peroxides. Thermal decomposition of diacyl peroxides (*1.1*) yields, in the first instance, acyloxy radicals (*1.2*). The most studied

$$RC\overset{O}{\underset{O-O}{\diagup}}\overset{O}{\underset{}{\diagdown}}CR \longrightarrow 2\,RC\overset{O}{\underset{O\cdot}{\diagup}}$$

$$(1.1) \qquad\qquad\qquad (1.2)$$

peroxides are benzoyl (R=Ph) and acetyl peroxide (R=Me). The energy of activation for the first-order decomposition of benzoyl peroxide is 30 kcal/mole which corresponds to the dissociation energy of the O—O bond.

Benzoyl peroxide has been widely used to provide radicals which initiate chain reactions such as polymerization, and as a source of phenyl radicals which are produced by decarboxylation of benzoyloxy radicals:

$$PhCOO\cdot \longrightarrow Ph\cdot + CO_2$$

3

Dissociation to give benzoyloxy radicals has, however, been shown to be the sole primary step in the decomposition of the peroxide; benzoyl hypoiodite (PhCOOI) is obtained quantitatively when decomposition is allowed to occur in the presence of iodine. It is characteristic of the homolytic dissociation of the peroxide that change of solvent does not change the *unimolecular* rate (but see Chapter 8) and that it is retarded by high pressures. Electron-withdrawing substituents in the aromatic nuclei lower the rate of decomposition. This suggests that dipole–dipole interaction (*1.3*) decreases the energy of activation for homolysis:

$$PhC\begin{matrix}O\\O\end{matrix} \xrightarrow{} \xleftarrow{} \begin{matrix}O\\O\end{matrix}CPh \qquad NO_2-\langle\bigcirc\rangle-COO-OCO-\langle\bigcirc\rangle-OMe$$

$$(1.3) \qquad\qquad\qquad\qquad (1.4)$$

The Hammett $\sigma\rho$ relationship (a reference is given at the end of Chapter 4) is followed with $\rho = -0.38$. The 'electronically distorted' peroxide (*1.4*) undergoes homolysis in non-polar solvents, but acid catalysed *heterolysis* in polar solvents.

Alkyl radicals are similarly produced by decarboxylation of aliphatic acyloxy radicals. Acetyl peroxide, in particular, has been widely used to generate methyl radicals, but being dangerously explosive requires careful handling.

Decomposition of peroxydicarbonates constitutes a valuable method for generating radicals at relatively low temperatures ($\sim$35°). Homolysis occurs with formation of alkoxy radicals:

$$\underset{\overset{\|}{O}}{ROC}O-O\underset{\overset{\|}{O}}{C}OR \longrightarrow RO\overset{\overset{O}{\|}}{C}O\cdot \longrightarrow CO_2 + RO\cdot$$

The isopropyl derivative (R = i-Pr) is commercially available.

Alkyl Peroxides and Hydroperoxides. The oxygen–oxygen bond strength in these compounds is near 38 kcal/mole and homolysis produces alkoxy radicals (together with hydroxyl radicals in the case of alkyl hydroperoxides). Decomposition of t-butyl peroxide is an important and typical example:

$$t\text{-}BuO\text{-}O\text{-}t\text{-}Bu \longrightarrow 2t\text{-}BuO\cdot \longrightarrow MeCOMe + Me\cdot$$

Alkoxy radicals are also unstable (Chapter 8); t-butoxy radicals, for example, give methyl radicals and acetone so that in reactions with t-butyl peroxide there is competition between the attack of butoxy radicals on the substrate and their fragmentation. Decompositions of t-alkyl peroxides are first order and rates are again insensitive to solvent changes.

Thermal scission of the oxygen–oxygen bond of hydroperoxides produces both hydroxyl and alkoxy radicals so that their reaction products are frequently complicated. They have so far been relatively little studied except in electron transfer reactions (next section and Chapter 8). Peroxyesters produce both acyloxy and alkoxy radicals:

$$ROOH \longrightarrow RO\cdot + \cdot OH$$

$$RC\!\!\begin{array}{c} {}^{\displaystyle O}\\[-2pt] \diagup\\[-6pt] \diagdown\\[-2pt] OOR' \end{array} \longrightarrow RC\!\!\begin{array}{c} {}^{\displaystyle O}\\[-2pt] \diagup\\[-6pt] \diagdown\\[-2pt] O\cdot + \cdot OR' \end{array}$$

Homolytic fission of the persulphate ion also occurs with $E_A = 33 \cdot 5$ kcal/mole and this reaction has been widely used in the initiation of vinyl polymerization in emulsion systems:

$$\overset{\ominus}{O_3}SO\!-\!O\overset{\ominus}{S}O_3 \longrightarrow 2\overset{\bullet\ominus}{S}O_4$$

Azo-compounds. Diazonium salts in neutral or alkaline aqueous solutions exist in equilibrium with the diazo-hydroxides which are probably substantially covalent. These undergo decomposition with formation of nitrogen and generation of aryl radicals:

$$Ar\!-\!\overset{\oplus}{N}\!\!\equiv\!\!N\ X^{\ominus} \xrightarrow{\ OH^{\ominus}\ } Ar\overset{\oplus}{N_2}\ \overset{\ominus}{O}H \rightleftharpoons ArN\!\!=\!\!N\!-\!OH \longrightarrow Ar\cdot + N_2 + \cdot OH$$

The high heat of formation of nitrogen doubtless favours this decomposition and related derivatives behave in a similar way:

$$Ar\!-\!N\!\!\equiv\!\!\overset{\oplus}{N}\ X^{\ominus} + Me_2NH \longrightarrow ArN\!\!=\!\!N\!-\!NMe_2 \longrightarrow Ar\cdot + N_2 + (\cdot NMe_2?)$$

$$ArN(NO)COMe \rightleftharpoons ArN\!\!=\!\!NOCOMe \longrightarrow Ar\cdot + N_2 + (\cdot OCOMe?)$$

$$ArN\!\!=\!\!N\!-\!CPh_3 \longrightarrow Ar\cdot + N_2 + \cdot CPh_3$$

$$ArNHNH_2 \xrightarrow{\ HgO\ } ArN\!\!=\!\!N\cdot \longrightarrow Ar\cdot + N_2$$

Simple azo-compounds such as azomethane, $CH_3N\!\!=\!\!NCH_3$, require high temperatures for appreciable decomposition ($E_{A \text{ dissociation}} = 50$ kcal/mole) but an important group of azo-compounds, the azonitriles, which contain α-cyano groups, decompose readily at ordinary temperatures:

$$NC\!-\!\underset{\underset{\displaystyle R'}{|}}{\overset{\overset{\displaystyle R}{|}}{C}}\!-\!N\!\!=\!\!N\!-\!\underset{\underset{\displaystyle R'}{|}}{\overset{\overset{\displaystyle R}{|}}{C}}\!-\!CN \longrightarrow N_2 + 2\cdot\underset{\underset{\displaystyle R}{|}}{\overset{\overset{\displaystyle R}{|}}{C}}\!-\!CN$$

5

The decompositions strictly obey first-order kinetics and the rates are unaffected by change in solvent. It is interesting that when the groups R and R′ are β-branched alkyl groups, the higher rates of decomposition found are put down to assistance caused by steric interaction across the N=N double bond.

(b) Photolytic Cleavage of Covalent Bonds. Absorption of electromagnetic radiation by a molecule increases its energy and if the quantum size is great enough, bond dissociation may follow. At 270 mμ, for example, the quantum size is equivalent to 100 kcal/mole, enough to break most bonds (cf. Table, p. 167) provided that the energy is not dissipated in other ways. Photolysis is often used instead of thermal dissociation for radical production from some of the sources considered in the previous section, but the following are typical instances in which photodissociation is useful:

$$Cl_2 \longrightarrow 2Cl\cdot$$
$$CH_3COCH_3 \longrightarrow CH_3CO\cdot + CH_3\cdot$$
$$CH_3HgI \longrightarrow CH_3\cdot + Hg + I\cdot$$
$$ArI \longrightarrow Ar\cdot + I\cdot$$
$$CH_2N_2 \longrightarrow CH_2: + N_2$$

A commonly used alternative to direct photolysis is to use 'photosensitizers' which readily absorb radiation and can pass on the absorbed energy so as to cause dissociation of non-absorbent molecules. Photoexcitation of olefins to diradical states is the first stage in many photosyntheses. In the technique known as 'Flash Photolysis', devised by Norrish and Porter for the study of very short lived radicals in the gas phase, the reactants are dissociated by a very powerful flash and very shortly (10^{-3} sec) afterwards the spectra of the radicals produced are recorded by absorption from a second flash.

Production of radicals by high-energy radiolysis may also be included in this section. γ-Radiation from, e.g., ^{60}Co, produces radicals from many substrates but reactions are frequently very complex. Much work has been carried out in aqueous systems (in which hydroxyl radicals are produced) because of its importance in connection with the effects of radiation on biological systems.

(c) Electron Transfer. Transfer of one electron to or from a species containing only paired electrons must result in radical formation, and cases are known in which transfer of electrons to and from both neutral molecules and ions occurs. Examples of each type are given below:

$$RCO_2^{\ominus} \xrightarrow[\text{(anode)}]{-e} RCO_2\cdot \qquad \text{(cf. Chapter 10)}$$

$$NH_2-\!\!\!\langle\rangle\!\!\!-NH_2 \xrightarrow{-e} NH_2-\!\!\!\langle\rangle\!\!\!-\overset{\cdot\oplus}{N}H_2 \qquad \text{(cf. Chapter 2)}$$

$$H_2O_2 \xrightarrow[\text{Fe}^{++}\to\text{Fe}^{+++}]{+e} \bar{O}H + \cdot OH \qquad \text{(cf. Chapter 10)}$$

$$\overset{+}{N}H_3OH \xrightarrow[\text{Ti}^{3+}\to\text{Ti}^{4+}]{+e} \cdot NH_2 + H_2O \qquad \text{(cf. Chapter 10)}$$

Metal ions are commonly used as the electron donors or acceptors and application of this method to aqueous media is particularly important as other methods are frequently unsuitable. Further examples are given in succeeding chapters.

DETECTION OF RADICALS

It must be emphasized at this point that for the overwhelming majority of the reactions described in later chapters, there is no *proof* of the formation of radical intermediates. The characteristics (p. 14) of most of these reactions strongly suggest that radicals are involved, but their direct detection by physical methods has been limited to a few instances. Direct methods of radical detection have, in the main, been applied to radicals in the 'long-life' category, the arbitrary definition of which is given at the beginning of Chapter 2.

Electron Spin Resonance. The unpaired electron of a free radical behaves like a small magnet and when subjected to an external magnetic field takes up a spin orientation parallel or anti-parallel to the applied field. Those electrons which are aligned anti-parallel to the field will have an energy $\frac{1}{2}g\beta H$ greater than the zero field value (where β is the Bohr magneton, H the field strength, and g the 'spectroscopic' splitting factor or 'g value'). Similarly, electrons aligned parallel to the field will have an energy $\frac{1}{2}g\beta H$ less than the zero field value. The 'g value' measures the contribution of spin and orbital angular momenta to the total angular momentum and has a value of 2·0023 for a free spin. The 'g values' of most radicals are close to this value because, due to delocalization of the unpaired electron, there is little coupling between spin and orbital motions.

Absorption of energy from incident radiation can cause promotion of electrons from the lower to the higher energy states which appear when a magnetic field is applied. The energy difference between the states is very small even at high values of H, and for field strengths normally used, corresponds to absorption of energy in the microwave region. Absorption of energy will occur when:

$$h\nu = g\beta H,$$

where $h\nu$ is the quantum energy of of the incident radiation. For a free electron this gives, on inserting numerical values:

$$\nu \text{ (Mc/sec)} = 2\cdot8 \times H \text{ (gauss) for a free electron.}$$

7

In practice, a field strength of about 3000 gauss is most convenient. A frequency v, of about 9000 Mc/sec ($\lambda = 3$ cm) is then needed to induce electron resonance. The sample is irradiated with 'monochromatic' microwave radiation in a strong homogeneous magnetic field whose strength can be varied slightly so as to sweep the region in which the spin-orientation energy difference is equal to that of the microwave quantum.

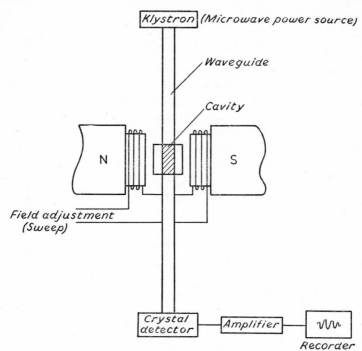

Fig. 1.2. Diagram of an ESR Spectrometer

For the simple detection of radicals, ESR measurements have two important advantages over other methods: (i) ESR absorption is an absolute property of the system depending only upon the presence of the unpaired electron and does not require the corrections that have to be applied to magnetic susceptibility measurements (below); (ii) the method is extremely sensitive. Concentrations of radicals down to about 10^{-10} M are detectable, and can be measured by comparison with standards of 'pure' radicals such as diphenylpicrylhydrazyl (below). The great sensitivity of the technique allows determination of radical lifetimes down to about 10^{-7} sec.

Refinements in technique have recently allowed the study, by ESR methods, of radicals with very short lifetimes. These involve the formation of radicals by irradiation at low temperatures in the cavity of the spectrometer, or the use of flow systems.

Hyperfine Splitting. A more significant aspect of electron spin resonance spectroscopy, however, is the information that the technique can yield about the structure of radicals. For reasons outlined above, most radicals have nearly the same g-value but in the great majority of them the absorption line is seen to be split into a number of components, an effect which is termed 'hyperfine splitting'. This arises from the fact that magnetic nuclei such as H, N, F (but not ^{12}C, ^{16}O or ^{32}S) in the orbital of the unpaired electron effectively add to or subtract from the external field

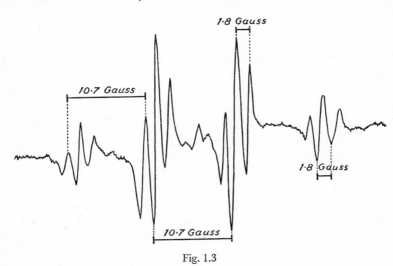

Fig. 1.3

depending upon the relative orientations of the nuclear magnetic moment to the external field. In general, for a nucleus of spin I there will be $2I+1$ possible orientations and the resonance line will be split into $2I+1$ components, with respect to this nucleus. Splitting by protons is most commonly encountered and examples in this book will be limited to proton splitting. For splitting by one proton (spin $\frac{1}{2}$), there will be $2 \cdot \frac{1}{2}+1 = 2$ components of the resonance line and for n equivalent protons, $2n \cdot \frac{1}{2}+1 = n+1$ components. The degree of splitting, or spacing between the components (see Fig. 1.3), is expressed by a 'hyperfine coupling constant' which is dependent upon the extent of interaction between the magnetic nucleus and the free electron. The size of the coupling constant in turn depends upon the situation of the magnetic nucleus and it can be seen that hyperfine splitting is thus extremely important not only for deciding radical structure but also in determining the extent of interactions of magnetic nuclei with the electronic magnetic moment of the unpaired electron.

When two sets of equivalent protons interact with the free electron, the resonance line should be split $(n + 1)$ $(n' + 1)$ times. The electron spin resonance spectrum† of the 2,6-di-t-butyl-4-methylphenoxy radical (*1.5*) in which the odd electron is delocalized (see Chapter 2) illustrates several points:

(*1.5*)

The spectrum shows twelve lines composed of a widely spaced quartet of narrowly spaced triplets; the unpaired electron interacts, therefore, with three equivalent protons and with two equivalent protons $[(2 + 1)(3 + 1) = 12]$. The stronger (quartet) splitting of 10·7 gauss is due to interaction of the odd electron with the three hydrogen nuclei of the 4-methyl group. The weaker (triplet) splitting of 1·8 gauss is due to the hydrogen nuclei attached to the *m*-carbon atoms. The simple theory of interaction actually predicts that neither nuclear nor side chain protons should interact with the free electron. The nuclear protons are situated in a plane at right angles to the π orbital in which the electron moves and the methyl protons are situated outside this orbital. Interaction with nuclear protons (a universal feature of aromatic radicals in which the free electron is delocalized in a π-orbital) can be accounted for by arguments presented elsewhere. Interaction with the methyl protons is a manifestation which has long been familiar in chemical experience, that of hyperconjugation. It is significant that the latter interaction is greater, in this instance, than the former.

Several further examples of ESR measurements are given in later chapters. A simple problem on ESR is given at the end of Chapter 2.

Magnetic Susceptibility. The presence of an unpaired electron confers a permanent magnetic moment on the molecule in which it is situated. In an unhomogeneous magnetic field, a force will act upon a sample containing radicals drawing it into the field to an extent dependent upon the magnetic susceptibility of the species present. The situation is somewhat complicated by the *dia*magnetic (out of the field) susceptibility of molecules with paired electrons. Diamagnetic susceptibility can

---

† The spectrum shown is a first derivative tracing—each crossing of the base line by a downstroke which follows an upstroke corresponds to one peak. It is reproduced by permission of Dr. G. Scott and the Faraday Society.

be calculated, so that values of paramagnetic susceptibility are obtained from the difference of observed and calculated magnetic susceptibility. Before the development of ESR methods, paramagnetic susceptibility was the most absolute and important method for the diagnosis of radicals. Estimations of the degree of dissociation of hexa-arylethanes (Table 2.1, Chapter 2) were made by this method.

(c) Spectra. The unpaired electron of a radical is usually much more susceptible to electronic excitation than one belonging to an electron-pair, whether bonded or not. On this account, the electronic spectra of radicals frequently differ strikingly from the spectra of the molecules from which they are derived. The longer wavelength absorption maxima shown by the triphenylmethyl radical (p. 18) are probably due to the greater ease of electronic excitation in the radical as a whole, as well as to the intrinsically easy excitation of the unpaired electron itself. Spectra of 'short-life' radicals have been obtained by trapping them in rigid glasses at low temperatures and in 'flash-photolysis' experiments when absorption, either from the flash producing the radicals or from a second one following after a short interval, can be detected. Spectra of benzyl and phenoxy radicals, for example, have been obtained in this way.

REACTION TYPES

Before dealing with specific radical reactions it is desirable to outline the types of reaction that radicals have been found to undergo. These are more numerous than non-radical reactions and frequently do not have heterolytic counterparts. Furthermore, a radical jargon has grown up and it as well to explain it at this stage.

(a) Combination.

$$R\cdot + R'\cdot \longrightarrow R{-}R'$$

e.g. $Ph_3C\cdot + PhCH_2\cdot \longrightarrow Ph_3CCH_2Ph$

This reaction is frequently referred to as 'dimerization', but this implies the involvement of identical radicals and the term will be reserved for that special case. Combination is an energetically favourable reaction as the heat of formation of the new bond is liberated, and it frequently proceeds with little or no energy of activation. Removal of the energy liberated is no problem in the liquid phase but requires a third body or surface in the gas phase. The rate of the reaction depends upon the product of radical concentrations and hence it is characteristic rather of 'long-life' radicals capable of existing in relatively high concentrations than of 'short-life' radicals for which radical-molecule reactions are statistically favoured. Combination of 'short-life' radicals is, however, observed when they are produced in high local concentrations as in the Kolbé reaction

(Chapter 10), or when other reactions are suppressed as in aqueous media (Chapter 10). Velocity constants for combination of alkyl radicals have been obtained from polymerization studies (Chapter 7) and are of the order 1×10^6 mole^{-1} sec^{-1}.

(b) Aromatic Substitution.

$$R \cdot + ArY \longrightarrow RAr + Y \cdot$$
$$\text{e.g.} \quad Ph \cdot + PhH \longrightarrow PhPh + [H \cdot]$$

Aromatic substitution is discussed in Chapter 3, where it will be seen that the simple expression of the reaction given above is very much of an oversimplification. Y is nearly always hydrogen, but a few instances of the displacement of other atoms are known.

(c) Abstraction.

$$R \cdot + R'Y \longrightarrow RY + R \cdot$$
$$\text{e.g.} \quad Cl \cdot + CH_4 \longrightarrow HCl + CH_3 \cdot$$

This very common and important reaction is also referred to as 'transfer', particularly when polymerizations are discussed. The radicals R· and R'· may vary widely in structure but only in rare examples is R' = aryl. The group Y is nearly always hydrogen or halogen. The new radical R'· produced is often capable of performing a similar abstraction, so that the process may be repeated many times. This leads to 'chain reactions' of the type discussed in Chapters 4, 5, and 6.

(d) Addition to Multiple Bonds.

$$R \cdot + X = Y \longrightarrow R - X - Y \cdot$$
$$\text{e.g.} \quad Ph \cdot + CH_2 = CHPh \longrightarrow PhCH_2 \overset{\cdot}{C}HPh$$

Usually X and Y are both carbon and the bond between them is usually double. Some instances are known of addition to acetylenes and to carbonyl groups. Addition to olefins is of immense importance both as the propagation stage of radical polymerization (Chapter 7) and as the first stage of the chain sequences which produce small molecules (Chapter 6). It may be noted that the rate-determining stage of homolytic aromatic substitution (p. 35) is an example of this type of reaction.

(e) Rearrangement.

$$R \cdot \longrightarrow R' \cdot$$
$$\text{e.g.} \quad CH_3 \overset{\cdot}{C} \overset{O}{\diagup\diagdown} CH_2 \longrightarrow CH_3COCH_2 \cdot$$

Homolytic rearrangements are discussed in Chapter 8. Although analogous to heterolytic rearrangements, their variety is much more restricted. Migration of aryl groups β to the carbon bearing the unpaired electron have been most studied, but migration of hydrogen and halogen

12

atoms is also known. The reactions may be pictured as the intramolecular versions of aromatic substitution and abstraction.

(f) Fragmentation.

$$R \cdot \longrightarrow R' \cdot + Y$$

e.g. $Me_3CO \cdot \longrightarrow MeCOMe + Me \cdot$

Fission of a bond occurs in certain radicals with formation of a non-radical fragment and a new radical. Oxygen-containing radicals are particularly prone to fragmentation and some important examples are discussed in Chapter 8.

(g) Displacement. (S_R)

$$R \cdot + R'Y \longrightarrow RR' + Y \cdot$$

e.g. $Ph \cdot + MeCOCOMe \longrightarrow PhCOMe + MeCO \cdot$

This type is formally the same as (b) but applies to the cases in which R′ is alkyl and Y a group of atoms. It is encountered only in special cases and the bond broken is usually between oxygen atoms. It is designated S_R and is the homolytic counterpart of an $S_N 2$ reaction.

(h) Disproportionation.

$$2 \; \overset{\overset{\displaystyle H}{|}}{\underset{|}{C}}{-}\overset{\cdot}{\underset{}{C}} \longrightarrow \; C{=}C + \overset{\overset{\displaystyle H}{\cdot}}{\underset{|}{C}}{-}\overset{|}{\underset{|}{C}}{-}H$$

e.g. $2CH_3CH_2 \cdot \longrightarrow CH_2{=}CH_2 + CH_3CH_3$

This reaction involves transfer of hydrogen between radicals and is energetically favourable as two new bonds are made for one broken. Mechanistically the reaction has been little investigated and it will be mentioned only incidentally. The structural requirement of β-hydrogen is obvious and the reaction is consequently found with alkyl radicals higher than methyl.

The following simple example of the products obtained from a radical reaction illustrates types (a), (c), (e), (f), and (h):

$$PhC(Me)_2CH_2C\overset{\displaystyle O}{\underset{\displaystyle H}{<}} + t\text{-}BuO \cdot \xrightarrow{(c)} PhC(Me)_2CH_2C\overset{\displaystyle O}{\cdot}$$

$$\downarrow (f)$$

$$PhCH_2\overset{\cdot}{C}\overset{\displaystyle Me}{\underset{\displaystyle Me}{<}} \xleftarrow{(e)} PhC(Me)_2CH_2 \cdot + CO$$

$$\begin{array}{l} PhCH{=}CMe_2 \\ PhCH_2C\overset{\displaystyle Me}{\underset{\displaystyle CH_2}{<}} \\ PhCH_2CH(Me)_2 \end{array} \Bigg\} \quad \overset{(h)}{\swarrow} \qquad \overset{(a)}{\swarrow} \qquad \overset{(c)}{\searrow}$$

$$PhC(Me)_2CH_2CH_2C(Me)_2Ph \qquad PhC\overset{\displaystyle Me}{\underset{\displaystyle Me}{-Me}}$$

(c = abstraction; f = fragmentation; e = rearrangement; a = combination; h = disproportionation.)

13

Note that, apart from long-life radicals, no radicals remain in the system at the end of a reaction. They are removed in reactions (a) and (h).

CHARACTERISTICS OF RADICAL REACTIONS

The patterns of radical reactivity will emerge from the following chapters, but it may be useful to have them summarized briefly at this point.

(i) Radicals react so as to share the unpaired electron by bond formation, the driving force being the energy liberated in the formation of the bond. This process occurs in each of the reaction types considered above.

(ii) Most radicals are electrically neutral and tend, therefore, to be weakly susceptible to polar influences either in the solvent or at the reaction site. They consequently show considerably less selectivity than is usual for heterolytic reagents. In consequence, radical reactions normally give mixtures of several products.

(iii) The very common abstraction and addition reactions produce a new radical capable of repeating the type of reaction from which they were derived. These processes can therefore be self-perpetuating giving 'chain-reactions', and a large turnover of reactants can be achieved for a small investment of radical generation. On the other hand, very small amounts of inhibitors (capable of 'trapping' radicals) can prevent reaction by reducing the small numbers of radicals which sustain chain reactions.

(iv) Radicals show a strong tendency to take up a planar configuration (or to invert very rapidly), and reactions which involve homolysis of a bond attached to an asymmetric centre usually give racemized products. The methyl radical, for example, is known from flash photolysis spectra and ESR measurements to be flat; stereochemical aspects of radical reactions are dealt with in later chapters as they arise. Usually, steric effects are very slight; abstraction occurs at the molecular periphery and it is in addition reactions requiring penetration that effects have chiefly been noticed.

ENERGETICS

The reactions to be discussed involve homolytic fission of covalent bonds and are not usually subject to the strong electronic or steric effects which powerfully influence the energies of activation of heterolytic processes. Certain broad conclusions can reasonably be drawn, therefore, from consideration of the energy profile of a typical radical reaction (Fig. 1.4).

The first and most obvious point is that the energy of activation (E_A) for an endothermic reaction (dotted line) must be at least as great as the endothermicity. The combination reaction (a) (p. 11) with a low energy of activation, is always available for radicals, so that significantly endothermic reactions are never likely to be encountered.

Formation of the transition state R---Y---R' involves partial fission of the R'—Y bond and partial formation of the R—Y bond; it is reasonable to suppose that the energy of activation will be lowered by a weak R—Y bond and a strong R—Y bond. Superimposed upon this simple picture of partial bond formation in the transition state will be the effect of repulsions (i) between the attacking radical and the substrate and (ii) between the new molecule and the new radical. We can associate non-coulombic interaction with 'steric effects' and these are often slight for the reasons

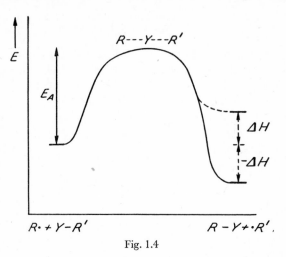

Fig. 1.4

given earlier. Electrostatic interactions are more specific and may either raise activation energies as in halogenation reactions (Chapter 4) or lower them as in certain aromatic substitutions (Chapter 3).

Because radicals are electrically neutral, electrostatic interactions are generally small and the relative strengths of bonds made and broken, i.e. the heat content changes, parallel activation energies. Thermochemical data are hence of the first importance for broad prediction of the relative ease of radical reactions, and the data required are those concerned with the energy required to break *specific* bonds. This energy is termed bond-dissociation energy and it is to be distinguished from 'average bond strength' which for a simple molecule like methane would be one-fourth of the energy required to separate methane into a carbon and four hydrogen atoms, i.e.

Bond Dissociation Energy, $D(CH_3$—$H) = \Delta E$ for CH_3—$H \longrightarrow CH_3\cdot + H\cdot$
Average Bond Strength $= \frac{1}{4}\Delta E$ for $CH_4 \longrightarrow C + 4H$

Bond dissociation energies vary very much with structure as exemplified by the series [D(C—H) in kcal/mole]:

CH₃—H	t-Bu—H	PhCH₂—H	CH₃CO—H	ĊH₂CH₂—H
101	89	78	78	40

This must be borne in mind when predictions of heat content change, and the conclusions thereby drawn, are made. As bond dissociation energies will continually be referred to, a Table is given on p. 167; extracts from it will be given in appropriate sections of later chapters.

For further reading

BERSOHN, 'Electron Paramagnetic Resonance of Organic Molecules' in Nachod and Phillips, *Determination of Organic Structure by Physical Methods*, Vol. 2. Academic Press, 1962.

INGRAM, *Free Radicals as Studied by Electron Spin Resonance*. Butterworths, 1958.

SWARC, *The Transition State in Radical Reactions*. Chemical Society Special Publication No. 16. 1962.

16

CHAPTER 2

'LONG-LIFE' RADICALS

It must be repeated that the term 'long-life' is an arbitrary one—the difference between the radicals discussed in this chapter and those dealt with in succeeding ones is merely one of degree of reactivity and not of any more fundamental property. The line between 'long-life' and 'short-life' radicals has been roughly drawn at the point where radicals can be detected directly by physical methods at 25°. The use of flow systems coupled to ESR spectrometers, however, has enabled the detection of radicals with lifetimes of 10^{-7} sec. We shall be concerned here with radicals of very much longer lifetimes. The significant property of 'long-life' radicals is their greatly reduced reactivity and the more limited range of reaction types displayed by them. In the past they have been mainly of theoretical interest but they are becoming of technical importance in connection with their characteristic property of combining with reactive radicals and hence inhibiting the chain reactions of which these reactive radicals are the carriers (Chapters 5 and 7).

TRIPHENYLMETHYL AND RELATED RADICALS

The discovery of triphenylmethyl by Gomberg in 1900 opened the era of radical chemistry. The discovery, like so many fundamental ones, was accidental; Gomberg was attempting to prepare a series of polyphenyl-substituted hydrocarbons and found that hexaphenylethane was obtained from trityl chloride and silver only with rigorous exclusion of oxygen:

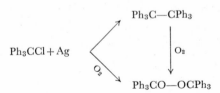

Contrary to expectation, the colourless hydrocarbon dissolved in organic solvents giving yellow solutions which rapidly yielded *triphenylmethyl* derivatives on the addition of reagents such as oxygen and iodine. Gomberg suggested that dissociation of the hydrocarbon with formation of triphenylmethyl radicals best accounted for his results, contrary as

17

this belief was to current theories of organic chemistry. Dissociation into radicals was soon supported by physical measurements; cryoscopic molecular weight determinations on more highly dissociated derivatives showed that the apparent molecular weights were well below that of the associated molecule. Spectrophotometry established that solutions of hexaphenylethane did not obey Beer's law. The intensity of absorption increased relatively with dilution as would be expected for dissociation of a colourless compound into a coloured radical. Electronic absorption data for triphenylmethyl and triphenylmethane are as follows:

$$Ph_3C \cdot \begin{cases} \lambda_{max.}\ 3450\ \text{Å} \quad \epsilon = 11,000 \\ \lambda_{max.}\ 5100\ \text{Å} \quad \epsilon = 210 \end{cases} \quad Ph_3CH\ \lambda_{max.}\ 2620\ \text{Å} \quad \epsilon = 870$$

Absolute methods of radical detection—magnetic susceptibility and electron spin resonance measurements—have placed the reality of hexa-arylethane dissociation beyond doubt.

Equilibrium constants for the dissociation of a series of hexa-aryl-ethanes are given in Table 2.1.

Table 2.1. Dissociation Constants of Hexa-aryl Ethanes
(*in benzene at 25°*)

Substituents	$K_{eq.} \times 10^3$	Substituents	$K_{eq.} \times 10^3$
Hexaphenyl	0·22	Diphenyl tetra-*p*-tolyl	1·3
Tetraphenyl di-*o*-tolyl	33	Tetraphenyl di-*α*-naphthyl	11
Tetraphenyl di-*m*-tolyl	1·8	Tetraphenyl di-*β*-naphthyl	1·5
Tetraphenyl di-*p*-tolyl	1·1	Hexa-*p*-biphenylyl	∞
Diphenyl tetra-*o*-tolyl	1500	Hexa-*p*-nitrophenyl	∞

Two factors chiefly determine the position of the equilibrium:

$$Ph_3CCPh_3 \rightleftharpoons 2Ph_3C \cdot$$

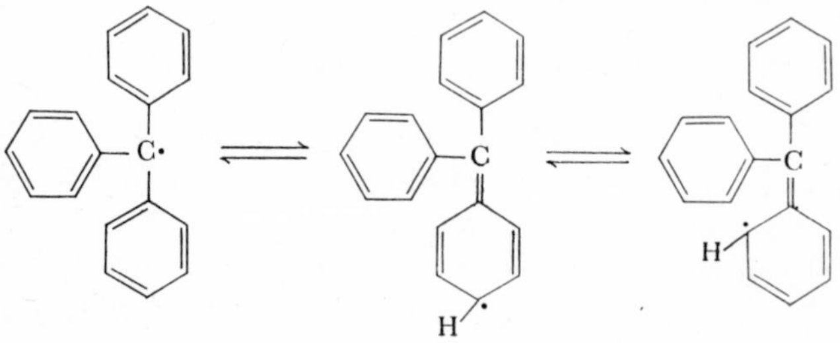

(i) *Radical Stability.* The odd electron is delocalized in the triarylmethyl radical and by virtue of this delocalization, conjugation between aryl nuclei in the radical becomes possible. The triphenylmethyl radical thus shows absorption in the visible spectrum, while triphenylmethane is colourless (cf. p. 18). Further, the fluorine atom in compound (*2.1*) is inert to silver but is removed in the derived radical (*2.2*). This shows that the latter has partial allylic character as represented in the extreme mesomeric form (*2.3*).

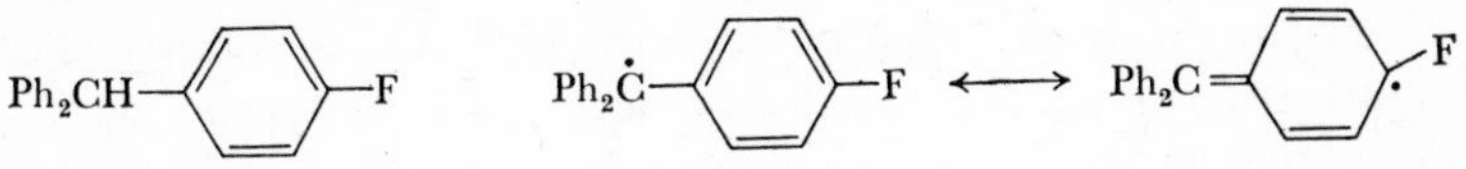

(*2.1*)	(*2.2*)	(*2.3*)

The high values of the equilibrium constants for the *p*-phenyl- and *p*-nitro-substituted compounds show the effect of increase in the extent of delocalization upon the degree of resonance stabilization. The degree of resonance stabilization in all of these compounds is, however, rather less than would be expected. This is because interference between the *ortho*-hydrogen atoms causes twisting of the aromatic nuclei out of the plane of the molecule giving triphenylmethyl a 'propeller' shape. This lowers the extent of delocalization. The bonds connecting the aryl nuclei to the central carbon atom are on average, all in one plane; the planar structure is demonstrated by infrared measurements and by the failure to obtain optically active triarylmethyl radicals.

(ii) *Steric Factors*. Non-bonded interactions favour the right-hand side of the equilibrium (i.e. formation of radicals) in two ways. First, repulsion between aryl groups across the central carbon–carbon bond in the associated molecule extends (and weakens) this bond which has a length 1·58 Å instead of the normal C—C value of 1·54 Å. In support of this argument, the molecule (*2.4*), which has two of the aryl groups on each side of the central bond 'tied back', is not appreciably dissociated at ordinary temperatures.

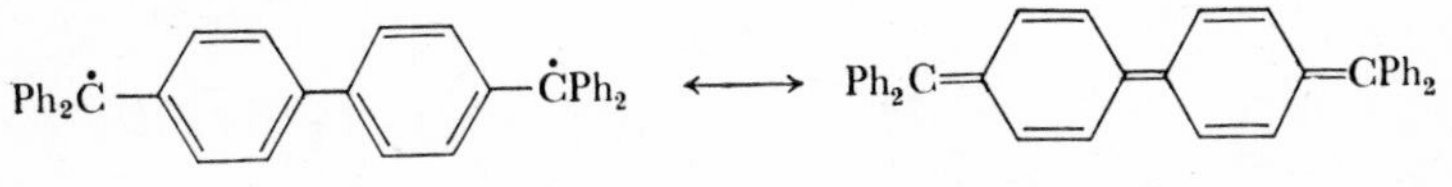

(*a*)	(*b*)

(*2.5*)

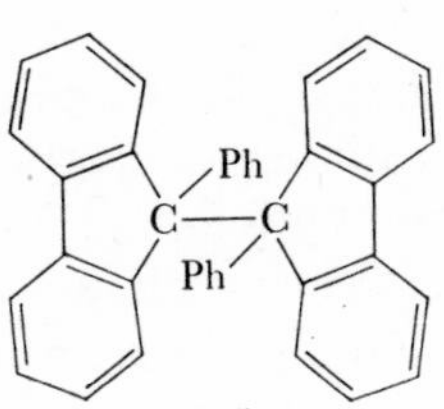

(*2·4*)

Secondly, there is steric hindrance to recombination. *Ortho-* substituents, which markedly favour radical formation, not only assist dissociation but, as recombination of radicals involves closing down the valency angles of 120° in the radical to 109° in the associated molecule, they magnify the consequent increase of steric interaction in the radical itself.

Diradical formation is, in principle, possible when two triarylmethyl centres are present in one molecule. In the biphenyl derivative (*2.5*) the quinonoid structure (*2.5b*) with *paired* electrons is favoured and electron spin resonance measurements show only 4–5% of the diradical (*2.5a*). In this situation, electron pairing requires both conjugation between the centres and coplanarity. When either condition is not satisfied, diradical forms are favoured as in the *meta*-linked derivative (*2.6*) and the molecule (*2.7*). In the latter case, coplanarity is prevented by interference between *o*-chlorine atoms:

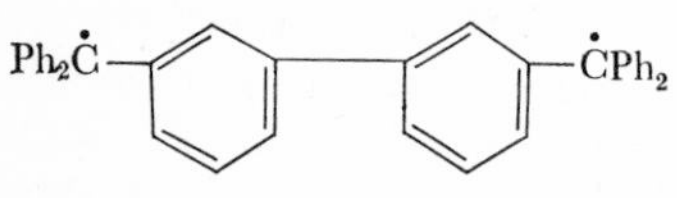

(*2.6*) 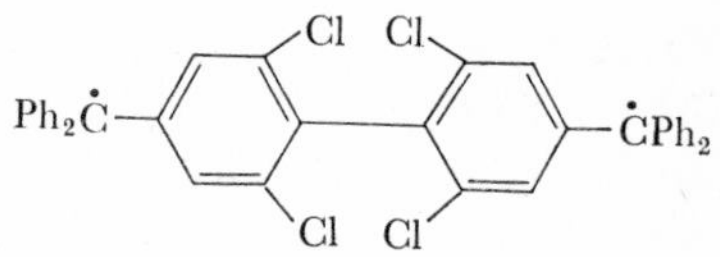   (*2.7*)

Reactions of Triphenylmethyl. The most characteristic reaction of triphenylmethyl and its analogues is combination, a process which requires a low energy of activation and relatively high radical concentrations. Typical examples are the reactions with species possessing unpaired electrons such as oxygen (a paramagnetic diradical), iodine atoms, sodium atoms, and nitric oxide.

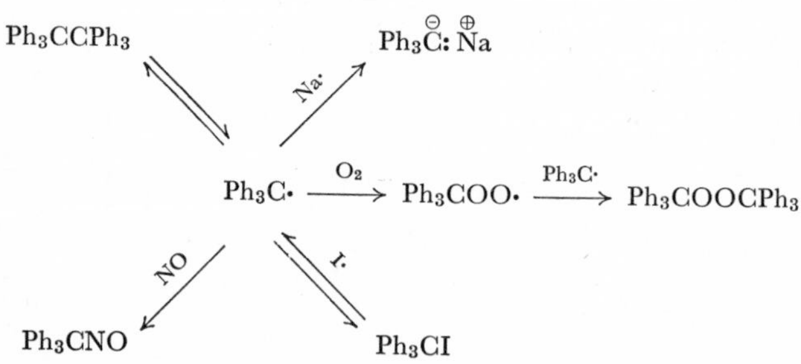

Reaction between hexaphenylethane and nitric oxide is zero order in nitric oxide; the rate determining stage is dissociation into triphenylmethyl radicals. The reaction with iodine is reversible, triphenylmethyl iodide being 20–40% dissociated even in non-ionizing solvents. Electron-transfer occurs with sodium atoms; the resulting triphenylmethylsodium is a brick-red *salt*.

20

Addition to olefins also occurs with triphenylmethyl, but normally the resulting radical has itself to be stabilized:

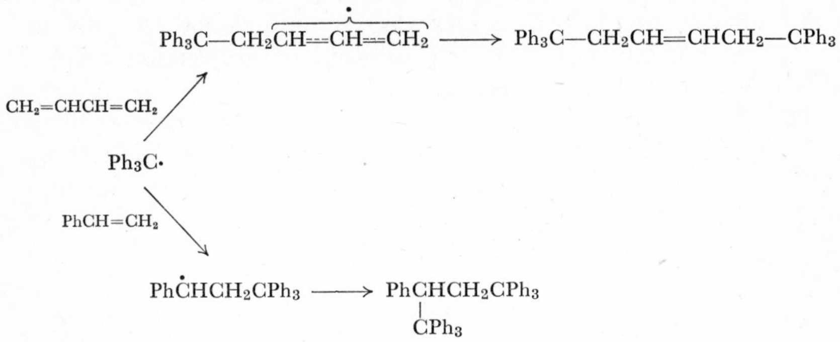

$$Ph_3C—CH_2\overset{\displaystyle \cdot}{\overbrace{CH{=}{=}{=}CH{=}{=}{=}CH_2}} \longrightarrow Ph_3C—CH_2CH{=}CHCH_2—CPh_3$$

CH$_2$=CHCH=CH$_2$

Ph$_3$C·

PhCH=CH$_2$

$$Ph\overset{\displaystyle \cdot}{C}HCH_2CPh_3 \longrightarrow \underset{\displaystyle CPh_3}{PhCHCH_2CPh_3}$$

In these cases the radicals from butadiene and styrene are of the allylic and benzylic type respectively. Addition to benzoquinone is important as the prototype of the mechanism of radical chain inhibition (Chapters 5 and 7) but is unusual in occurring at the oxygen of the carbonyl group. Here, the radical produced is a phenoxy-radical, isoelectronic with and stabilized in the same way as a benzyl radical:

Ph$_3$C· + O=⟨⟩=O ⟶ Ph$_3$C—O-⟨⟩-O· ⟶ Ph$_3$C—O-⟨⟩-O—CPh$_3$

Cf. ⟨⟩-ĊH$_2$ ⟷ ⟨⟩=CH$_2$ ⟷ ⟨⟩=CH$_2$

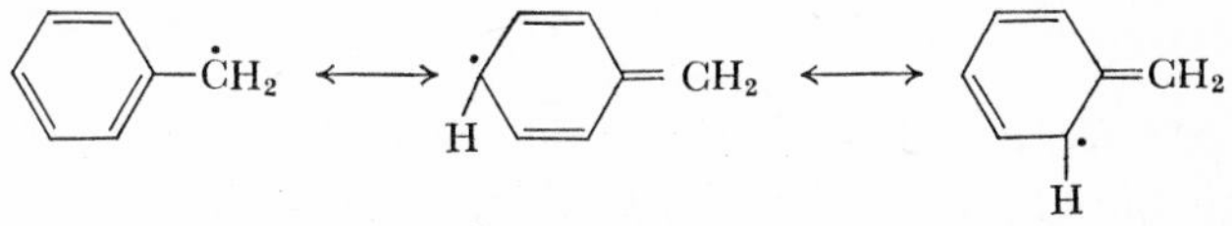

OTHER 'LONG-LIFE' RADICALS

Hydrocarbons. An interesting example of the incredulity with which some early work was treated has been described by Koelsch (1957). In a paper submitted for publication in 1932, he reported that treatment of α,γ-bisdiphenylene-β-phenylallyl chloride with mercury gave the red-brown radical α,γ-bisdiphenylene-β-phenylallyl:

Ph
C=C—Ċ

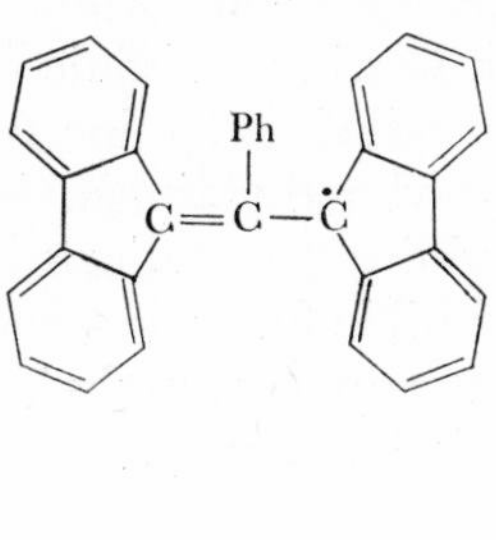

The radical reacted with sodium but was found to be inert towards oxygen. The paper, however, was rejected on the grounds that the properties of the compound were inconsistent with its formulation as a radical. A quarter of a century later the paper was resubmitted (and accepted) and ESR measurements showed that the radical had survived unchanged in contact with air during this period!

Addition of perinaphthene (*2.8*) to sodium methoxide gives the red anion (*2.9*). In contact with oxygen, solutions of the anion rapidly assume a green colour and addition of water gives the blue perinaphthyl radical (*2.10*) (and dust jacket). Formation of the radical involves electron transfer to oxygen (cf. p. 7).

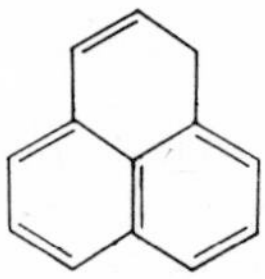

(2.8)

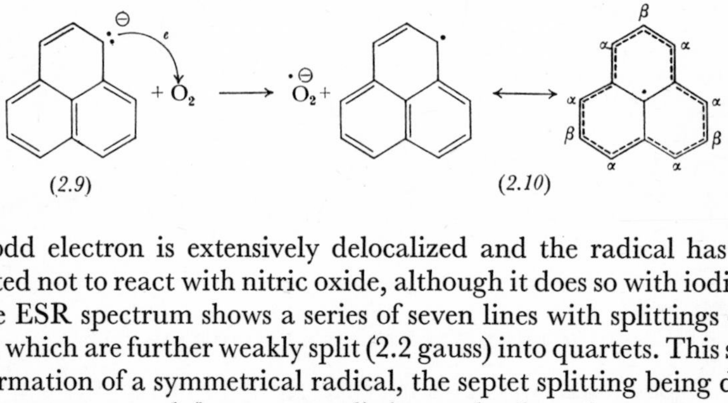

(2.9)   (2.10)

The odd electron is extensively delocalized and the radical has been reported not to react with nitric oxide, although it does so with iodine.

The ESR spectrum shows a series of seven lines with splittings of 7·3 gauss, which are further weakly split (2.2 gauss) into quartets. This shows the formation of a symmetrical radical, the septet splitting being due to the six α-protons and the quartet splitting to the three β-protons.

Hydrocarbon radical ions are mentioned briefly below.

Nitrogen Derivatives. Oxidation of diphenylamine gives tetraphenylhydrazine as a colourless solid whose solutions in non-ionizing solvents become green on heating and fade on cooling. Reaction with nitric oxide gives *N*-nitrosodiphenylamine (*2.11*) and with triphenylmethyl radicals, *N*-triphenylmethyldiphenylamine (*2.12*) is obtained. Dissociation into diphenylnitrogen radicals evidently occurs, electron delocalization being responsible for their stability. Although the area of delocalization is less than in triphenylmethyl, dissociation is favoured by the low N—N bond dissociation energy.

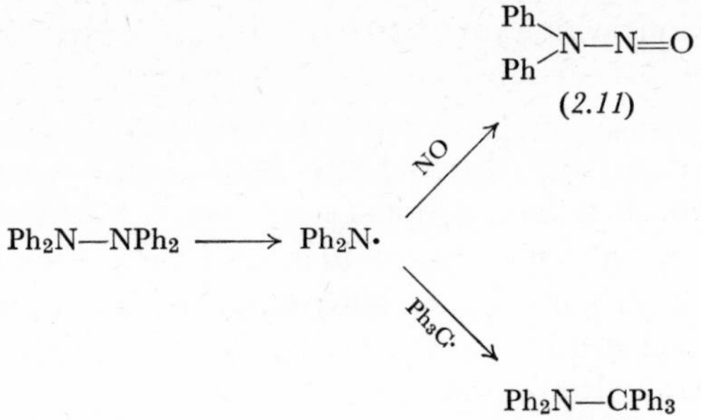

$$\begin{array}{c} Ph \\ _{\diagdown} N-N=O \\ Ph^{\diagup} \end{array}$$
$$(2.11)$$

$$Ph_2N-NPh_2 \longrightarrow Ph_2N\cdot \quad \nearrow^{NO}$$

$$\searrow_{Ph_3C\cdot}$$

$$Ph_2N-CPh_3$$
$$(2.12)$$

Similarly, the triphenylhydrazyl radical (*2.13*) is produced by oxidation of triphenylhydrazine and forms analogous combination products with triphenylmethyl radicals and nitric oxide.

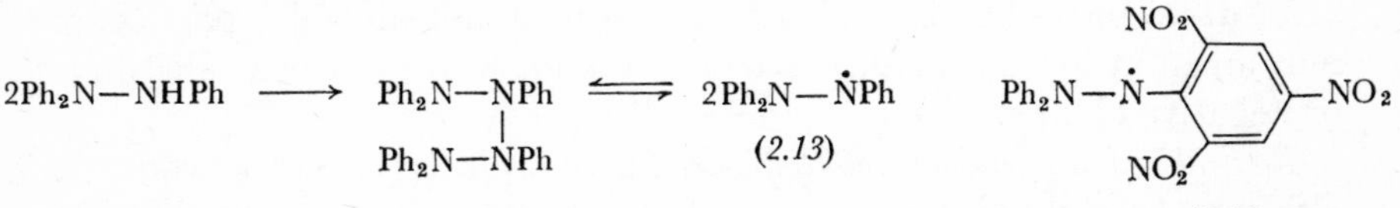

$$2Ph_2N-NHPh \longrightarrow \begin{array}{c} Ph_2N-NPh \\ | \\ Ph_2N-NPh \end{array} \rightleftharpoons 2Ph_2N-\overset{\cdot}{N}Ph \qquad Ph_2N-\overset{\cdot}{N}\!\!-\!\!\!\underset{NO_2}{\overset{NO_2}{\diagup}}\!\!-\!\!NO_2$$
$$(2.13) \qquad\qquad\qquad\qquad (2.14)$$

An important derivative of this radical, diphenylpicrylhydrazyl (*2.14*), is readily obtained as a violet-black solid by mild oxidation of the hydrazine, and has no associated dimer. Diphenylpicrylhydrazyl has been widely used as a 'radical scavenger', as it readily combines with radicals of all types, and as these combination products are much less intensely coloured than the radical, the rate of radical production (e.g. in polymerizations, Chapter 7) can be followed. It is also used as a convenient primary standard for ESR and magnetic susceptibility measurements.

Oxygen and Sulphur Derivatives. Removal of a hydrogen atom from the hydroxyl group of phenol leaves the resonance-stabilized phenoxy-radical (*2.15*) which, although too reactive for detection under normal conditions, except in flow systems, shows the characteristic

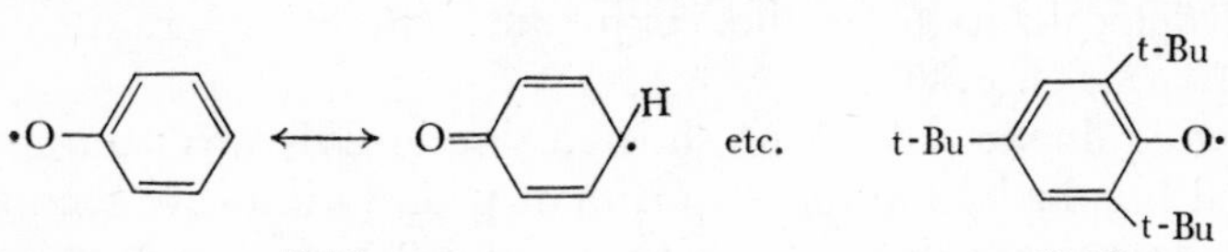

$$\cdot O\!\!-\!\!\langle\ \rangle \longleftrightarrow O\!\!=\!\!\langle\ \rangle\!\!\overset{H}{\cdot} \quad etc. \qquad t\text{-}Bu\!\!-\!\!\langle\ \rangle\!\!-\!\!O\cdot$$
$$(2.15) \qquad\qquad\qquad (2.16)$$

reactions of long-life radicals in coupling reactions. The latter are of great synthetic and biosynthetic significance (Chapter 10). The 2,4,6-tri-t-butylphenoxy radical is much less reactive and it, together with several other polyalkyl phenoxy radicals, has been detected by ESR in

23

oxidation reactions which involve O—H homolysis. In the radical (*2.16*), resonance stabilization must be adversely affected by steric inhibition of resonance (the oxygen atom is pushed out of the plane of the nucleus by *o*-t-butyl groups) but this is more than compensated for by steric repression of combination reactions.

When solutions of diaryl disulphides are heated they become yellow reversibly and Beer's law is not obeyed. In the presence of triphenyl-methyl, trityl aryl sulphides, which appear to result from combination with arylthio radicals are obtained:

$$ArSSAr \rightleftharpoons ArS\cdot \xrightarrow{Ph_3C\cdot} ArS—CPh_3$$

Reactions of short-lived thio radicals are discussed in subsequent chapters.

Radical Ions. This is an important group of radicals which possess not only an atom bearing an unpaired electron but also one bearing a positive or negative charge.

Radical Anions. Semiquinone Radicals. These radicals (*2.17*) are produced either by careful oxidation (removal of one electron) of the dianion of a hydroquinone, or by reduction (addition of one electron) of a benzo-quinone, both reactions requiring to be carried out in basic media.

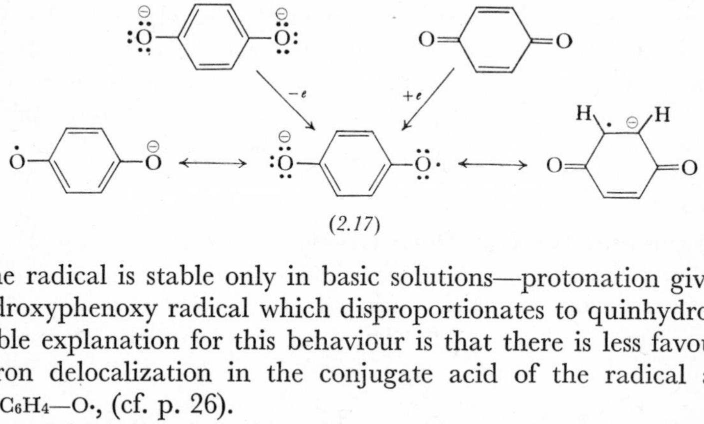

(*2.17*)

The radical is stable only in basic solutions—protonation gives the *p*-hydroxyphenoxy radical which disproportionates to quinhydrone. A possible explanation for this behaviour is that there is less favourable electron delocalization in the conjugate acid of the radical anion, $HO—C_6H_4—O\cdot$, (cf. p. 26).

The semiquinone radical ion shows a simple ESR spectrum in which the signal is split by the four equivalent protons into five components with an intensity ratio of $1:4:6:4:1$. The 2,5-di-t-butylsemiquinone radical ion (*2.18*) is interesting because it shows a simple three line ESR spectrum, the splitting being caused by the equivalent 3,6 protons. In addition, however, the centre line under high resolution shows closely spaced multiple splitting which is evidently due to a rather surprising interaction with the β-hydrogens of the t-butyl groups.

Ketyls. Ketones without hydrogen α- to the carbonyl group (especially diaryl ketones) give intensely coloured solutions on treatment with strongly electropositive metals such as sodium. Magnetic susceptibility measurements have shown these solutions to contain the ketyls (*2.19*) which exist in equilibrium with the dimer (*2.20*)—a metal pinacolate:

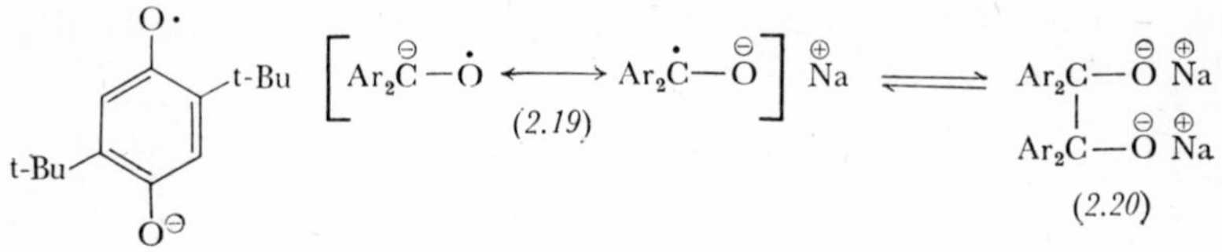

Chemical behaviour supports this formulation because ketyls show reactivity different from sodium pinacolates; oxygen, for example, regenerates ketone and yields sodium peroxide. The familiar reduction of aromatic ketones to pinacols by magnesium–magnesium iodide probably involves ketyl formation and intense colours are produced during the reactions. The extent of dissociation in pinacolate–ketyl systems varies very much with the metal, and as it increases with its electropositive character, electrostatic repulsion in the dimer is probably an important factor.

The potassium ketyl obtained from di-t-butyl ketone shows the expected ESR spectrum which involves splitting by γ-protons, although two of the nineteen lines are too weak for detection. This ESR spectrum is interesting in that the main group of lines is split into two weak replicas by interaction with the small natural content of magnetic ^{13}C nuclei.

Hydrocarbon Radical Anions. 'Long-life' radical anions have been obtained from a wide range of aromatic hydrocarbons by treatment with strongly electropositive metals in good electron transfer solvents such as tetrahydrofuran. The reaction of naphthalene with sodium to give the naphthalene radical anion (*2.21*) is a typical example:

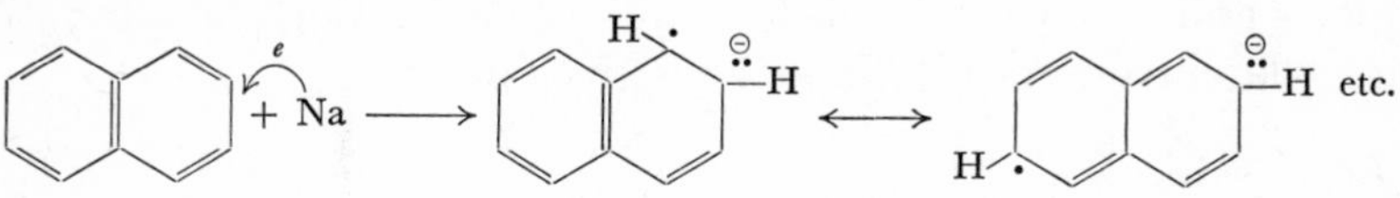

The ESR spectra of this and other related radicals have been determined and the results are important because the degree of splitting by each type of proton is related to the electron density at the carbon atom to which the proton is attached. The values obtained from ESR measurements thus serve as a direct check on molecular orbital calculations of electron densities. Agreement in the case of the naphthalene radical

3

anion is very good and the fact that a seventeen line spectrum is observed instead of the expected spectrum of twenty-five lines $(4+1\alpha \times 4+1\beta$ proton splittings) is accounted for in terms of an integral relationship between the electron densities at the α and β carbon atoms.

Radical Cations. Treatment of triarylamines with mild oxidizing agents such as bromine or lead peroxide in the presence of acids, causes removal of one of the lone pair electrons and formation of salts of triarylaminium radical cations (*2.22*)

$$Ar_3\overset{\oplus}{N}H \overset{\ominus}{X} \xrightarrow{-e} Ar_3\overset{\oplus\bullet}{N} \overset{\ominus}{X}$$

$$(2.22)$$

These radicals are isoelectronic with triphenylmethyl and although unstable do not appreciably associate; electrostatic repulsion, of course, militates against this process.

Closely related to the aminium radical ions are the 'Wurster' salts (*2.23*) obtained by oxidation of derivatives of *p*-phenylenediamine:

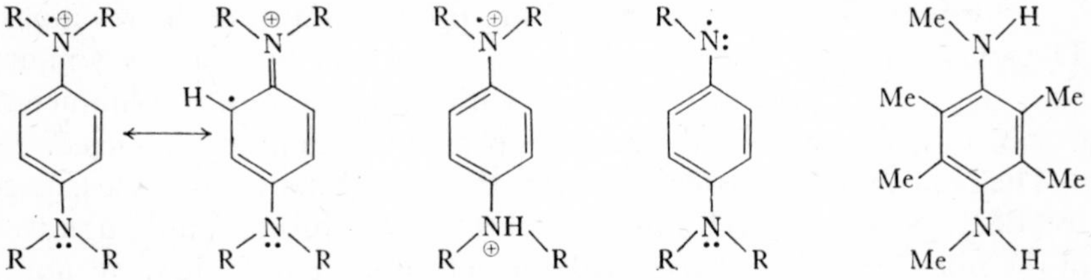

$$(2.23) \qquad\qquad (2.24) \qquad\qquad (2.25) \qquad\qquad (2.26)$$

The simple derivatives (*2.23*; R=H) are stable only in a limited *p*H range (3·5–6) and resemble in this respect the semiquinone radical ions (p. 24). Under strongly acid conditions, protonation of the other nitrogen atom (*2.24*) reduces conjugation, while under basic conditions the uncharged radical (*2.25*), whose resonance structures involve considerable charge separation, is formed. Co-planarity of the nucleus and nitrogen atoms is a condition for stability of the Wurster salts; *NN'*-dimethylaminodurene (*2.26*) does not give one.

For further reading

BACHMANN in Gilman's *Organic Chemistry—An Advanced Treatise*, Chapter 6. Wiley, 1943. See also the works listed at the end of Chapter 1.

PROBLEMS

1. Explain the following:

(*a*) Oxidation of triacetone amine (1) with hydrogen peroxide gave a red solid $C_9H_{16}NO_2$ which gave a pink paramagnetic oxime and an orange paramagnetic 2,4-dinitrophenylhydrazone.

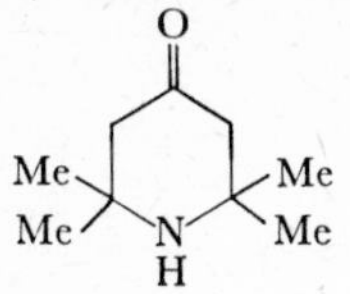

(1)   (2)   (3)

p-NO$_2$C$_6$H$_4$NHPh   Ph$_2$N—O—C(Ph)$_2$C$_6$H$_4$CPh$_3$—p

(*b*) Oxidation of *NN*-diphenylhydroxylamine with silver oxide in ether gives a dark red solid which reacts with nitric oxide to give diphenylhydroxylamine and compound (2). Triphenylmethyl reacts with the red compound to give diphenyl-hydroxylamine and the compound (3).

2. Solutions of p-bromophenyldiphenylmethyl chloride in xylene were shaken under nitrogen with an excess of silver. Oxygen absorption by the solutions and the amounts of halide ion released were determined at intervals with the results below:

Time	Oxygen uptake (moles/mole of chloride)	Halide ion released (equiv./mole of chloride)	
		Br$^-$	Cl$^-$
20 min	0·5	0·01	0·97
20 days	0·25	0·51	1·01

Account for these results.

3. (*a*) Oxidation of the phenol (4) with lead dioxide in cyclohexane and immediate observation of the ESR spectrum showed a triplet of triplets with hyperfine splitting constants of 12·3 and 2·0 gauss. After an interval, the spectrum showed a triplet with a hyperfine splitting constant of 1·25 gauss. Suggest an explanation for these observations

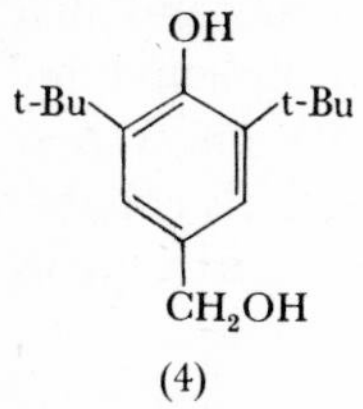

(4) 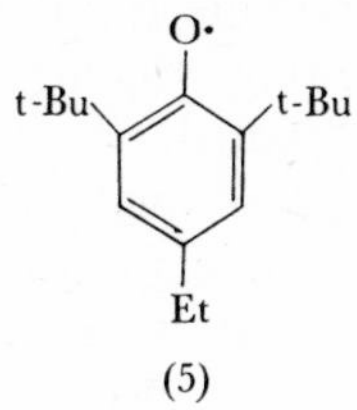   (5) 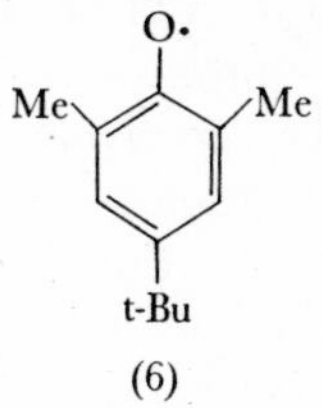   (6)

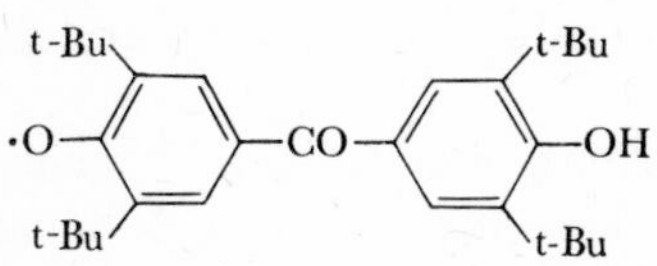

(7)   (8)   (9)

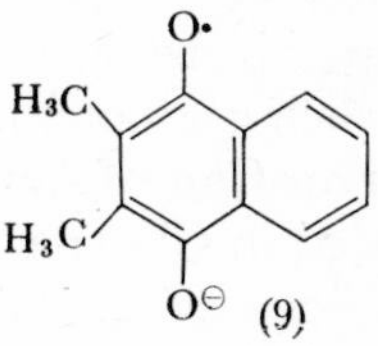

(*b*) What ESR patterns would you expect from radicals (5) to (9)?

CHAPTER 3

AROMATIC SUBSTITUTION

This Chapter deals with reactions in which a radical displaces a group attached to an aromatic nucleus:

$$R \cdot + ArY \longrightarrow ArR + [Y \cdot]$$

In practice the group Y is nearly always hydrogen. Arylation (R = Ar) will be discussed in most detail both because of its synthetic utility (Chapter 10) and because more quantitative work has been carried out on arylation than on any other homolytic aromatic substitution.

ARYLATION

The first clear evidence for the formation of reactive 'short-life' radicals in solution was obtained by Hey (1934) in a reinvestigation of several well-known reactions which gave biaryls as the products of aromatic substitution. He found that whatever substituent was present in the aromatic substrate, *some p*-isomer could always be detected. Thus, decomposition of benzoyl peroxide (p. 3) in toluene and in nitrobenzene gave product mixtures from which *p*-methylbiphenyl and *p*-nitrobiphenyl respectively were obtained. These observations were in marked contrast to the contemporary studies of Ingold and his collaborators on aromatic nitration in which ionic species were clearly involved. The incursion of phenyl *radicals* was postulated in order to account for this insensitivity to electronic effects and, in support of this conclusion, decomposition of benzoyl peroxide in equimolecular mixtures of toluene and ethyl benzoate gave roughly comparable amounts of biaryl derived from each compound.

Formation of Aryl Radicals. Formation of radicals in general was discussed in Chapter 1. The main methods for aryl radicals depend on (i) cleavage of aryl-nitrogen bonds with evolution of nitrogen, (ii) decarboxylation of aroyloxy radicals, and (iii) photolysis of a weak aryl-atom bond (usually to a metal).

(i) *Aryl-N fission.*

Gomberg reaction:

$$\overset{\oplus}{Ar-N} \equiv \overset{\ominus}{N} \; OH \rightleftharpoons ArN = NOH \xrightarrow{20°} Ar \cdot + N_2 + [\cdot OH]$$

Nitrosoacylarylamines:

$$ArN(NO)COR \rightleftharpoons ArN{=}N{-}OCOR \xrightarrow{20°} Ar{\cdot} + N_2 + [\cdot OCOR]$$

Triazens:

$$ArN{=}N{-}NHR \longrightarrow Ar{\cdot} + N_2 + [\cdot NHR]$$

Arylazotriarylmethanes:

$$ArN{=}N{-}CAr_3 \longrightarrow Ar{\cdot} + N_2 + \cdot CAr_3$$

Oxidation of arylhydrazines:

$$ArNHNH_2 \longrightarrow ArN{=}N{\cdot} \longrightarrow Ar{\cdot} + N_2$$

(ii) *Decarboxylation of Aroyloxy Radicals.* These radicals can be generated from a variety of sources:

Diacyl peroxides:

$$ArCOO{-}OCOAr \xrightarrow{80°} 2ArCOO{\cdot} \longrightarrow Ar{\cdot} + CO_2$$

Iodosoacylates:

$$PhI(OCOAr)_2 \xrightarrow{130°} 2ArCOO{\cdot} + PhI$$

Lead tetrasalts:

$$Pb(OCOAr)_4 \xrightarrow{130°} 2ArCOO{\cdot} + Pb(OCOAr)_2$$

Electrolysis of acids:

$$ArCO_2^{\ominus} \xrightarrow{-e} ArCOO{\cdot}$$

Silver iodide–Acid complexes:

$$AgI(OCOAr)_2 \xrightarrow{130°} 2ArCOO{\cdot} + AgI$$

Subsequent decarboxylation of aryoyloxy radicals yields aryl radicals. Except for the last reaction, these methods have also been applied to the production of alkyl radicals.

(iii) *Photolytic Methods.*

$$ArI \longrightarrow Ar{\cdot} + I{\cdot}$$

$$Ar{-}Hg{-}X \longrightarrow Ar{\cdot} + Hg + X{\cdot} \quad (X = Ar, \text{ halogen, etc.})$$

$$Ar_4Pb \longrightarrow Ar{\cdot} + Pb$$

Mechanistic Aspects of Homolytic Arylation. The early qualitative work of Hey and Waters left little doubt as to the involvement of aryl radicals. Detailed quantitative data, however, were required for the

29

discussion of electronic and steric effects upon the substitution process, and for the comparison of theoretical predictions with experimental results. Such data became available with the development of appropriate analytical techniques, notably infrared spectroscopy and gas chromatography, in the early 1950s. In any discussion of a substitution process in an aromatic system, information on two important aspects is required: (i) the orientating effect of substituents in the substrate, (ii) the effect of substituents upon nuclear activation (usually relative to a standard).

Orientation of Substitution. In most of the quantitative work on homolytic arylation, benzoyl peroxide has been used to provide phenyl radicals. This source provides 'cleaner' products than others, and the

Table 3.1. Isomer Ratios in Phenylation with Benzoyl Peroxide

(Reactions at 80° with 0·02 M peroxide)

Substrate	%			Substrate	%		
	o-	*m-*	*p-*		*o-*	*m-*	*p-*
PhNO$_2$	62	10	28	PhMe	67	19	14
PhF	54	31	15	PhEt	53	28	19
PhCl	50	32	18	Ph.i-Pr	31	42	27
PhBr	49	33	18	Ph.t-Bu	24	49	27
PhI	52	32	16	PhCF$_3$	29	41	30
PhOMe	70	14	16	PhCCl$_3$	12	49	39
PhCN	60	10	30	Naphthalene	α-82	β-18	
Ph–Ph	49	23	28				

biaryl fraction, upon which interest is focussed, is readily separated from other products (p. 38) of the reactions. Isomer distributions for phenylation of a number of aromatic compounds are given in Table 3.1.

As phenyl radicals are electrically neutral, one might expect little influence to be exerted by the substituent and that consequently the isomer ratio would be close to the statistical value of *o-*, 40%; *m-*, 40%; *p-*, 20%. The results of Table 3.1 show distinct deviations from these values but the pattern is totally different from that found in a heterolytic substitution such as nitration (Table 3.2).

It is significant that in reactions with phenyl radicals, all three isomers are formed in substantial amounts, and that the selectivity in substitution is low when compared with nitration. The low selectivity is understandable; the attacking species does not cause the 'electronic distortion' in approach to the substrate which the electrophilic nitronium ion produces, and does not require delocalization of an electron *pair* at the site of substitution. Further, *o*-substitution predominates irrespective of the substituent except in those cases, such as t-butylbenzene, in which steric

Table 3.2. Isomer Distribution in Nitration

(*by* NO$_2^\oplus$)

Substrate		%	
	o-	*m-*	*p-*
PhNO$_2$	6	93	1
PhCl	30	1	69
PhMe	57	3	40
Ph.i-Pr	30	8	62
Ph.t-Bu	12	9	79
Naphthalene	α-90	β-10	

effects operate. These steric effects operate in heterolytic nitration also (Table 3.2).

The results provide strong evidence for substitution by phenyl *radicals* and the values in Table 3.3 show that the pattern of isomer distribution is not significantly changed when other phenylating agents are used. There can be little doubt that a single reactive species is common to all of these reactions and that this is the phenyl radical.

Table 3.3. Isomer Distributions with Various Phenylating Agents

Reagent	Pyridine (%)			Substrate nitrobenzene (%)			Chlorobenzene (%)		
	2-	3-	4-	*o-*	*m-*	*p-*	*o-*	*m-*	*p-*
Bz$_2$O$_2$	58	28	14	62	10	28	50	32	18
Gomberg	—	—	—	—	—	—	60	25	13
Pb(OBz)$_4$	52	33	15	55	16	29	—	—	—
PhI(OBz)$_2$	58	28	14	58	14	28	—	—	—
PhN:NCPh$_3$	53	31	16	—	—	—	58	28	14
Ph$_3$Bi	48	31	21	—	—	—	—	—	—
PhCO$_2$H (electrolysis)	56	35	9	—	—	—	—	—	—
PhNHNH$_2$/Ag$_2$O	—	—	—	—	—	—	65	22	13
AgI(OBz)$_2$	—	—	—	—	—	—	60	24	16
Ph.N(NO).Ac	46	43	11	—	—	—	—	—	—

Activation of Substitution. A complete picture of the effect of substituents in substitution requires information on the effect of these substituents upon the *reactivity* of the nucleus. Reactivity can, in principle, be determined by direct rate measurements. In phenylations with benzoyl peroxide, however, dissociation of the peroxide is a slow process which is followed by very rapid attack of phenyl radicals upon the aromatic nucleus. An indication of the difficulty of this sort of measurement is provided by the rate data for radical hydroxylation of benzene. This reaction has a specific rate of 4×10^9 mole^{-1} sec^{-1} at 23°. A simpler method is to obtain relative rates from competitive reactions in which a mixture of two substrates compete for a limited number of phenyl radicals. Analysis of the biaryl mixture produced then gives the extent of attack upon each. Activation (or deactivation) is then expressed as a rate ratio $\left(\substack{X\\H}K\right)$ with respect to a standard, normally benzene. An example is the determination of $\substack{PhNO_2\\PhH}K$. The analytical data for a biaryl mixture obtained from a competitive experiment with nitrobenzene and benzene was as follows:

Analytical Procedure

	$C_6H_5C_6H_4NO_2$		$C_6H_5C_6H_5$	
	Wt.-%	*Moles-%*	*Wt.-%*	*Moles-%*
(1) Titanous sulphate reduction	78·4	73·8	21·6	26·2
(2) Vapour phase chromatography	79·7	75·5	20·2	24·5

Mean value for $\substack{NO_2\\H}K$ for this expt. $= \dfrac{74·65}{25·35} = 2·94$

The results of such competitive reactions are given in Table 3.4, together with values for heterolytic nitration.

Two striking features emerge from Table 3.4. Selectivity in phenylation is very small when compared with nitration, and this is again in keeping with the radical nature of the reaction. Secondly, all substituents *activate* the nucleus irrespective of their inductive and mesomeric effects. The only exceptions involve bulky substituents, and can reasonably be accounted for on steric grounds. Further, the effects of substituents are additive as shown by the values for the polychlorobenzenes.

The rate ratio $\substack{X\\H}K$, expresses the overall reactivity of the nucleus. Combination of the rate ratio with the isomer ratio (Table 3.1) for a particular substrate, allows the reactivity of a particular position in the substrate to be expressed relative to a single position in benzene. This reactivity is expressed as a *partial rate factor*, k, such that:

$$6\substack{X\\H}K = 2k_{o\text{-}} + 2k_{m\text{-}} + k_{p\text{-}}$$

Table 3.4. Effect of Substituents on Reactivity towards the Phenyl Radical and Nitronium Ion

Substrate	$\frac{X}{H}K(Ph\cdot)$	$\frac{X}{H}K(NO_2{}^{\oplus})$
PhH	1	1
Ph–Ph	4·0	8
PhNO$_2$	2·9	$\sim 1 \times 10^{-6}$
PhCl	1·4	0·033
PhBr	1·7	0·03
PhI	1.8	0·18
PhCO$_2$Me	2·4	0·0037
PhMe	1·7	25
PhEt	1·2	—
Ph.i-Pr	0·87	—
Ph.t-Bu	0·87	15·7
p-t-BuC$_6$H$_4$t-Bu	0·63	—
p-ClC$_6$H$_4$Cl	2·7	—
s-Cl$_3$C$_6$H$_3$	5·0	—
Naphthalene	9·9	400

for nitrobenzene, for example, the isomer ratio is *o*-, 62%; *m*-, 10%; *p*-, 28%, and the rate ratio is 2·94, i.e.

$$6.2\cdot94 = 2k_{o\text{-}} + 2k_{m\text{-}} + k_{p\text{-}}$$

$$k_{o\text{-}} = \tfrac{1}{2}.6.2\cdot94.0\cdot63 = 5\cdot6$$

$$k_{m\text{-}} = \tfrac{1}{2}.6.2\cdot94.0\cdot1 = 0\cdot86$$

$$k_{p\text{-}} = 6.2\cdot94.0\cdot28 = 4\cdot9$$

Some values of partial rate factors are given in Table 3.5.

Table 3.5. Partial Rate Factors for Homolytic Phenylation

Substrate	$k_{o\text{-}}$	$k_{m\text{-}}$	$k_{p\text{-}}$
PhNO$_2$	5·5	0·86	4·9
PhCl	2·2	1·4	1·6
PhBr	2·1	1·8	1·8
PhI	2·1	1·7	1·8
PhMe	3·5	1·0	1·4
PhEt	2·0	1·0	1·4
Ph.i-Pr	0·8	1·1	1·4
Ph.t-Bu	0·6	1·3	1·4
Ph–Ph	2·9	1·4	3·4

33

Effect of Substitution in the Radical. Quantitative investigations of both activation and orientation have recently been extended to reactions involving substituted phenyl radicals. A selection of results is given in Table 3.6.

It can be seen that the rate ratios $\frac{X}{H}K$, are markedly influenced by substitution in the radical. Thus nitrobenzene is much less readily attacked by *p*-nitrophenyl and *p*-chlorophenyl radicals than by phenyl radicals. It is reasonable to conclude that the substituents exert their $-I$ effects and confer electrophilic character upon *p*-nitro and *p*-chlorophenyl radicals. There is no *resonance* interaction of substituents with the unpaired electron so that mesomeric effects do not operate in the radical.

Table 3.6. Substituent Effects on Radical Reactivity

Substrate	Radical	*Isomer ratio*			$\frac{X}{H}K$
		o-	*m-*	*p-*	
PhNO$_2$	*p*-NO$_2$C$_6$H$_4$	57	15	27	0·94
PhNO$_2$	*p*-ClC$_6$H$_4$	59	14	27	1·5
PhNO$_2$	Ph	62	10	28	2·9
PhNO$_2$	*p*-CH$_3$C$_6$H$_4$	59	12	29	3·4
PhCl	*p*-NO$_2$C$_6$H$_4$	60	24	16	1·17
PhCl	Ph	50	32	18	1·49
PhCl	*p*-CH$_3$C$_6$H$_4$	—	—	—	2·05
PhCH$_3$	*p*-NO$_2$C$_6$H$_4$	—	—	—	2·61
PhCH$_3$	Ph	67	19	14	1·68
PhCH$_3$	*p*-CH$_3$C$_6$H$_4$	—	—	—	1·03

Similarly, the *p*-nitrophenyl radical attacks chlorobenzene less readily than the phenyl radical does. Chlorobenzene, like nitrobenzene, is poorly reactive towards electrophiles (Table 3.2). Toluene, on the other hand, which is readily attacked by electrophiles, is more readily attacked by the *p*-nitrophenyl radical than by the phenyl radical.

The situation is reversed when the *p*-tolyl radical is compared with the phenyl radical. The methyl group, by electron release, confers *nucleophilic* character upon the *p*-tolyl radical which attacks nitrobenzene *more* readily than does the phenyl radical. Toluene, on the other hand, is *more* reactive towards the phenyl radical than towards the *p*-tolyl radical.

The isomer distributions are less affected by substitution in the radical. Data are rather limited but fit into the picture of electrophilic and nucleophilic character in radicals. With nitrobenzene as substrate, the electrophilic *p*-chlorophenyl radical is directed to the *m*-position to a greater extent than the phenyl radical. Conversely, the extent of *m*-substitution in chlorobenzene is depressed when *p*-nitrophenyl radicals are used instead of phenyl radicals.

Mechanism of Substitution. Many details of the mechanism of homolytic aromatic substitution are still controversial but there is general agreement on the broad features of the process. The first step is addition of the radical to the π-electron system of the nucleus, one of whose π-electrons becomes localized in the formation of a new bond. A resonance-stabilized cyclohexadienyl radical (*3.1*) is produced. This is the radical (Wheland intermediate) considered in many theoretical treatments of the process (p. 37). The chief reaction paths followed by the arylcyclohexadienyl radical (*3.1*) are outlined in the scheme. In path (i) biaryls are formed directly when a hydrogen atom is removed by another radical. In phenylations with benzoyl peroxide roughly half of the peroxide is converted into free benzoic acid, which is shown by deuterium labelling to be derived from abstraction by the benzoyloxy radical. This hydrogen atom is particularly easy to remove on account of its 'doubly allylic' situation (cf. p. 67).

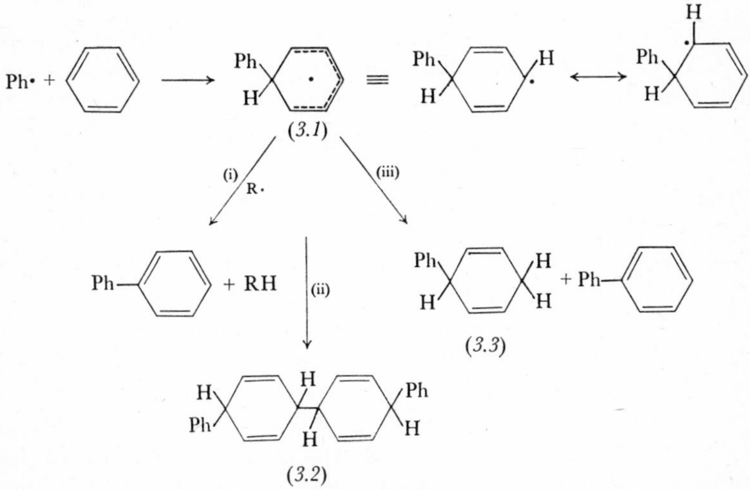

Reaction paths (ii) and (iii) involve respectively, the combination and disproportionation of the cyclohexadienyl radical. The products, tetrahydroquaterphenyl (*3.2*) and dihydrobiphenyl (*3.3*) have been isolated from experiments using dilute solutions and with exclusion of air. Unless precautions are taken, oxidation of these hydro-compounds occurs to give quaterphenyl together with biphenyl.

Further direct evidence for the intermediate radical (*3.1*) has been obtained from the phenylazotriphenylmethane-pyridine reaction, which yields the combination product (*3.4*). On oxidation, this compound subsequently gives the phenyltriphenylmethyl-pyridine (*3.5*).

$$PhN=N-CPh_3 \longrightarrow Ph\cdot + N_2 + \cdot CPh_3$$

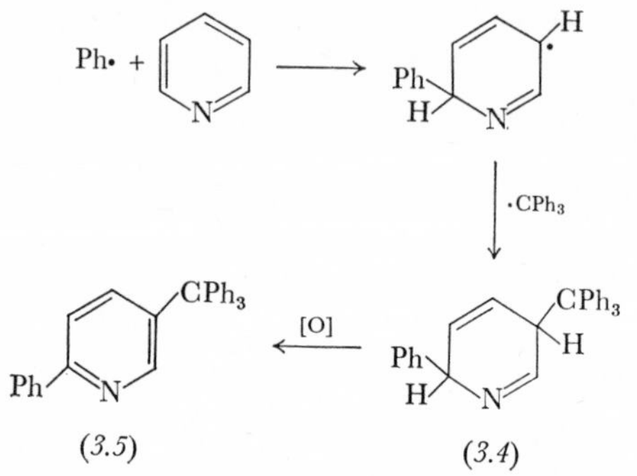

(*3.5*)   (*3.4*)

Arylations with benzoyl peroxide, when conducted in an atmosphere of oxygen, give very much increased yields of biaryl. Evidently removal of hydrogen from the arylcyclohexadienyl radical is favoured under these conditions, and more benzoyloxy radicals are available to give phenyl radicals.

Isotope Effects. When isotopically labelled substrates are phenylated with benzoyl peroxide, the recovered substrate is found to be isotopically unchanged. The addition step is, therefore, irreversible. The *product* isotope effect, however, varies from 1·0 to 6·6 and phenylation of PhD yields some dideuterodiphenyl. It is probable that an arylcyclohexa-dienyl radical containing D at the tetrahedral carbon atom is less likely to give biaryl by path (i) (p. 35) (because of the stronger C—D bond) than one with hydrogen at this position. The deutero-radical is hence more likely to give disproportionation-dimerization products. It is in dispro-portionation, therefore, that isotopic discrimination enters; biphenyls formed by this path become isotopically enriched.

To sum up the quantitative work on homolytic phenylation, it is evident that in general, substituent effects are slight but the tendency is for all positions to be activated (steric factors apart). It has been sug-gested that the usually greater activation at *o*- and *p*- positions is due to the greater degree of delocalization that is possible in the cyclohexadienyl radical that is produced (cf. p. 35). No clear rationalization of orienta-tion and activation effects in homolytic aromatic substitution has been given. The experimental observations were, however, correctly predicted

36

in a qualitative sense by Wheland and later workers, from calculations of the energy required to delocalize an electron at the seat of substitution:

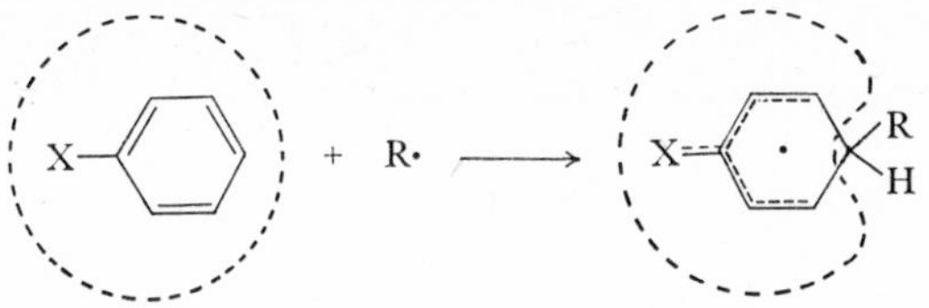

The dotted line surrounds the area of delocalization. Details of the theoretical treatments of homolytic aromatic substitution are given by Williams (1960).

Reactions Accompanying Nuclear Substitution. It is characteristic of radical reactions that they are rarely specific. Arylation is no exception, and some important side reactions will now be considered.

(i) *Attack on the Substituent.* This type of reaction is observed chiefly in alkyl and halogenomethyl benzenes. Abstraction of hydrogen or halogen from the side chain competes with nuclear substitution. The reaction between ethylbenzene and benzoyl peroxide gives an isomeric mixture of ethylbiphenyls together with an equimolecular mixture of *meso-* and racemic dimethyldibenzyls.

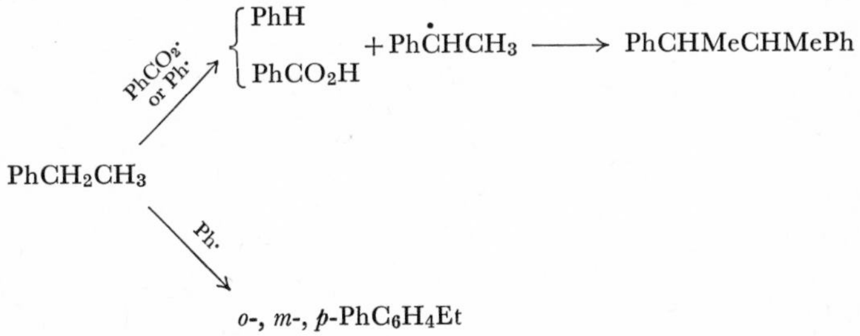

The extent of side-chain abstraction in alkylbenzenes lies in the order: Ph.t-Bu, 0%; PhMe, 13%; PhEt, 55%; Ph.i-Pr, 61%. The absence of side chain reaction in t-butylbenzene is understandable; removal of α-hydrogen from the other members of the series gives a resonance-stabilized benzylic radical, but in t-butylbenzene only β-hydrogens are available. The order of increasing side-chain attack indicates that the tertiary hydrogen in isopropylbenzene is more readily removed than either the secondary hydrogen in ethylbenzene or the primary one in toluene. The same order is found in halogenation (next chapter) and it can be accounted for in terms of maximum hyperconjugative stabilization of the tertiary radical.

37

(ii) *Hydrogen Abstraction from the Nucleus*. In mononuclear aromatics, this type of reaction is not generally encountered. Its occurrence would lead to the formation of disubstituted biaryls:

$$\text{ArH} + \text{Ph} \cdot \longrightarrow \text{PhH} + \text{Ar} \cdot \xrightarrow{\text{ArH}} \text{Ar—Ar} + (\text{H} \cdot)$$

These have been looked for in reactions of this type but no significant amounts are obtained. Abstraction from the nucleus is common, however, in the higher polycyclics. Naphthalene and benzoyl peroxide give a 35% yield of isomeric binaphthyls which result from the abstraction of nuclear hydrogen and subsequent attack of α- and β-naphthyl radicals on naphthalene.

(iii) *Nuclear Benzoyloxylation*. Although benzoyloxy radicals decarboxylate readily, a proportion survives long enough to participate in nuclear substitution. In monocyclic compounds, formation of arylbenzoates is unimportant ($\sim 10\%$ of the nuclear substituted products), but in the polycyclics, which are highly reactive towards nuclear substitution (p. 40), benzoyloxylation is favoured. Ester formation even in naphthalene exceeds the yields of phenylnaphthalenes and binaphthyls combined.

ALKYLATION

Alkylation has been more studied than any other radical substitution with the exception of arylation. Alkylation is, however, usually more complex than arylation and the yields of simple alkylation products are generally poor. Alkylbenzenes, the primary products of substitution, possess vulnerable benzylic C—H bonds, and side-chain abstraction becomes a serious side reaction. In addition, there is a greater tendency in alkylation for the alkyl cyclohexadienyl radical to be diverted to disproportionation or combination. This is because the gain in resonance energy associated with arylation is largely absent. The products of alkylation are more difficult to separate from starting materials than in phenylation, and this fact doubtless hampered the earlier investigations of the reaction.

Sources of Alkyl Radicals. The primary sources (i.e. generation *ab initio* and not in a secondary reaction such as transfer) are closely related to the methods for generating aryl radicals. An important exception is the use of t-butyl peroxide for producing methyl radicals (this is actually a secondary reaction; see Chapter 8).

A wide variety of aromatic alkylations (listed by Williams) have been examined quantitatively; monoalkyl derivatives are usually obtained only in low yield. Alkylation of pyridine is rather exceptional and high yields (up to 86%) of alkylpyridines can be obtained using acetyl and

$$RCOO—OCOR \xrightarrow{\text{heat}} 2RCOO\cdot \longrightarrow R\cdot + CO_2 \quad \text{(all types)}$$

$$RCOO^{\ominus} \xrightarrow[\text{electrolyse}]{-e} RCOO\cdot \longrightarrow R\cdot + CO_2 \quad (\text{,,} \quad \text{,,})$$

$$RHgI \xrightarrow{h\nu} R\cdot + HgI \qquad (\text{,,} \quad \text{,,})$$

$$\left. \begin{matrix} Pb(OCOR)_4 \\ PhI(OCOR)_2 \end{matrix} \right\} \xrightarrow{\text{heat}} \left\{ \begin{matrix} Pb(OCOR)_2 + 2RCOO\cdot \longrightarrow R\cdot + CO_2 & \text{(esp. Me·)} \\ PhI \quad\quad + 2RCOO\cdot \longrightarrow R\cdot + CO_2 & (\quad \text{,,} \quad) \end{matrix} \right.$$

$$Me_3CO—OCMe_3 \xrightarrow{\text{heat}} 2Me_3CO\cdot \longrightarrow MeCOMe + Me\cdot$$

higher acyl peroxides. Methylation of trinitrotoluenes with acetyl peroxide, lead tetra-acetate, phenyliodoso acetate, and the electrolysis of sodium acetate, all give trinitro-*m*-xylene in comparable yields. A common mechanism involving methyl radicals is probable.

Decomposition of t-butyl peroxide in anisole gives, in addition to an isomeric mixture of methylanisoles [reaction (3.1)], a mixture of phenoxymethylanisoles. The latter arise from substitution by phenoxymethyl radicals produced in the transfer reaction (3.2):

$$Me_3CO—OCMe_3 \longrightarrow Me_3CO\cdot \longrightarrow MeCOMe + Me\cdot$$

$$Me\cdot + PhOMe \longrightarrow o\text{-},m\text{-},p\text{-}MeC_6H_4OMe \qquad \ldots(3.1)$$

$$Me_3CO\cdot + PhOMe \longrightarrow PhOCH_2\cdot + Me_3COH \qquad \ldots(3.2)$$

$$PhOCH_2\cdot + PhOMe \longrightarrow o\text{-},m\text{-},p\text{-}PhOCH_2C_6H_4OMe$$

Intramolecular alkylation is also known. Decomposition of 5-phenylpentanoyl peroxide yields tetralin:

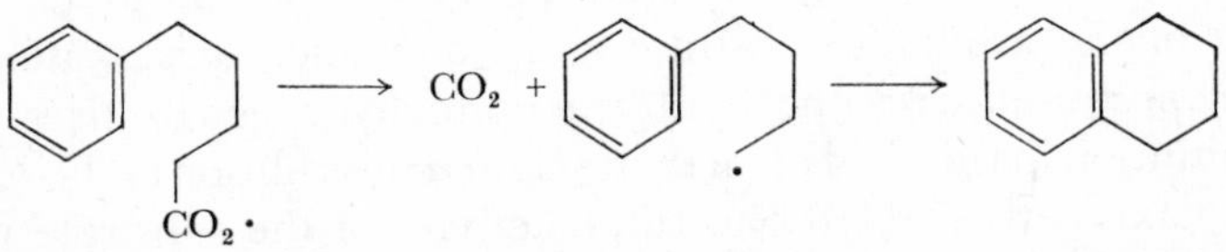

Quantitative Aspects of Alkylation.

Comparison of the orientation and activation effects of substituents towards methyl and phenyl radicals is obviously important for a fuller understanding of the factors involved in homolytic aromatic substitution.

Orientation in alkylation has been much less studied than for phenylation. Isomer ratios for some methyl radical substitutions are given in Table 3.7.

Table 3.7. Isomer Ratios for Homolytic Methylation

Substrate	%			Substrate	%		
	o-	*m-*	*p-*		*o-*	*m-*	*p-*
PhCl	64	25	11	PhCN	48	9	43
PhNO$_2$	66	6	28	PhOMe	74	15	11
PhMe	56	27	17				

The typical pattern of homolytic substitution is clear but nitrobenzene and benzonitrile show a clear preference for *o-/p-*substitution. It seems possible that methyl is more nucleophilic than phenyl; *m/p* ratios are higher in methylation than phenylation for $+E$ substituents and the reverse is true for $-E$ substituents. This conclusion fits with the fact that the ionization potential for methyl

$$(CH_3 \cdot \longrightarrow CH_3^{\oplus} + e)$$

is less than the electron affinity

$$(CH_3 \cdot \xrightarrow{+e} CH_3^{\ominus})$$

Further, the electronegativity of sp^3 carbon is less than that of sp^2.

Activation in homolytic alkylation is hard to determine by the competitive methods used for phenylation on account of the complexity of the reaction products and the incursion of secondary reactions. Some information on relative reactivities of aromatic substrates towards methyl radicals has been obtained by Swarc and his collaborators. They have measured 'Methyl Affinities' by allowing methyl radicals to react with a mixture of the aromatic substrate and iso-octane. It is assumed that methane produced arises only by abstraction of hydrogen from iso-octane; the diminution in the yield of methane caused by addition of the substrate to iso-octane is then related to the reactivity of the substrate towards addition of methyl radicals. Results obtained in this way are given in Table 3.8.

Table 3.8. Relative Methyl Affinities

Benzene	1	PhCN	12
PhCH$_3$	1·7	Naphthalene	22
PhCl	4·2	Anthracene	820
PhPh	5	Benzoquinone	15,200

The method suffers from lack of attention to products derived from the substrate; the large assumptions involved are discussed elsewhere. Reactivities of mono-nuclear compounds are of the same order of magnitude as towards aryl radicals. The steep rise in reactivity observed with polynuclear compounds fits well with theoretical predictions of their reactivity. The unpaired electron of the radical produced by addition to benzoquinone is extensively delocalized, and the high reactivity of the quinone is thus not surprising. On this account, benzoquinone finds frequent use as a 'radical catcher', causing inhibition of radical chain reactions.

HYDROXYLATION

Homolytic hydroxylation is similar to alkylation in that the yields of primary substitution products are low because of secondary reactions, and complex product mixtures are produced. A further difficulty encountered in the study of the reaction is that the methods of generating hydroxyl radicals all involve the simultaneous formation of a variety of other reactive species.

The most convenient source of hydroxyl radicals is Fenton's reagent, in which they are produced by electron transfer from ferrous ion to hydrogen peroxide:

$$Fe^{++} + H_2O_2 \longrightarrow Fe^{+++} + \cdot OH + \overset{\ominus}{O}H$$

Direct radiolytic fission of water is also used:

$$H_2O \xrightarrow[\text{X-rays}]{\gamma\text{-rays}} H\cdot + \cdot OH$$

A number of simple aromatic compounds have been hydroxylated with hydroxyl radicals generated in these ways. An idea of the complexity of the reactions can be gained from the results obtained with nitrobenzene. Radiolysis of saturated aqueous nitrobenzene gave a nitrophenol mixture with the composition: *o*-, 34%, *m*-, 31%; *p*-, 35%, together with phenol and isomeric dinitrobiphenyls. The isomer ratio is itself pH dependent. The values above are for reactions at pH 2; at pH 12 there is less *o*- and more *p*-isomer produced.

The mechanism of substitution is the same as for phenylation. The hydroxycyclohexadienyl radical (*3.6*; X=H) has been directly detected by ESR observations on a flowing system of benzene and hydroxyl radicals:

4

The subsequent loss of a hydrogen atom (presumably transferred to another radical) by path (i) yields the phenol. It is suggested that the alternative pathway (ii), while unfavourable in arylation and alkylation, is favoured in hydroxylation. Thus path (i) is exothermic by 3 kcal/mole, while (ii) is 16 kcal/mole exothermic. The aryl radical produced in (ii) then attacks the aromatic substrate with the formation of disubstituted biaryls, $X-C_6H_4.C_6H_4-X$. Aryl radicals may, of course, be produced directly by abstraction of hydrogen from the nucleus (path iia). This is energetically much more advantageous with hydroxyl than with phenyl radicals on account of the strong $O-H$ bond (p. 167) produced. Phenol is considered to arise in the nitrobenzene reaction from displacement of nitro-groups by hydroxyl radicals.

Data on reactivity towards hydroxyl radicals are also available. The compounds PhOMe, PhH, PhCl, PhNO₂ have the reactivity order 6·35:1: 0·55:0·14. These figures demonstrate the electrophilic character of the hydroxyl radical (cf. phenylation, Table 3.4) and this is confirmed by distinct *o-/p-* or *m-* direction by appropriate substituents.

Benzenoid compounds foreign to the animal body are frequently hydroxylated before excretion, and it is significant that all three isomers may be obtained from benzoic acid, for example. It appears likely that some type of homolytic process is involved. The general study of hydroxyl radical reactions in biological systems has become very important in connection with tissue damage caused by radiation.

Certain other reactions which appear to involve homolytic aromatic substitution have been described. Amino radicals (NH₂·) are produced from the hydroxylamine-titanous system (p. 7), and with benzene give ammonia, biphenyl, and aniline in small amounts. Arylsulphonyl-nitrenes (Chapter 9) replace hydrogen in aromatic systems and the activating effects of substituents confirm the homolytic nature of the reactions. Aromatic mercuration under certain conditions also appears to be homolytic; details are given by Williams (1960).

42

For further reading

Augood and Williams, *Chem. Rev.*, 1957, **57**, 123.
Dermer and Edmison, *Chem. Rev.*, 1957, **57**, 77.
Williams, *Homolytic Aromatic Substitution*. Pergamon, London, 1960.

PROBLEMS

1. The isomer ratio given for the phenylation of pyridine with phenylazotriphenylmethane (Table 3.3) is corrected for formation of the compound (*3.5*) (p. 36). This compound (2·75 g) together with isomeric phenylpyridines (2·02 g) was obtained from a reaction of phenylazotriphenylmethane with pyridine. Calculate the actual isomer ratio that was observed and, given that $\frac{\text{Pyridine}}{\text{Benzene}}$ K = 1·04, calculate the partial rate factors for the phenylation of pyridine.

2. Comment on the following sets of data obtained from reactions of aroyl peroxides with:

(*a*) Naphthalene:

	Products (*moles/mole of peroxide*)	
Peroxide	$ArCOOC_{10}H_7$	$ArC_{10}H_7$
Benzoyl	0·55	0·20
o-Nitrobenzoyl	0·87	0·00
p-Nitrobenzoyl	0·80	0·00
p-Chlorobenzoyl	0·61	0·11
o-Chlorobenzoyl	0·68	0·17

(*b*) Alkyl benzenes:

	Side chain attack (*moles-%*)		
Peroxide	$PhCH_3$	$PhCH(CH_3)_2$	$PhCCl_3$
Benzoyl	12	55	66
p-Methylbenzoyl	42	—	—
p-Nitrobenzoyl	0	0	0
p-Chlorobenzoyl	11	38	0

3. Account for the fact that treatment of anthracene and benzenediazonium zincichloride in acetone with zinc dust gives 9,10-diphenylanthracene (12%), but a negligible quantity of 9-phenylanthracene.

CHAPTER 4

HALOGENATION

Formation of alkyl halides in the reactions of alkanes with halogens is one of the earliest reactions encountered in the study of organic chemistry. The first stage of the reaction in a very simple case is given in reaction (4.1):

$$CH_4 + Cl_2 \longrightarrow CH_3Cl + HCl \qquad \ldots(4.1)$$

This type of reaction is frequently referred to as halogen substitution but from a mechanistic point of view this term is misleading as it implies a reaction type analogous to that discussed in the previous chapter. The term 'halogenation' will be used for the type of process exemplified by reaction (4.1). This is clearly different from homolytic halogen addition (Chapter 6).

CHARACTERISTICS OF HOMOLYTIC HALOGENATION

Ethane and chlorine do not react in the dark even at 120° but illumination of the mixture or introduction of a compound known to give radicals at this temperature, e.g. $Pb(Et)_4$, causes rapid reaction. Furthermore, the reaction is found to be slowed down by the addition to the mixture of oxygen, which has already been seen to react rapidly with radicals. The reactions are thus homolytic in character and the simplest mechanism which embraces the known features of the reactions is as follows (X = halogen):

$X_2 \longrightarrow 2X\cdot$	...(4.2a)	Photolytic	INITIATION
$In\cdot† + X_2 \longrightarrow InX + X\cdot$	...(4.2b)	Radical	INITIATION
$In\cdot + RH \longrightarrow InH + R\cdot$	...(4.2c)	Radical	INITIATION
$X\cdot + RH \longrightarrow R\cdot + HX$	...(4.3a)		PROPAGATION
$R\cdot + X_2 \longrightarrow RX + X\cdot$	...(4.3b)		PROPAGATION
$R\cdot + R\cdot \longrightarrow RR$	...(4.4a)		TERMINATION
$R\cdot + X\cdot \longrightarrow RX$	...(4.4b)		TERMINATION
$X\cdot + X\cdot \longrightarrow X_2$	...(4.4c)		TERMINATION

† The symbol In (initiator) denotes a reactive radical produced from a source of radicals present in low concentration relative to the reactants.

Evidence for the initiation steps has already been mentioned; photo-initiatiation is very convenient for either gas or liquid phase reactions and has the advantage that extraneous reactants are not introduced. Use of radical initiators, such as benzoyl peroxide, is, however, common. Steps (4.3a) and (4.3b) constitute a reaction sequence common in radical chemistry—*the chain reaction*. The halogen atom X•, produced in reaction (4.3b) attacks a new alkane molecule in reaction (4.3a) and steps (4.3a) and (4.3b) are then repeated. The mechanism is thus an abstraction–abstraction chain and evidence is presented later that direct substitution, reaction (4.6a) (below), is not involved. Reactions (4.3a) and (4.3b) may be repeated many times before termination [reaction (4.4)] intervenes. Typical quantum yields in photochlorination are of the order of 10^4. The mechanism of termination is not clear; while products of reactions (4.4b) and (4.4c) are, of course, indistinguishable from the reactants or products, dimers, from reaction (4.4a), are not usually isolated. The long chain sequences that are frequently observed imply that termination products will, in any event, be produced only in very small amounts.

The characteristics of the reactions with different halogens are understandable (and largely predictable) on the basis of the energetics of the propagation steps. These are given in Table 4.1 for fluorine, chlorine, and bromine.

Table 4.1. Enthalpy changes in the Propagation Steps of Homolytic Halogenation

Reaction	F_2	Cl_2	Br_2
(4.3a) $RH + X• \longrightarrow R• + HX$	-33	-3	$+13$
(4.3b) $R• + X_2 \longrightarrow RX + X•$	-71	-24	-21
[$D(R—H)$ is taken as 100 kcal/mole, cf. p. 167)]			

Both propagation steps in reactions of aliphatic hydrocarbons with fluorine are strongly exothermic, step (4.3a) by virtue of the large H—F bond strength, and step (4.3b) by virtue of the low F—F bond strength. As might be expected, fluorination of alkanes is an extremely vigorous reaction, and its control is the chief obstacle to its preparative use for fluorocarbons.

CHLORINATION

Most of the quantitative work on halogenation has been done with chlorine and accordingly most space will be devoted to its consideration. Both propagation steps are still exothermic if $D(C—H) = 100$ kcal/mole,

45

or less, but as carbon–halogen bonds are stronger than the corresponding halogen–halogen bonds, reaction (4.3b) is always exothermic and the energetics of reaction (4.3a) are decisive.

Oxygen causes inhibition of chlorination by reaction with the 'chain-carrying' alkyl radical, reaction (4.5):

$$R\cdot + O_2 \longrightarrow ROO\cdot \qquad \ldots(4.5)$$

Alkyl peroxy radicals are less reactive than alkyl radicals (cf. Chapter 5) and are less well able to continue the chain process.

A conceivable alternative mechanism for the propagation of chlorination is given in equations (4.6a) and (4.6b):

$$Cl\cdot + RH \longrightarrow RCl + H\cdot \qquad \ldots(4.6a)$$
$$H\cdot + Cl_2 \longrightarrow HCl + Cl\cdot \qquad \ldots(4.6b)$$

This mechanism has been ruled out, however, by the demonstration that chlorination of (+)-1-chloro-2-methyl butane (*4.1*) gives the *racemic* dichloride (*4.3*). Inversion of configuration in reaction (4.6a) would reasonably be expected; racemization shows that the reaction takes the course indicated in reactions (4.3a) and (4.3b) *via* the configurationally unstable radical (*4.2*) [cf. Chapter 9, but see p. 54]. Reaction (4.6a) is, in any event, endothermic to the extent of 22 kcal/mole, while energies of activation for the attack of chlorine atoms on alkanes are in the region of 1–2 kcal/mole.

$$\underset{(4.1)}{ClCH_2-\overset{\displaystyle Me}{\underset{\displaystyle H}{\overset{|}{\underset{|}{C}}}}-Et} \longrightarrow \underset{(4.2)}{ClCH_2-\overset{\displaystyle Me}{\underset{\displaystyle \bullet}{\overset{|}{C}}}-Et} \longrightarrow \underset{(4.3)}{ClCH_2-\overset{\displaystyle Me}{\underset{\displaystyle Cl}{\overset{|}{\underset{|}{C}}}}-Et}$$

Structural Effects. The product of halogenation depends upon which hydrogen atom is removed by the halogen atom in reaction (4.3a). The choice is decided chiefly by the C—H bond strength at the site of reaction and by the polar and steric effects on the transition state for hydrogen abstraction. In alkanes, the reactivity of C—H bonds lies in the order: tertiary > secondary > primary. Chlorination of 2-methylbutane at 300° gives the following pattern of reactivity:

$$\overset{\displaystyle 34\% \quad CH_3 \ 28\%}{\underset{\displaystyle 22\% \qquad 16\%}{CH_3-CH-CH_2-CH_3}}$$

When statistical correction for the available numbers of each type of hydrogen atom is applied, the reactivity ratio is roughly $4:3:1$ for tertiary, secondary, and primary hydrogens respectively. The results suggest that the tertiary radical is the most stable. This stability is due to hyperconjugation which is also responsible for the greater stability of tertiary rather than primary or secondary carbonium ions. A further illustration of the magnitude of structural effects is given in Table 4.2, the reactivities of secondary and tertiary C—H bonds being expressed relative to that of the primary C—H bond.

Table 4.2. Abstraction by Halogen Atoms

(reactivity relative to primary C—H)

Atom	CH₃	CH₂	CH
F	1	1·2	1·4
Cl	1 (1)	3·9 (0·52)	5·1 (0·35)
Br	1	82	1600

(CH₃ and CH₂ in butane; CH in 2-methylpropane.)
Energies of activation in parentheses

The selectivity greatly increases from F to Br, i.e. with decrease in the reactivity of the atom. The very high selectivity of bromine atoms is discussed later (p. 53).

Polar Effects. The pattern of orientation found in simple alkanes is profoundly influenced by polar substituents. Electron withdrawing groups generally slow down the removal of hydrogen by chlorine atoms from carbon atoms adjacent to them. The effects are shown in Tables 4.3 and 4.4.

Table 4.3. Effect of β-Substituents on Chlorination

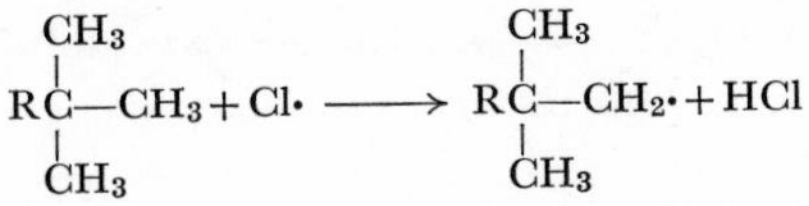

$$\underset{\overset{|}{CH_3}}{\overset{\overset{CH_3}{|}}{RC}}-CH_3 + Cl\cdot \longrightarrow \underset{\overset{|}{CH_3}}{\overset{\overset{CH_3}{|}}{RC}}-CH_2\cdot + HCl$$

R	Relative rate
t-Bu	1·2
Ph	1
p-NO₂C₆H₄	0.5
C₆H₅CO	0.4
ClCO	0.19
CN	0.17

47

Table 4.4. Relative Reactivities of C—H bonds towards Chlorine Atoms

C—C—CO₂H 1 0·6	C—C—C—C 1 3·6 3·6 1
C—C—C—CO₂H 1 3 0·2	C—C—C—C—F 1 3·7 1·7 0·9
C—C—CN 1 0·5	C—C—C—C—Cl 1 3·7 2·1 0·8
	C 0·25
C—C—C—O.COMe 1 1·3 0·8	C—C—C—Cl 1 3·5 3·7
C—C—C—CO₂Me 1 3·5 0	C—C—C—CF₃ 1 1·25 0
C—C—SO₂Cl 1 0	

The results of Table 4.3 show that a $-I$ effect, uncomplicated by resonance effects, causes deactivation towards *halogen atom* attack. It is evident that the chlorine atom is an electron acceptor and prefers reaction sites of high electron density. This effect is even more strikingly shown by the results in Table 4.4. There is no doubt that C—H bonds adjacent to carbonyl groups, for instance, are weakened and that the radical produced is resonance stabilized:

$$-\overset{\cdot}{\underset{|}{C}}-\overset{O}{\overset{\|}{C}}- \quad \longleftrightarrow \quad -\underset{|}{C}=\overset{\overset{O\cdot}{|}}{C}-$$

In these compounds, the chlorine atom is faced with the choice between (i) attack upon a weakly bound hydrogen atom α- to the substituent in a situation of low electron density, and (ii) attack further along the chain away from the substituent. In general, the inductive effect is more important and α-positions are deactivated. That this is not always so is shown by the values for 2-chlorobutane (Table 4.4). Tedder (1960) has discussed this situation in detail.

The reality of polar effects upon halogen atoms is demonstrated by the contrast shown between the α-C—H reactivities of isobutyryl chloride (*4.4*) towards chlorine atoms and methyl radicals:

$$\underset{\underset{H}{|}}{\overset{\overset{Me}{|}}{Me\overset{}{C}}}-COCl \xrightarrow{Cl_2} \underset{\underset{Cl}{|}}{\overset{\overset{Me}{|}}{Me\overset{}{C}}}-COCl + \underset{\underset{H}{|}}{\overset{\overset{CH_2Cl}{|}}{Me\overset{}{C}}}-COCl$$

(*4.4*)   reactivity ratio: αH:βH = 1.5:1

$$\underset{\underset{D}{|}}{\overset{\overset{Me}{|}}{Me\overset{}{C}}}-COCl \xrightarrow{Me\cdot} MeD(\alpha):MeH(\beta) = 12:1$$

(*4.4*)

Ignoring isotope effects, α-hydrogen abstraction for the non-polar methyl radical is very much more favourable than for the chlorine atom. The effect is even greater when allowance is made for the isotope effect; $k_H/k_D = 1.22$.

Quantitative measurements of polar effects in homolytic halogenation have been made using nuclear-substituted toluenes. Attack occurs at the methyl group and relative reactivities have been determined by competitive methods. The results for chlorination are given in the first column of Table 4.5 and show the progressive decrease in reactivity with increase in the electron withdrawal by the substituent. The Hammett† plot ($\log k/k_0 = \rho\sigma$) is linear with $\rho = -0.76$. An interesting consequence of the sensitivity of the chlorine atom to polar effects is seen in the fact that cyclohexane is four times as reactive as toluene (per C—H bond) in spite of the fact that resonance stabilized benzyl radicals are produced from the latter. It has been suggested that, as both reactions are exothermic, there is in any case little energy of activation to be reduced by stabilization of the radical produced (cf. p. 15) and electron accession to the reaction site consequently becomes the dominant effect. Cyclohexane is thus more reactive than toluene because the electron density

Table 4.5. Radical Attack on Substituted Toluenes

(Reactivities relative to toluene)

Substituent	Cl•	Br•	CCl₃•
p-MeO	—	6·6	14·2
p-Ph	1·59	—	—
p-t-Bu	1·44	1·51	—
p-Me	1·62	—	—
m-Me	1·33	—	1·58
None	1	1	1
m-MeO	—	—	0·87
p-Cl	0·72	—	0·73
m-Br	—	0·42	0·25
m-Cl	0·54	—	—
p-CN	0·38	0·25	—
p-NO₂	0·06	0·13	—
Relationship	σ	σ^+	σ^+

in the methyl group of the latter is lowered by the adjacent aromatic nucleus. Polar effects are considered further in the final section of this chapter.

† References to the Hammett equation are given at the end of the chapter.

Solvent Effects. In Chapter 1 it was pointed out that, owing to the electrical neutrality of radicals, solvent effects should be slight. An example of a specific type of solvent effect in alkane chlorination has, however, been observed by Russell (1958). 2,3-Dimethylbutane possesses only primary and tertiary C—H bonds and measurement of the extent of attack at each type of bond in a variety of solvents gave the results in Table 4.6.

Table 4.6. Chlorination of 2,3-Dimethylbutane

Solvent	tertiary/primary k_{rel}
2,3-Dimethylbutane	3·7
Carbon tetrachloride	3·5
Nitromethane	3·4
Nitrobenzene	4·7
Benzoyl chloride	6·4
Chlorobenzene	10
Benzene	14
Mesitylene	17
t-Butylbenzene	24
1-Chloronaphthalene	37

The tertiary/primary ratio obtained using the hydrocarbon itself as solvent is little changed in non-aromatic solvents but in aromatic solvents the selectivity increases greatly with increase in the basicity of the aromatic nucleus. This solvent effect is put down to the occurrence of π-complexing between the aromatic nucleus and the chlorine atom; π-complexed chlorine atoms (*4.5*) and (*4.6*) are considered to be capable

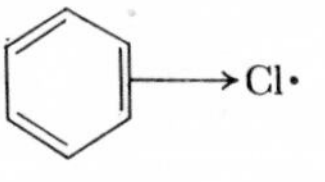

(*4.5*) 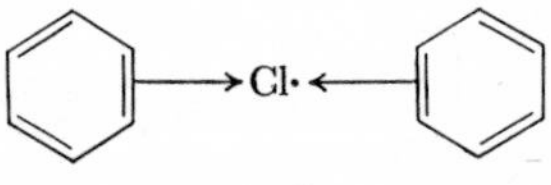   (*4.6*)

of the removal of tertiary hydrogens only; selectivity consequently increases with the increasing extent of complexing power of the solvent. Later work (Walling, 1959) has shown that not only specificity but the electrophilic character of the chlorine atom is increased by complex formation.

Steric Effects. The first transfer step (4.3a) (p. 44) of the chain sequence involves removal of a hydrogen atom and as this occurs at the molecular periphery, only slight steric effects are to be expected.

Table 4.7. Halogenation of Pentachloroethylbenzene

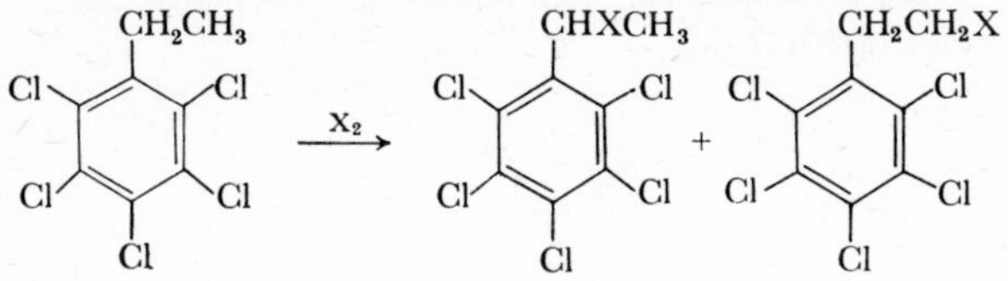

X	α-, %	β-, %
Cl_2	40	60
Br_2	100	0
Cl_2 (Ethylbenzene)	85	15

α-Chlorination in pentachloroethylbenzene (Table 4.7) is partially suppressed relative to ethylbenzene, but this effect is undoubtedly due in some measure to deactivation of the α-C—H bond by the nuclear chlorine atoms (cf. Table 4.5). Likewise the fluoro-derivative (*4.7*) reacts normally with chlorine at the α-position while the corresponding chloro-derivative (*4.8*) does not react under the same conditions. In these cases steric effects appear to operate in the attack of the chlorine atom upon the molecule [reaction (4.3a)], but instances of effects on the attack of the alkyl radical on the halogen molecule [reaction (4.3b)] have also been found. Norbornane (*4.9*) with molecular chlorine gives a mixture of chlorides and

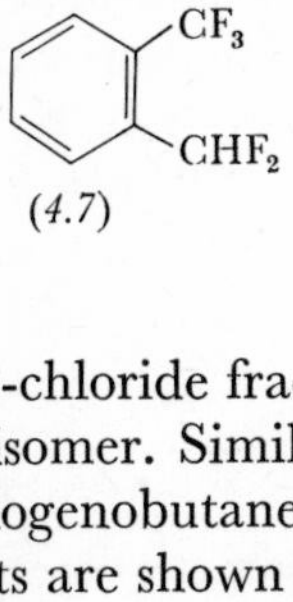

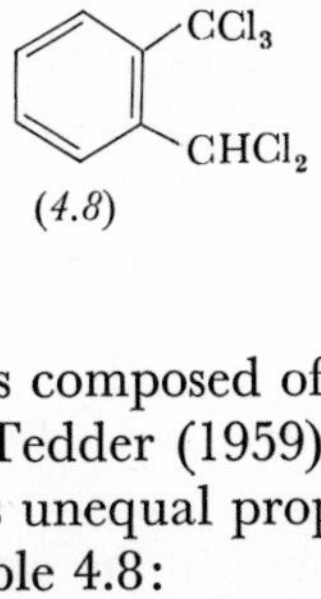

the 2-chloride fraction is composed of 70% of the *exo*- and 25% of the *endo*-isomer. Similarly, Tedder (1959) has shown that halogenation of 2-halogenobutanes gives unequal proportions of the 2,3-dihalides. The results are shown in Table 4.8:

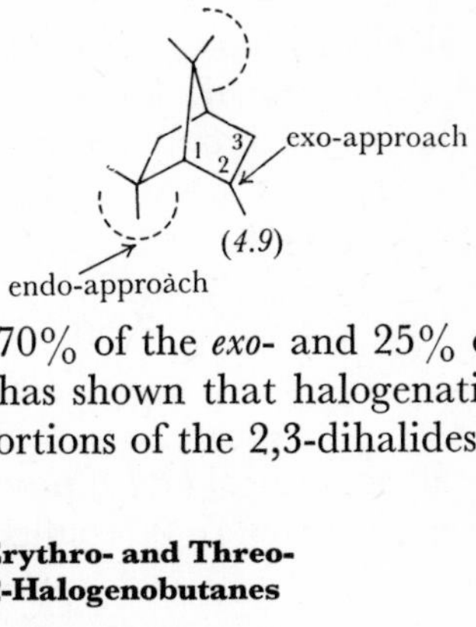

Table 4.8. Percentages of Erythro- and Threo-Dihalides obtained from 2-Halogenobutanes

$$CH_3CHYCH_2CH_3 \xrightarrow{X_2} CH_3CHYCHXCH_3$$

Halogen	Substituent	% Erythro	% Threo
Cl_2	Cl	71	29
F_2	Cl	67	33
Cl_2	F	59	41
F_2	F	60	40

51

In the most favourable conformation (*4.10*) of the 2-halogeno-1-methylpropyl radical, attack will occur on the side remote from Y, leading to erythro-dihalide.

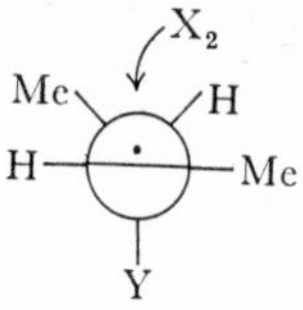

(*4.10*)

Table 4.8 shows that is it is the size of Y rather than X which is the main factor responsible for stereoselectivity.

Chlorination with Hypochlorites. Tertiary hypochlorites are easily prepared and are moderately stable but at temperatures around 50° are capable of chlorinating a variety of substrates. A chain mechanism involving transfer at the weak O—Cl bond is probable, e.g. for toluene and t-butyl hypochlorite:

$$t\text{-BuOCl} \longrightarrow t\text{-BuO}\cdot + \text{Cl}\cdot \qquad \ldots(4.7)$$

$$\text{PhCH}_3 + t\text{-BuO}\cdot \longrightarrow \text{PhCH}_2\cdot + t\text{-BuOH} \qquad \ldots(4.8)$$

$$\text{PhCH}_2\cdot + t\text{-BuOCl} \longrightarrow \text{PhCH}_2\text{Cl} + t\text{-BuO}\cdot \qquad \ldots(4.9)$$

When olefins with α-C—H bonds react with t-butyl hypochlorite, allylic chlorides are formed. An interesting example is the reaction with *cis*-but-2-ene in which only the *cis*-allylic chloride (*4.11*) is obtained:

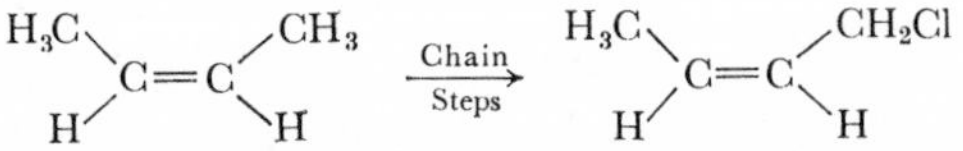

(*4.11*)

The allylic radical (*4.12*) produced in the first transfer step of propagation must therefore be configurationally stable. This configurational

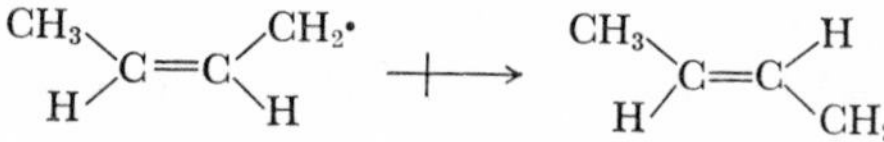

(*4.12*)   (*4.13*)

stability is understandable because maximum orbital overlap (corresponding to a resonance energy of 25 kcal/mole) is attained only when (*4.12*) is planar. Conversion to the *trans*-configuration (*4.13*), which must

52

involve rotation through a non-planar conformation, would result in the loss of this interaction.

Alicyclic tertiary hypochlorites, e.g. (*4.14*), give ω-chloroketones (*4.17*) on decomposition. Carbon–carbon bond cleavage occurs in the tertiary

(*4.14*)　　　(*4.15*)　　　(*4.16*)　　　(*4.17*)

alkoxy radical (*4.15*) to give the alkyl radical (*4.16*) which subsequently removes a chlorine atom from the original hypochlorite. Further examples of ring cleavage in cyclic alkoxy-radicals are discussed in Chapter 8.

BROMINATION

The success of homolytic bromination is very dependent upon energetic considerations. The alkyl radical-halogen molecule reaction (4.3b) is still exothermic, but the hydrogen abstraction step is endothermic by about 13 kcal/mole for all but the weakest C—H bonds (Table 4.1). Accordingly, one can predict that chains will be short; bromine atoms will be little inclined to participate in endothermic hydrogen abstraction and will be diverted to the more energetically favourable (and chain-breaking) reactions such as recombination. These predictions are borne out experimentally; the quantum yield in the photobromination of cyclohexane is 2. Secondly, one can predict that structural factors affecting the stability of the alkyl radical produced in reaction (4.3a), and hence the endothermicity of the reaction, will become critical, leading to great selectivity. Thus neopentane, with primary C—H bonds only, fails to brominate under normal conditions and iso-butane yields 95% of the tertiary bromide. When structural factors lower the C—H bond strength to such an extent that hydrogen abstraction becomes exothermic, bromination proceeds readily with high quantum yields. The energetics for the propagation steps in the bromination of toluene are as follows [D(PhCH$_2$—H) = 78 kcal/mole]:

$$PhCH_3 + Br\cdot \longrightarrow PhCH_2\cdot + HBr \qquad -9 \text{ kcal} \qquad \ldots(4.10)$$

$$PhCH_2\cdot + Br_2 \longrightarrow PhCH_2Br + Br\cdot \qquad -5 \text{ kcal} \qquad \ldots(4.11)$$

In spite of the fact that both steps are exothermic, the reaction is still much more selective than chlorination. The isotope effect ($k_H/k_D = 4\cdot6$) is more than double the value for chlorination, and whereas cyclohexane is more reactive than toluene in chlorination, toluene is more than two hundred times as reactive towards bromine atoms than cyclohexane. Effects on radical stability now operate very favourably in the reduction of the activation energy, and slight polar effects are swamped. Similarly steric effects are overshadowed by the need for a weak C—H bond; bromination of pentachloroethylbenzene (Table 4.7) gives only α-bromide. Polar effects in substituted toluenes (Table 4.5) are more pronounced in bromination but discussion of these is deferred to the final section of this chapter.

Skell and his collaborators (1963) have found that photobromination of (+)-1-bromo-2-methylbutane gives (−)-1,2-dibromo-2-methylbutane of high optical purity (cf. p. 46). They suggest that a bridged radical (*4.18*) is formed which can hold its configuration until reacting with a bromine molecule. In reactions with chlorine or t-butyl hypochlorite, however, the second stage is slower; the bridged radical isomerizes to the open chain form (*4.19*) which racemizes and racemic bromo-chloride is produced.

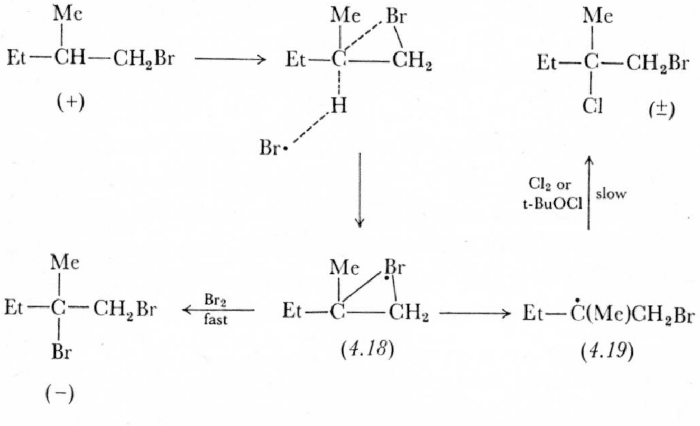

Bromination with N-Bromosuccinimide. This method of bromination has assumed great importance in organic chemistry particularly because of its use for selective allylic bromination of olefins without concurrent addition of bromine to the double bond. The reaction with cyclohexene, for example, gives the bromide (*4.20*) in 87% yield:

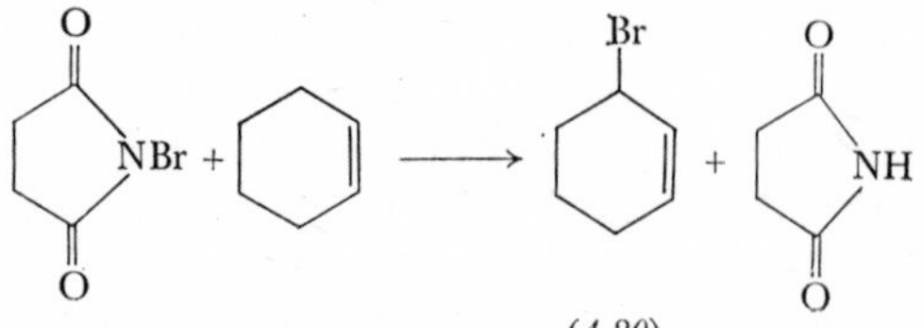

(*4.20*)

The reagent is also used for α-bromination of ketones and synthesis of benzylic bromides; in both reactions weak C—H bonds are involved. Cholestan-3-one yields the 2-bromo-ketone in 66% yield and fluorene gives 61% of the 9-bromide.

The reactions are catalysed by light and peroxides, and while a radical mechanism clearly operates, the details are controversial. Until recently, a chain mechanism involving succinimido-radicals was generally favoured:

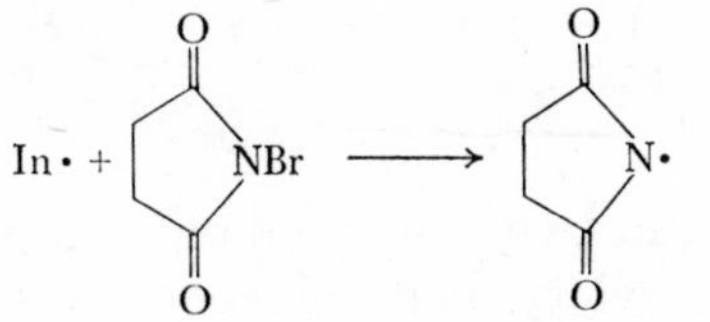

$$\text{In}\cdot + \underset{O}{\overset{O}{\text{NBr}}} \longrightarrow \underset{O}{\overset{O}{\text{N}\cdot}} \qquad \ldots(4.12)$$

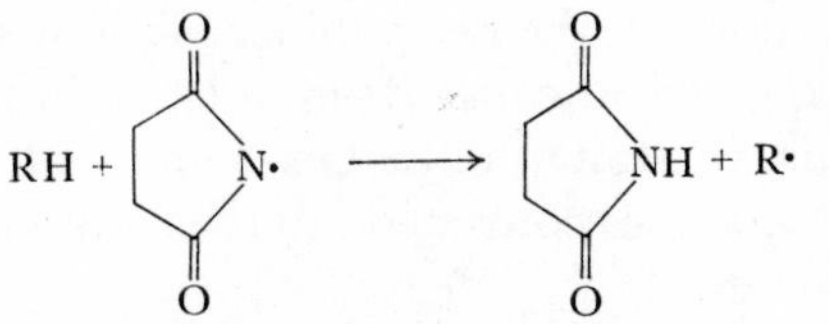

$$\text{RH} + \underset{O}{\overset{O}{\text{N}\cdot}} \longrightarrow \underset{O}{\overset{O}{\text{NH}}} + \text{R}\cdot \qquad \ldots(4.13)$$

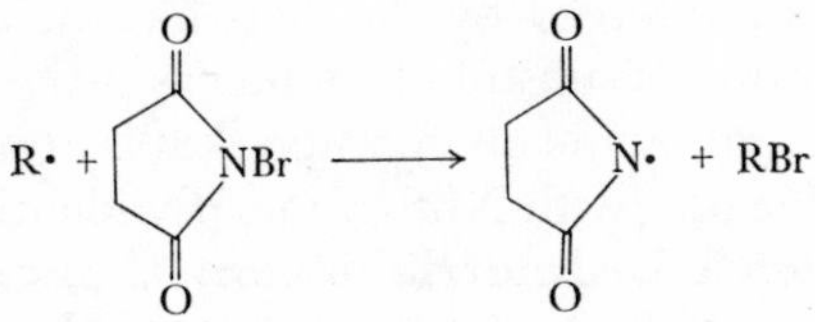

$$\text{R}\cdot + \underset{O}{\overset{O}{\text{NBr}}} \longrightarrow \underset{O}{\overset{O}{\text{N}\cdot}} + \text{RBr} \qquad \ldots(4.14)$$

A recent alternative view of the reaction is that the function of N-bromosuccinimide is to provide molecular bromine and hence bromine atoms in very low concentrations (reactions 4.15 and 4.16):

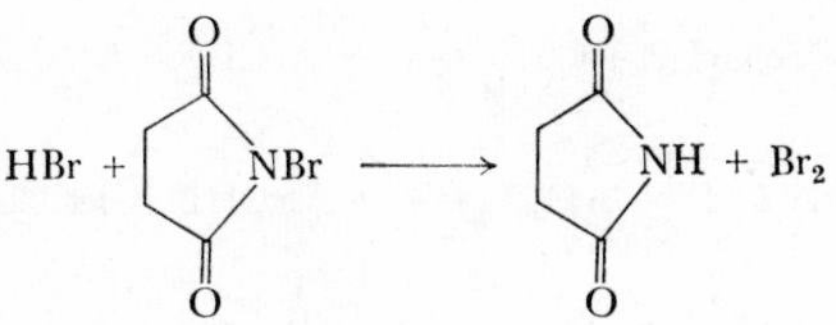

$$\text{HBr} + \underset{O}{\overset{O}{\text{NBr}}} \longrightarrow \underset{O}{\overset{O}{\text{NH}}} + \text{Br}_2 \qquad \ldots(4.15)$$

$$\text{Br}_2 \longrightarrow \text{Br}\cdot \qquad \ldots(4.16)$$

Addition of bromine to olefins is known from other studies (Chapter 6) to be reversible. Thus, at low concentrations of bromine, when there is less chance of radical (*4.21*) going on to dibromide, formation of the allylic radical (*4.22*) and hence of the allylic bromide (*4.23*) is favoured.

$$
\begin{array}{c}
\overset{\displaystyle \text{Br}}{\underset{|}{}} \\
-\text{CH}_2\overset{\cdot}{\text{C}}\text{HCH}- \xrightarrow{\text{Br}_2} \\
(4.21)
\end{array}
\qquad
\begin{array}{c}
\overset{\displaystyle \text{Br Br}}{\underset{|\ \ |}{}} \\
-\text{CH}_2\text{CHCH}- \\
\end{array}
\qquad \dots(4.17)
$$

Br· + —CH$_2$CH=CH—

$$
\text{HBr} + -\overset{\cdot}{\text{C}}\text{HCH}=\text{CH}- \xrightarrow{\text{Br}_2} -\overset{\overset{\displaystyle \text{Br}}{|}}{\text{C}}\text{HCH}=\text{CH}- \qquad \dots(4.18)
$$

$$(4.22) \qquad\qquad\qquad (4.23)$$

Allylic bromination can, in fact, be carried out with bromine instead of N-bromosuccinimide, provided that the concentration of bromine is kept low and the hydrogen bromide produced is removed. Further, if the latter mechanism is correct, the reversibility of the first stage of reaction (4.17) would be expected to cause *cis-trans* isomerization of olefins. In agreement with this, treatment of *cis*-hex-3-ene with small amounts of N-bromosuccinimide causes conversion to the *cis-trans* mixture in which the latter predominates.

The conclusion that the function of NBS is to provide low concentrations of bromine is reinforced by the fact that the $\sigma^+\rho$ correlation for side-chain bromination of substituted toluenes gives identical values of ρ for each reagent, and by the observation that isotope effects for bromination with bromine and with NBS are nearly identical.

Bromination with Bromotrichloromethane. Ultra-violet irradiation of mixtures of bromotrichloromethane and alkylbenzenes causes hydrogen–bromine interchange with formation of α-bromoalkylbenzenes according to the sequence:

$$\text{BrCCl}_3 \longrightarrow \text{Br}\cdot + \text{CCl}_3\cdot \qquad \dots(4.19)$$

$$\text{ArCH}_2\text{R} + \text{CCl}_3\cdot \longrightarrow \text{Ar}\overset{\cdot}{\text{C}}\text{HR} + \text{CHCl}_3 \qquad \dots(4.20)$$

$$\text{Ar}\overset{\cdot}{\text{C}}\text{HR} + \text{BrCCl}_3 \longrightarrow \text{ArCHBrR} + \text{CCl}_3\cdot \qquad \dots(4.21)$$

Trichloromethyl is the 'chain-carrying' radical.

The reaction is not of practical significance because N-bromosuccinimide is a more convenient reagent, but the results obtained for the relative reactivities of substituted toluenes (Table 4.5) are of interest. These give a measure of the polar affects on the abstraction of hydrogen by the trichloromethyl radical (below).

POLAR EFFECTS ON HYDROGEN TRANSFER DURING HALOGENATION

Russell has discussed this topic in detail and his conclusions may be summarized as follows:

In a reaction in which the abstracting radical, $x\cdot$, is highly reactive (i.e. E_A is low) the transition state is considered to resemble the reactants. Hence, in reactions with chlorine atoms, there is little bond breaking in the transition state (*4.24*) and the dominant effect on C—H bond reactivity is the electron density of the bond. This, in the case of substituted toluenes, is related to Hamett's σ and the linear relationship between $\log(k/k_0)$ and σ supports these conclusions. With less reactive radicals, the transition state resembles the products more closely, the degree of bond

$$R\text{—}H \quad \cdot X \qquad\qquad R \overset{\cdot\cdot}{\underset{\cdot}{\ldots}} H \overset{\cdot\cdot}{\ldots} X \longleftrightarrow \overset{+}{R} \overset{\cdot\cdot}{\ldots} H \overset{\cdot\cdot}{\underset{\cdot}{\ldots}} \overset{-}{X}$$

$$(4.24) \qquad\qquad\qquad\qquad (4.25)$$

breaking becomes considerable, and charge separation develops (*4.25*). For reactions with bromine, *N*-bromosuccinimide, and bromotrichloromethane, $\log(k/k_0)$ is no longer linearly related to σ. This is not surprising as resonance effects may now *directly* control the stability of the carbonium ion-like transition state. Direct resonance effects are much better accommodated by σ^+ values for substituents, which are a measure of their effect on the ease of carbonium ion formation in the solvolysis of $\alpha\alpha$-dimethylbenzyl halides. The transition state (*4.26*) for these reactions has obvious analogies with (*4.25*):

$$PhC(Me)_2Cl \longrightarrow [Ph\overset{+}{C}(Me)_2\overset{-}{Cl}] \longrightarrow Ph\overset{+}{C}(Me)_2 + \overset{-}{Cl}$$

$$(4.26)$$

For further reading

BIGELOW, 'Fluorination of Paraffins and Cycloparaffins', *Chem. Rev.*, 1947, **40**, 51.
Hypochlorites: WALLING, *J. Amer. chem. Soc.*, 1962, **84**, 3326, and preceding papers.
N-Bromosuccinimide: SKELL, *J. Amer. chem. Soc.*, 1963, **85**, 2849. McGRATH and TEDDER, *Proc. chem. Soc.*, 1961, 80.
TEDDER, *Quart. Rev.*, 1960, **14**, 336.
The Hammett Equation: JAFFE, *Chem. Rev.*, 1953, **53**, 191.
WALLING, *Free Radicals in Solution*, Chapter 8. Wiley, New York, 1957.

PROBLEMS

1. Sulphuryl chloride can replace chlorine in radical initiated chlorinations. Formulate a reaction scheme. The $\alpha:\beta$ ratio for side-chain attack on isopropylbenzene is 80 for sulphuryl chloride and 13 for chlorine. Suggest a reason for this difference.

2. Account for the observation that reaction of dibenzyl with N-bromosuccinimide gives chiefly the *meso-α,α'*-dibromide. How would you show which hydrogen atom is removed in the bromination of α-bromodibenzyl and which would you expect to be removed?

3. Cyclohexanone oxime is obtained from the irradiation of a mixture of cyclohexane and nitrosyl chloride. Write a mechanism for this reaction.

4. Decomposition of acetyl peroxide in 2-phenylbutane $[\alpha]_D = +9\cdot94$ gave the inactive dimer, 3,4-dimethyl-3,4-diphenylhexane. The recovered 2-phenylbutane had $[\alpha]_D = +9\cdot67$. What do you deduce from this experiment?

5. Bromination of $(+)$-1-bromo-2-methylbutane with N-bromosuccinimide gives $(\pm)$-1,2-dibromo-2-methylbutane (cf. p. 54). Suggest an explanation for this observation.

CHAPTER 5

AUTOXIDATION

Autoxidation is defined as 'the reaction of molecular oxygen with organic compounds which does not involve inflammation and occurs at temperatures not significantly in excess of 100°'. With the exception of radical polymerization (Chapter 7), autoxidation is probably the most important radical reaction from the technical standpoint. This is not only because of its occurrence in the drying of paints and the cumene process for phenol manufacture, but also because of its undesirable effects in, for example, the perishing of rubber and the deterioration of edible oils. A wide variety of functional groups react with oxygen by what are probably radical processes, but this discussion will be limited to those reactions in which C—H and O—H bonds are broken, and C—O bonds made.

AUTOXIDATIONS WITH CHAIN MECHANISMS

Carbon–hydrogen bonds are susceptible to attack by molecular oxygen, the initial products being of the type ROOH. The reactions are catalysed by light, radical sources such as azonitriles, and by the hydroperoxide products themselves. This last feature makes many autoxidations autocatalytic. Inhibition by hydroquinones and other general inhibitors of radical chain reactions points to a radical mechanism for the reactions.

Products of autoxidation are frequently complex because of side reactions but the following simple mechanism covers most observations (R = alkyl or acyl):

$$\text{In·} + \text{RH} \longrightarrow \text{R·} \qquad \ldots(5.1) \qquad \text{Initiation}$$

$$\left.\begin{array}{ll} \text{R·} + \text{O}_2 \longrightarrow \text{ROO·} & \ldots(5.2a) \\ \text{ROO·} + \text{RH} \longrightarrow \text{ROOH} + \text{R·} & \ldots(5.2b) \end{array}\right\} \text{Propagation}$$

$$\left.\begin{array}{l} \text{ROO·} + \text{R·} \longrightarrow \text{ROOR} \\ \text{R·} + \text{R·} \longrightarrow \text{RR} \qquad \ldots(5.3) \\ 2\text{ROO·} \longrightarrow \text{ROOR} + \text{O}_2 \end{array}\right\} \begin{array}{l} \text{Termination} \\ \text{(non-radical} \\ \text{products)} \end{array}$$

Hydrocarbons. The reaction scheme presented above is closely similar to that involved in halogenation (Chapter 4). Autoxidation, however, differs from chlorination in that the alkylperoxy radicals (ROO·) produced in reaction (5.2a) are much less reactive in hydrogen abstraction reactions (5.2b) than chlorine atoms. This weak reactivity of the alkylperoxy radical accounts for the inhibition of radical chlorination by oxygen, and restricts the range of C—H bonds that are susceptible to attack in reaction (5.2b).

The first propagation stage (5.2a) is very rapid as befits what is tantamount to a combination reaction. The polystyrene radical, for example, attacks oxygen about 10^5 times as fast as it reacts with a molecule of styrene (cf. Table 7.2, Chapter 7) and the ratio $k_{5\cdot2a} : k_{5\cdot2b}$ is known to be about 10^8.

On account of the weak reactivity of alkyl peroxy radicals, only tertiary C—H bonds are usually attacked to give good yields of hydroperoxide, unless other factors which reduce the C—H bond strength operate. Thus decalin is converted readily to the tertiary hydroperoxide (*5.1*) which is a key intermediate in the synthesis of C_{10} ring compounds.

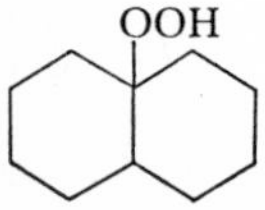

(*5.1*) 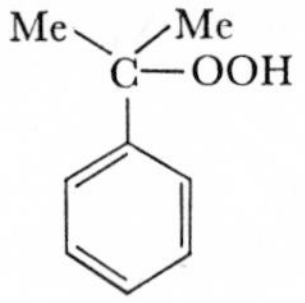   (*5.2*) 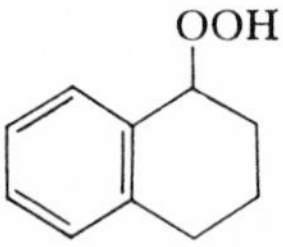   (*5.3*) 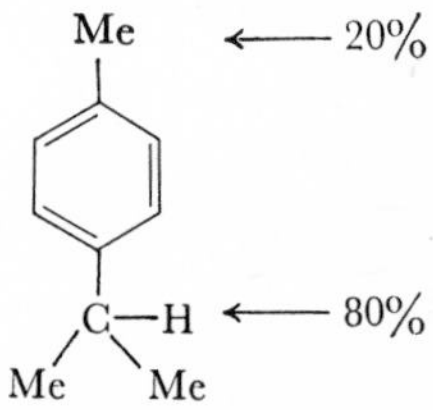   (*5.4*)

Compounds containing benzylic C—H bonds in which D(C—H) is reduced by 15–20 kcal/mole autoxidize readily, the hydroperoxides (*5.2*) and (*5.3*) being derived from cumene and tetralin respectively. Quite marked selectivity is however shown; the relative propagation rates in the series PhCH$_3$: PhEt : Phi–Pr are $0\cdot08 : 0\cdot6 : 1\cdot00$, and in *p*-cymene (*5.4*) only 20% of the primary hydroperoxide is formed. Allylic C—H bonds also take part readily in autoxidation. Cyclohexene gives cyclohexenyl hydroperoxide (*5.5*), and reaction with the allylic positions in unsaturated esters (p. 66) is the first stage of film formation from paints.

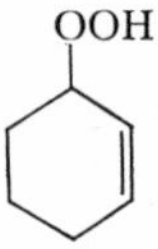

(*5.5*)

$$CH_3(CH_2)_6CD_2CH{=}CHCD_2(CH_2)_6CH_3$$

(*5.6*)

The isotope effect, $k_H/k_D = 5$, has been determined for the olefin (5.6) and this figure is comparable with that found for radical bromination of toluene (p. 53).

Initiation. Because of the slowness of many autoxidations, reactions are often carried out at around 100°, but at this temperature decomposition of the hydroperoxide becomes significant:

$$ROOH \longrightarrow RO\cdot + \cdot OH \qquad \qquad \ldots(5.4)$$

$$2ROOH \longrightarrow RO\cdot + H_2O + ROO\cdot \qquad \ldots(5.5)$$

A compromise must therefore be found between a useful reaction rate and serious loss of product. Initiation of chains by radicals derived from hydroperoxide decomposition is important, and accounts for the auto-catalysis mentioned earlier. In the early stages of the cyclohexene–oxygen reaction, the rate of oxygen uptake is proportional to the amount of oxygen already absorbed. Induction periods are frequent in autoxidations; they indicate the time lag required to build up a concentration of hydroperoxide sufficient to sustain initiation. The induction period of several hours in tetralin autoxidation disappears when 5% of tetralyl hydroperoxide is added initially. Radical sources, such as benzoyl peroxide and azonitriles can also initiate autoxidation; the rate is then proportional to $[\text{In}]^{1/2}$.

Catalysis and Inhibition. Transition metal ions, capable of donating or accepting single electrons, act as catalysts in autoxidations by reacting with the hydroperoxide to produce radicals. This catalysis has been formulated in a number of ways, the most common being given in reactions (5.6) and (5.7):

$$ROOH + M^{n+} \longrightarrow RO\cdot + OH^{\ominus} + M^{(n+1)+} \qquad \ldots(5.6)$$

$$ROOH + M^{(n+1)+} \longrightarrow ROO\cdot + H^{\oplus} + M^{n+} \qquad \ldots(5.7)$$

The sum of these consecutive reactions is equivalent to the bimolecular thermal decomposition, reaction (5.5), so that the role of the metal ion is genuinely catalytic. Cobalt and iron salts are widely used and have immense importance, both in inducing hydroperoxide decomposition in the autoxidation of unsaturated esters (p. 66) and in catalysis of the conversion of p-xylene to terephthalic acid for 'terylene' manufacture.

Inhibition of autoxidation is likewise of the first importance in prevention of the deterioration of organic compounds exposed to air. A wide variety of compounds, chiefly phenols and amines, have been used empirically for this purpose. Inhibition by hydroquinones is

61

considered to involve stepwise removal of hydroxyl hydrogens yielding benzoquinone via the semiquinone radical (*5.7*):

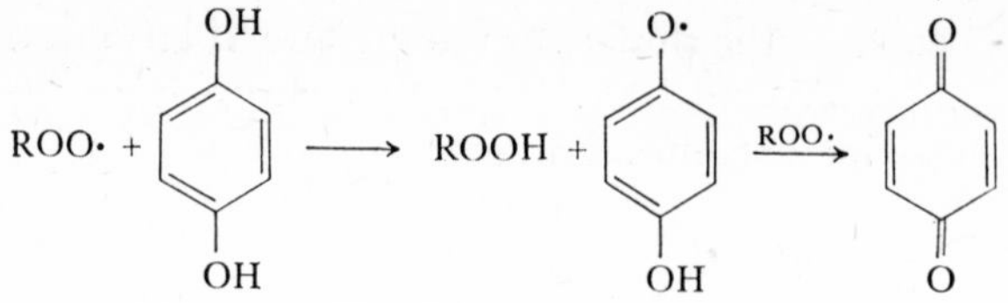

(*5.7*)

Inhibition by simple phenols involves an abstraction–combination sequence, e.g.:

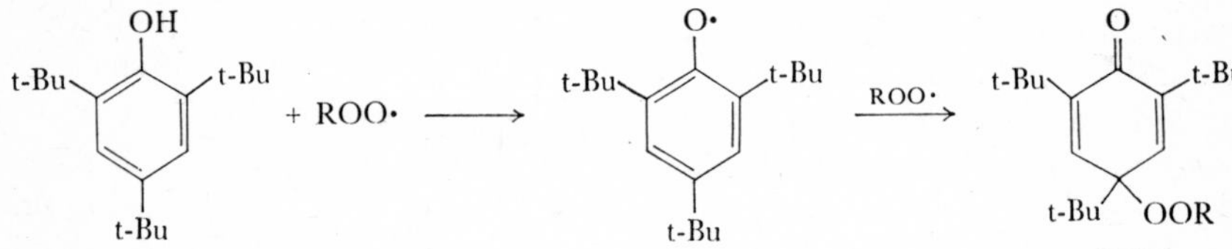

(*5.8*)

Cyclohexadienone peroxides, cf. (*5.8*), have been obtained by generation of alkyl radicals in the presence of oxygen and trialkylphenols, and parallels are found between inhibitor efficiency and oxidation–reduction potential. Inhibition mechanisms are, however, complex and there is not universal agreement about details.

Aldehyde Autoxidation. Autoxidation of aldehydes occurs very readily—the formation of 'collars' of benzoic acid on bottles of benzaldehyde is a familiar manifestation. The initial products of reactions with aldehydes are peracids:

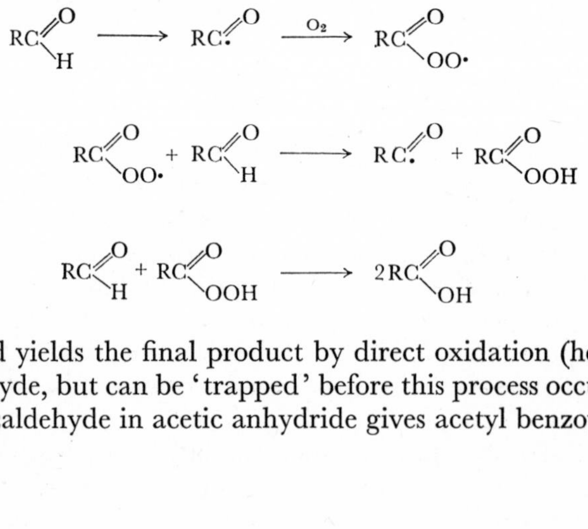

The peracid yields the final product by direct oxidation (heterolytic?) of the aldehyde, but can be 'trapped' before this process occurs. Oxidation of benzaldehyde in acetic anhydride gives acetyl benzoyl peroxide (*5.9*):

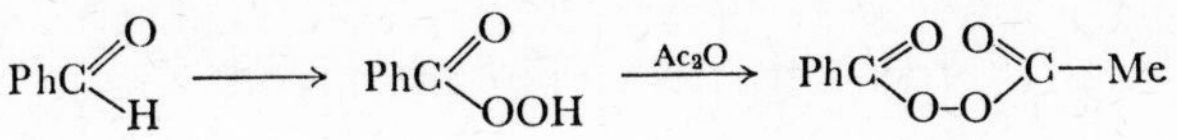

$$PhC\!\!\diagup_{H}^{O} \longrightarrow PhC\!\!\diagup_{OOH}^{O} \xrightarrow{Ac_2O} PhC\!\!\diagup_{O-O}^{O\ O}\!\!\diagdown C\!-\!Me$$

(5.9)

The high reactivity of aldehydes in autoxidation (Table 5.1) is accounted for by the comparatively weak $CO-H$ bond and the stability of the acyl radical produced.

Table 5.1. Relative Propagation Rates in Autoxidation

$ROO\cdot + RH \longrightarrow ROOH + R\cdot$	
Oct-1-ene	0.03
Cyclohexene	2
1-Methylcyclohexene	3.3
Tetralin	13
Ethyl linoleate	18
Decanal	2800
Benzaldehyde	8000

Aldehyde autoxidation is catalysed by transition metal salts acting as electron acceptors:

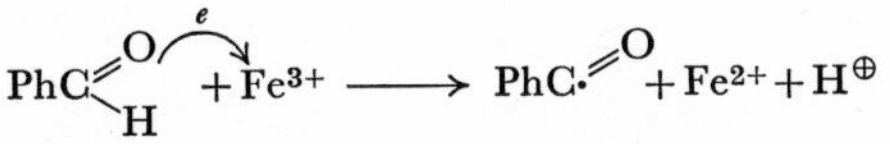

$$PhC\!\!\diagup_{H}^{O}\,\overset{e}{\frown}\,+Fe^{3+} \longrightarrow PhC\cdot\!\diagup^{O} + Fe^{2+} + H^{\oplus}$$

and is inhibited by iodide ion which donates electrons:

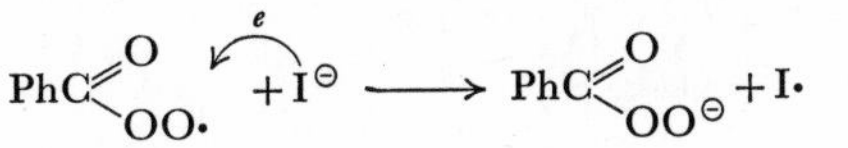

$$PhC\!\!\diagup_{OO\cdot}^{O}\,\overset{e}{\frown}\,+I^{\ominus} \longrightarrow PhC\!\!\diagup_{OO^{\ominus}}^{O} + I\cdot$$

The iodine atoms produced are too unreactive to participate in subsequent propagation steps.

Ethers. Provided that $C-H$ bonds α- to the oxygen atom are present, these compounds autoxidize readily with formation of α-hydroperoxy ethers (5.10). The $C-H$ bond adjacent to oxygen is particularly vulnerable to attack as the radical produced is significantly stabilized (cf. p. 154). The hazard associated with old specimens of ethers in contact with air is due to the formation of poly-alkylidene peroxides (5.11) by subsequent condensation of the α-alkoxy hydroperoxides:

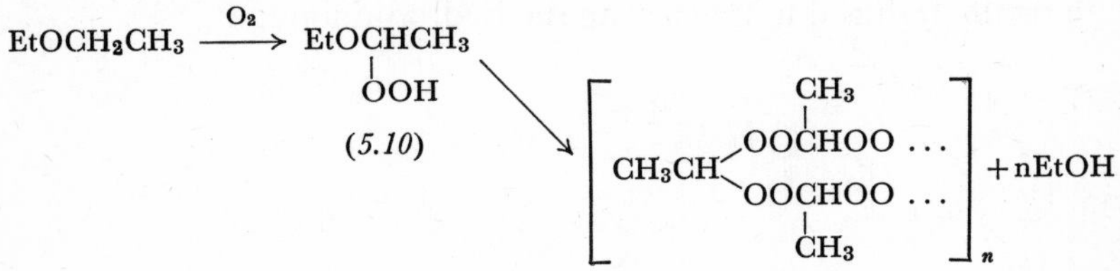

$$EtOCH_2CH_3 \xrightarrow{O_2} \underset{\underset{OOH}{|}}{EtOCHCH_3}$$

(5.10)

$$\left[CH_3CH\!\!\diagup_{OOCHOO\,\ldots}^{\overset{\overset{CH_3}{|}}{OOCHOO\,\ldots}}\underset{\underset{CH_3}{|}}{} \right]_n + nEtOH$$

(5.11)

63

NON-CHAIN AUTOXIDATIONS

O—H Homolysis. Solutions of hydroquinones in basic media react rapidly with oxygen, frequently giving highly coloured materials which are difficult to isolate and identify. The use of alkaline pyrogallol (1,2,3-trihydroxybenzene) for quantitative oxygen absorption is familiar. A simple instance of the reaction is that with durohydroquinone (*5.12*) which gives duroquinone (*5.13*) and hydrogen peroxide quantitatively:

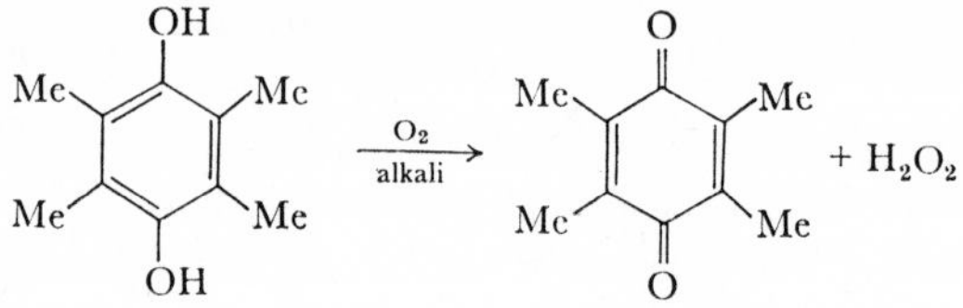

$$(5.12) \qquad\qquad (5.13)$$

This reaction, in contrast to those of the preceding section, is quinone *catalysed* and the rate is then independent of oxygen pressure. The mechanism is as follows:

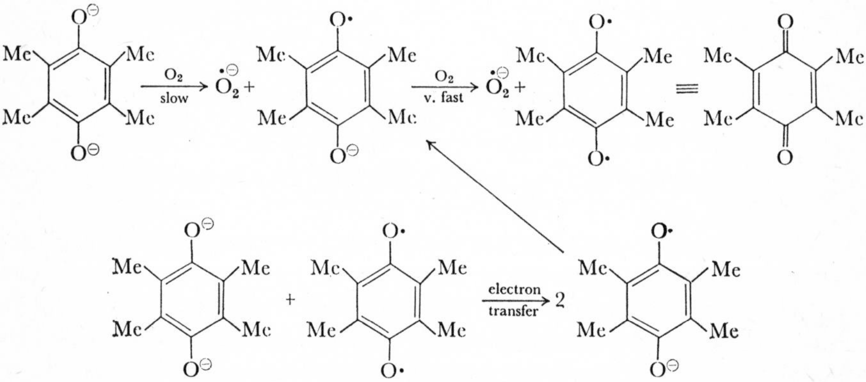

The peroxy radical ions ($O_2^{\cdot\ominus}$) which are produced, react rapidly with any oxidizable species present, e.g. hydroquinone, yielding hydrogen peroxide. In a process for hydrogen peroxide manufacture, 2-ethylanthrahydroquinone is autoxidized and the quinone produced is catalytically reduced to regenerate the hydroquinone:

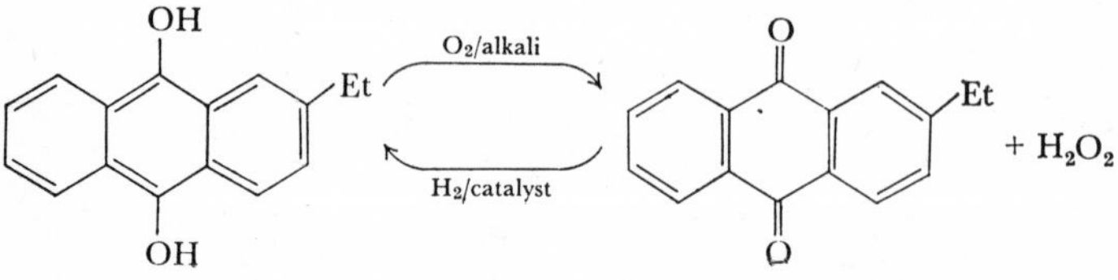

64

Most phenols, however, particularly members of the polyhydric series, give very complex product mixtures. This is due chiefly to the occurrence of nuclear coupling (cf. Chapter 10) and to combination of hydroperoxy radicals with radicals produced from the phenol. The peroxides formed in the latter case subsequently break down.

Photo-oxidation of Dienes. Irradiation of 1,3-dienes in the presence of oxygen yields cyclic peroxides of the general structure (*5.14*); the reaction has obvious analogies with the Diels–Alder reaction:

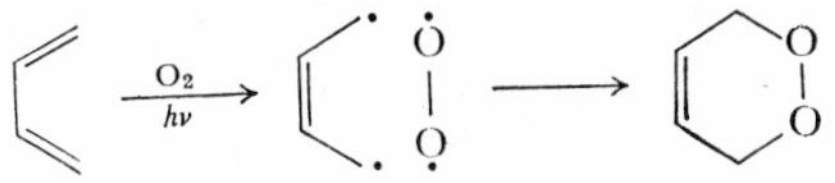

$$(5.14)$$

The original example was rubrene (*5.15*) whose solutions, when illuminated, absorb oxygen with formation of the endoperoxide (*5.16*)

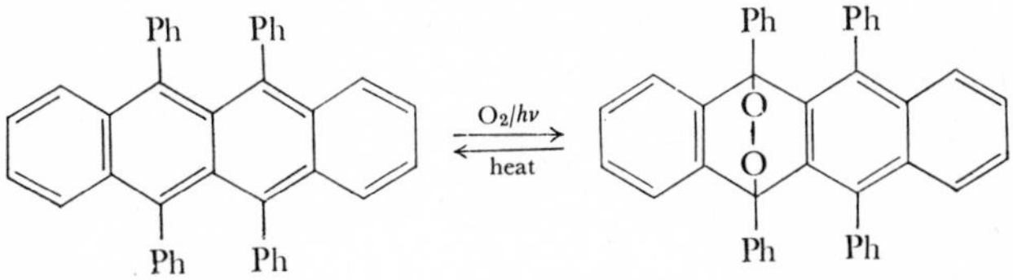

(*5.15*)   (*5.16*)

This reaction, unlike most other examples, is reversible; oxygen is regenerated when the endoperoxide is heated *in vacuo*. Similar photo-oxidation products are obtained from anthracene and the higher linear fused polycyclic aromatics. The reaction with hexacene occurs so easily that air must be excluded when handling the hydrocarbon.

Simple dienes require the presence of photosensitizers such as chlorophyll or eosin before endoperoxide formation takes place. One example is ascaridole (*5.18*), obtained from α-terpinene (*5.17*):

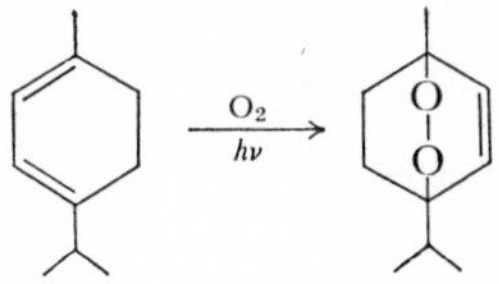

(*5.17*)   (*5.18*)

A number of endoperoxides derived from alicyclic dienes is listed by Davies (p. 67) and they have frequently been encountered in the

65

steroids. Formation of the endoperoxide (*5.20*) from ergosterol (*5.19*) was an early observation in structural investigations of vitamin D.

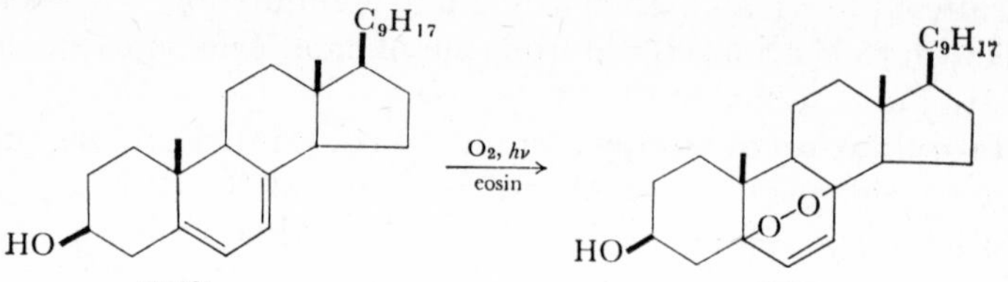

(*5.19*)   (*5.20*)

TECHNICAL IMPORTANCE OF AUTOXIDATION

Autoxidation is of great commercial significance in two respects— useful reactions can be exploited and undesirable ones prevented or inhibited.

A simple autoxidation of great technical importance is that of cumene. The product, cumene hydroperoxide (*5.21*), on acid hydrolysis, gives a mixture of phenol and acetone:

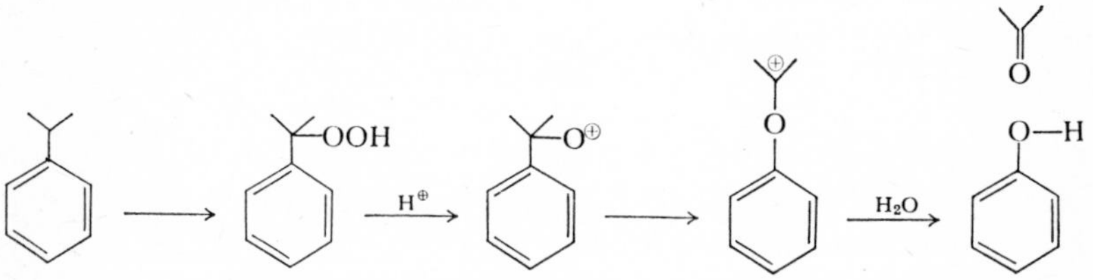

(*5.21*)

This process yielded 200,000 tons of phenol in 1959 and depends upon the ready availability from petroleum of propene and benzene, the starting materials for cumene manufacture.

The drying of paint to give a tough protective covering is due to the so-called 'drying oils' that it contains. These are predominantly the esters of the unsaturated acids, oleic, linoleic, and linolenic. It can be seen from the structures (below) that while oleic acid possesses two

	Relative autoxidation rates
$CH_3(CH_2)_6\overset{11}{C}H_2\overset{10}{C}H{=}\overset{9}{C}H\overset{8}{C}H_2(CH_2)_6CO_2H$ oleic	1
$CH_3(CH_2)_3\overset{14}{C}H_2\overset{13}{C}H{=}\overset{12}{C}H\overset{11}{C}H_2\overset{10}{C}H{=}\overset{9}{C}H\overset{8}{C}H_2(CH_2)_6CO_2H$ linoleic	12
$CH_3\overset{17}{C}H_2\overset{16}{C}H{=}\overset{15}{C}H\overset{14}{C}H_2\overset{13}{C}H{=}\overset{12}{C}H\overset{11}{C}H_2\overset{10}{C}H{=}\overset{9}{C}H\overset{8}{C}H_2(CH_2)_6CO_2H$ linolenic	25

'singly allylic' positions (8 and 11) in linoleic acid there is a 'doubly allylic' position (11) and in linolenic acid, two 'doubly allylic' positions (11 and 14). The relative rates of autoxidation suggest that, as would be expected, radical attack occurs at a 'doubly allylic' position if this is present. Conjugation is developed as autoxidation proceeds; attack of oxygen on the mesomeric radical (*5.22*) occurs so as to give the conjugated hydroperoxide:

$$—CH{=}CHCH_2CH{=}CH— \longrightarrow —CH{=}CH\overset{\cdot}{C}HCH{=}CH—$$

$$\begin{array}{c} OOH \\ | \\ —CHCH{=}CHCH{=}CH— \end{array} \quad\overset{O_2}{\longleftarrow}\quad —\overset{\cdot}{C}HCH{=}CHCH{=}CH— \qquad (5.22)$$

Analysis confirms that the hydroperoxy group in autoxidized linoleic acid is attached mainly at the 9 and 13 positions. 'Drying' of oils is caused by decomposition of the hydroperoxides. This is catalysed by 'driers'—transition metal salts—and polymerization follows by attack of the radicals produced on the unsaturated systems present.

$$ROOH + M^{++} \longrightarrow RO{\cdot} + \overset{\ominus}{O}H + M^{3+}$$
e.g. Co, Mn

Prevention of the undesired autoxidation of unsaturated compounds is similarly of the first importance. Natural rubber is a non-conjugated polyene and thus possesses allylic positions susceptible to oxidative attack. 'Perishing' is the familiar result and for this reason anti-oxidants are added. Popular ones are phenols, e.g. 2,6-di-t-butyl-*p*-cresol, and dihydroquinolines produced cheaply from ketones and primary aromatic amines.

Unsaturated fats and oils for dietary use deteriorate when in contact with air for the same reason. Inhibitors are again used as 'chain-breakers' in the autoxidation sequence. Esters of gallic (3,4,5-trihydroxybenzoic) acid are often employed for this purpose.

For further reading

Anti-oxidants: INGOLD, *Chem. Rev.*, 1961, **61**, 563.
Autoxidation and Antioxidants (ed. Lundberg). WILEY, 1961 (Vol. I); 1962 (Vol. II).
BATEMAN, *Quart. Rev.*, 1954, **8**, 147.
DAVIES, *Organic Peroxides*. Butterworths, London, 1961.
HAWKINS, *Organic Peroxides*. Spon, 1961.
RUSSELL, *J. chem. Educ.*, 1959, **36**, 111.
SCOTT, *Chem. & Ind.*, 1962, 271.
Technical Aspects: KIRK-OTHMER, *Encyclopedia of Chemical Technology*. Interscience, 1952.
WALLING, *Free Radicals in Solution*, Chapter 9. Wiley, 1957.

PROBLEMS

Explain the following:

(*a*) The bis-hydroperoxide (1) is obtained in 95% yield (based on oxygen uptake) from the reaction of 2,4-dimethylpentane with 0·1 mole of oxygen.

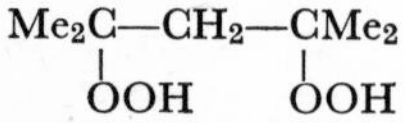

$$Me_2C-CH_2-CMe_2$$

$$\underset{OOH}{|} \qquad \underset{OOH}{|}$$

(1)

OAc

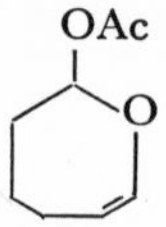

(2)    (3)

$(-SCH_2CH_2CH_2CH_2CHO)_2$

(4)

(*b*) Autoxidation of cyclohexane in acetic anhydride gives the acetate (2).

(*c*) Partial autoxidation of the sulphide (3) gives the disulphide (4).

(*d*) Autoxidation of methylcyclopentane gives 6-hydroperoxyhexan-2-one.

(*e*) Autoxidation of 2-ethylhexanal gives heptane and 3-hydroperoxyheptane.

(*f*) Autoxidation of 2-nitropropane under basic conditions gives acetone and nitrite ion.

CHAPTER 6

ADDITION TO OLEFINS—SMALL MOLECULE FORMATION

Addition of a radical A· to an olefin yields a new radical (6.1) whose subsequent behaviour will be considered in this and the following Chapter. This new radical may add to another molecule of olefin, reaction (6.2), and if successive additions occur, the process is termed *polymerization*. If, however, the radical participates in abstraction, reaction (6.3), with a molecule A—B possessing readily removable atoms, the product (6.2) is a 1:1 adduct of the addendum A—B and the olefin.

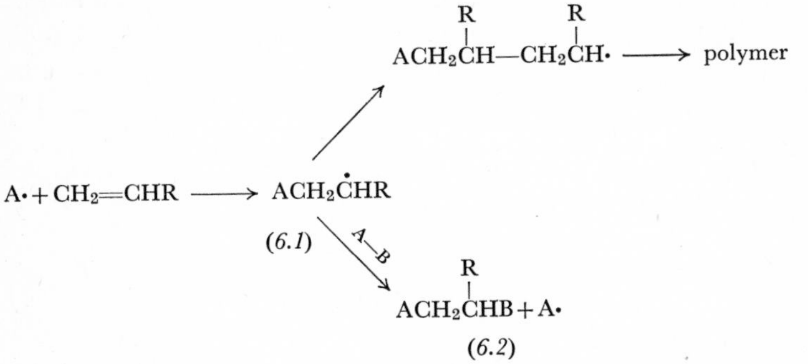

$$ACH_2\overset{R}{\underset{|}{C}}H—CH_2\overset{R}{\underset{|}{C}}H· \longrightarrow polymer \qquad ...(6.2)$$

$$A·+CH_2{=}CHR \longrightarrow ACH_2\overset{·}{C}HR \qquad ...(6.1)$$

$$(6.1) \overset{A}{\underset{B}{\diagdown}}$$

$$ACH_2\overset{R}{\underset{|}{C}}HB+A· \qquad ...(6.3)$$

$$(6.2)$$

A new radical A· is simultaneously produced which is capable of repeating the sequence of addition and transfer that leads to the formation of small molecules. These alternatives are exemplified in the

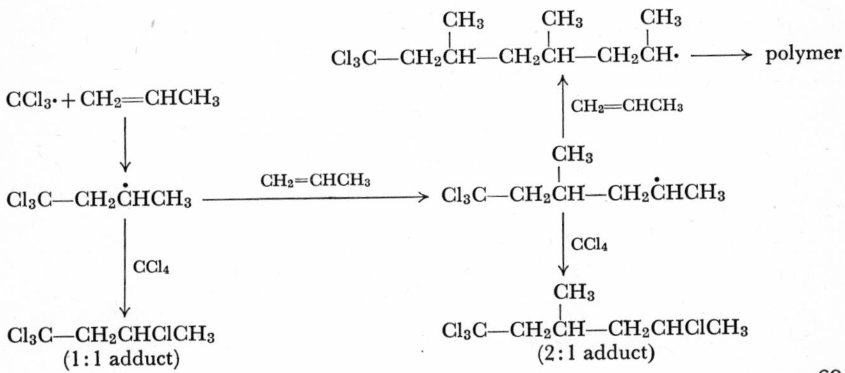

$$Cl_3C—CH_2\overset{CH_3}{\underset{|}{C}}H—CH_2\overset{CH_3}{\underset{|}{C}}H—CH_2\overset{CH_3}{\underset{|}{C}}H· \longrightarrow polymer$$

$$\uparrow CH_2{=}CHCH_3$$

$$CCl_3·+CH_2{=}CHCH_3$$

$$\downarrow$$

$$Cl_3C—CH_2\overset{·}{C}HCH_3 \xrightarrow{\ CH_2{=}CHCH_3\ } Cl_3C—CH_2\overset{CH_3}{\underset{|}{C}}H—CH_2\overset{·}{C}HCH_3$$

$$\downarrow CCl_4 \qquad\qquad\qquad\qquad \downarrow CCl_4$$

$$\begin{array}{cc} Cl_3C—CH_2CHClCH_3 & Cl_3C—CH_2\overset{CH_3}{\underset{|}{C}}H—CH_2CHClCH_3 \\ (1:1\ adduct) & (2:1\ adduct) \end{array}$$

addition of carbon tetrachloride to propylene, a reaction which gives a 1:1 adduct [cf. reaction (6.3)] together with products which contain larger proportions of the olefin [cf. reaction (6.1)]

Both reactions are further examples of self-sustaining chain reactions— we shall be concerned with the latter in this chapter. It must be pointed out here that the radical A· may also abstract hydrogen from the olefin, particularly when C—H bonds are adjacent to the double bond:

$$A \cdot + RCH_2CH{=}CH_2 \longrightarrow AH + R\overset{\cdot}{C}HCH{=}CH_2 \qquad \ldots (6.4)$$

and the radical (6.1) may dimerize or disproportionate rather than participate in reactions (6.2) and (6.3). These alternatives are considered together under the heading of 'termination' (p. 73).

Small Molecule Formation versus Polymerization. For the chain sequence of reactions (6.1) and (6.3) to be sustained, the individual steps must be able to compete favourably with the alternative process of polymerization. Qualitative predictions of the circumstances favourable to small molecule formation may be made from consideration of the energetics of the steps involved. These predictions are uncertain in that exothermic reactions may yet have high activation energies or highly negative entropies of activation. Because of the general lack of polar and steric influences on radical reactions, however, this is not usual experience.

The enthalpy changes for the stepwise addition of a selection of molecules to ethylene is given in Table 6.1.

Table 6.1. Enthalpy Changes (kcal/mole) for the Propagation Steps in Additions to Ethylene

A—B	D(C—A)	D(A—B)	Reaction (6.1) ΔH A·+CH₂=CH₂	Reaction (6.3)† ΔH ACH₂CH₂·+A—B	D(C—B)
HO—H	90	120	−32	+22	98
Cl—H	80	103	−22	+5	98
Br—H	67	87	−9	−11	98
I—H	53	71	+5	−27	98
Br—Br	67	46	−9	−21	67
CCl₃—H	72	90	−14	−8	98
CCl₃—Cl	72	68	−14	−12	80
CH₃CO—H	74	78	−16	−20	98
PhS—H	73	88	−15	−10	98

† [D(C—H) in ethane ~98 kcal/mole]

The 'opening energy' of the π-bond in ethylene is about 58 kcal/mole and as the dissociation energies of most bonds to carbon have values greater than this, reaction (6.1) is exothermic in nearly all cases. An exception is the C—I bond [D(C—I) = 53 kcal/mole]; iodine and hydrogen iodide do not add with any facility to simple olefins (but see p. 86).

For reaction (6.3) to be exothermic, the C—B bond must be stronger than the A—B bond and it is this criterion which determines the ease of most simple homolytic additions. Water and hydrogen chloride are two important examples in which, because of the high O—H and H—Cl bond strengths, the abstraction reaction becomes endothermic. For the other examples given, both steps are exothermic and radical addition readily occurs with formation of small molecules. It must be realized, however, that the energetics of the competing reaction of polymerization are also very favourable; the heat content change in reaction (6.2) is of the order of − 22 kcal/mole, and in practice, excess of the addendum A—B is usually used to favour small molecule formation.

The energetic situation presented for ethylene may be greatly altered when other olefins are considered. With styrene, for example, attack by radicals on the olefin becomes much easier because a benzylic radical is produced:

$$A\cdot + CH_2{=}CHPh \longrightarrow A{-}CH_2\dot{C}HPh$$

On the other hand, the abstraction stage becomes much more difficult for this weakly reactive radical. The situation is illustrated in Table 6.2.

Table 6.2. Energetics of Chain Steps in Additions to Styrene

A—B	ΔH A·+CH$_2$=CHPh	ΔH ACH$_2\dot{C}$HPh+A—B
Cl—H	−49	28
Br—H	−28	13
Cl—Cl	−49	−6
CH$_3$CO—H	−39	3
CCl$_3$—Cl	−37	5

The greater difficulty of the transfer step restricts the range of molecules that can satisfactorily be added to styrene. The radical produced in the addition step prefers the easier reaction path of addition to a new molecule of olefin with the ultimate formation of telomers (short-chain polymers containing 2–5 molecules of olefin) and polymers. Further, additions to styrene become very sensitive to the A—B bond strength in the addendum:

PhCH=CH$_2$ + CCl$_4$ (50 moles excess) ⟶ Telomers only
D(CCl$_3$—Cl) = 68

PhCH=CH$_2$ + CBr$_4$ (6 moles excess) ⟶ PhCHBrCH$_2$CBr$_3$
D(CBr$_3$—Br) = 50   96%

Initiation. Photo-initiation and radical initiation are both used for starting the chain sequence that leads to the formation of small molecules. Photo-initiation involves the direct generation of radicals from the addendum:

$$A\text{—}B \xrightarrow[\gamma\text{-rays}]{h\nu} A\!\cdot+B\!\cdot$$

The requirements for photolytic generation of radicals have already been outlined (Chapter 1), and the types of possible addenda are consequently somewhat restricted. This method is, however, widely used particularly for low temperature reactions in which thermal initiation is impossible. Additions of thiols and hydrogen halides are particularly well suited to this type of initiation.

Alternatively, radical initiation may be used. Benzoyl and t-butyl peroxides are frequently employed to provide radicals which start chains, and electron transfer reactions producing radicals such as hydroxyl (cf. Chapter 10) are also suitable. When radical initiation is used, the chain reaction may start in two ways. Radicals from the initiator either remove the abstractable atom (B), reaction (6.5), from the addendum (A—B) leaving the radical A· to perform the first act of the sequence:

$$\text{e.g.} \qquad (\text{PhCO}_2)_2 \longrightarrow \text{ or } \left.\begin{array}{l}\text{PhCO}_2\cdot\\ \text{Ph}\cdot\end{array}\right\} + A\text{—}B \longrightarrow \text{ or } \left.\begin{array}{l}\text{PhCO}_2\text{B}\\ \text{PhB}\end{array}\right\} + A\cdot \quad \ldots(6.5)$$

$$A\cdot + CH_2\!\!=\!\!CHR \longrightarrow ACH_2\overset{\bullet}{C}HR$$

or they attack the olefin directly. In this case the new radical subsequently removes B from A—B and A· continues the sequence:

$$\text{e.g. } (\text{PhCO}_2)_2 \longrightarrow \text{ or } \left.\begin{array}{l}\text{PhCO}_2\cdot\\ \text{Ph}\cdot\end{array}\right\} + CH_2\!\!=\!\!CHR \longrightarrow \text{ or } \left.\begin{array}{l}\text{PhCO}_2CH_2\overset{\bullet}{C}HR\\ \text{PhCH}_2\overset{\bullet}{C}HR\end{array}\right\}$$

$$\text{PhCO}_2CH_2\overset{\bullet}{C}HR + A\text{—}B \longrightarrow \underset{\underset{B}{|}}{\text{PhCO}_2CH_2CHR} + A\cdot$$

This process is termed *addition-initiation*.

In many radical additions, the chain lengths (the number of times the sequence is repeated for one act of initiation) are very large. Accordingly, the proportion of product that contains fragments of the initiator is very small and it is not often possible to tell which is the predominant type of initiation. In the benzoyl peroxide initiated addition of carbon tetrachloride to cyclohexene, however, chain lengths are only about 2 and significant yields of products derived directly from the initiator have been isolated. The products from this reaction are given in Table 6.3 and they illustrate several important features of radical addition.

Table 6.3. Products† from the Carbon Tetrachloride/Cyclohexene/Benzoyl Peroxide Reaction

Initiation		*Propagation*		*Termination*	
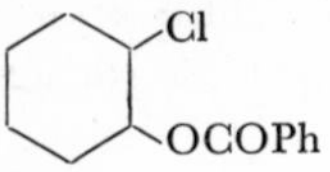 (6.3)	55	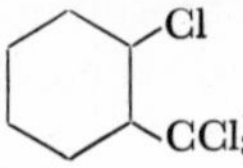 (6.4)	89	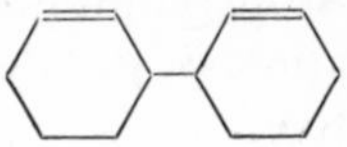	60
PhCl 10					
PhH 8			11		
PhCO₂H 12		CHCl₃ 65			

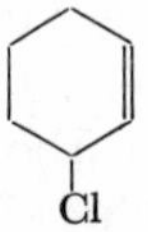

† Moles per 100 moles of peroxide.

The main product, 2-trichloromethylcyclohexyl chloride (6.4) is formed in the propagation sequence:

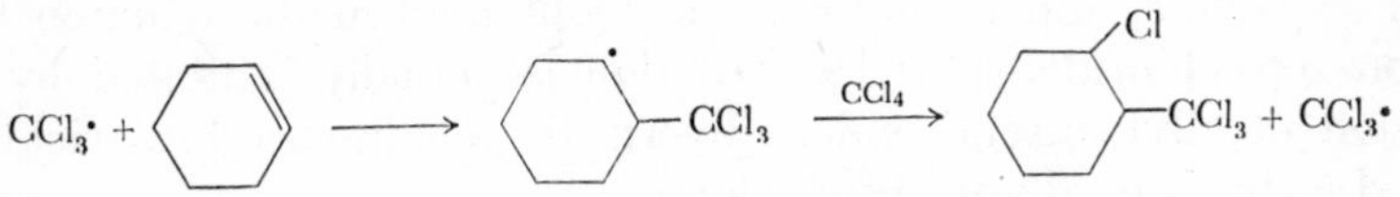

Those products which contain fragments of the initiator show that both types of initiation occur:

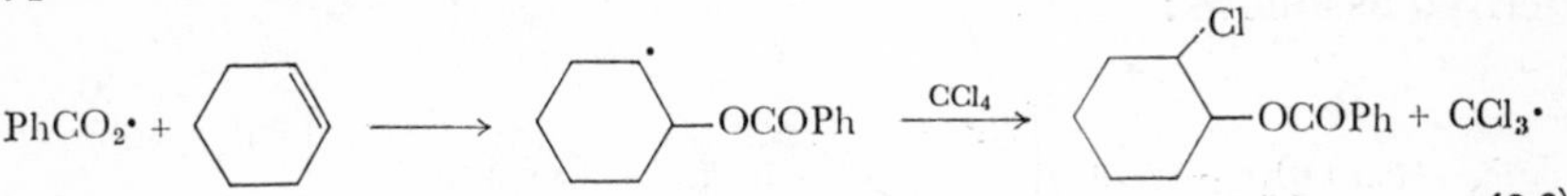

...(6.6)

$$Ph\cdot + CCl_4 \longrightarrow PhCl + CCl_3\cdot \qquad ...(6.7)$$

The high yield of 2-chlorocyclohexyl benzoate (6.3) shows that addition-initiation is predominant in this instance. The reverse is true, however, of the addition of bromotrichloromethane to stilbene when initiated by t-butyl peroxide. In this case 64% of the peroxide appears as t-butyl hypobromite:

$$(t\text{-BuO})_2 \longrightarrow t\text{-BuO}\cdot \xrightarrow{BrCCl_3} t\text{-BuOBr} + CCl_3\cdot$$

Termination. At the end of reactions no radicals remain; the chain sequence stops when the chain-carrying radicals combine or disproportionate. Termination by disproportionation is discussed in the

6

following chapter as there is limited evidence for its occurrence in simple radical-chain additions. Combination, on the other hand, is frequently encountered; hexachloroethane, for instance, which is obtained from the peroxide-initiated carbon tetrachloride/t-butylethylene reaction, results from combination of trichloromethyl radicals. This mode of termination is, of course, favoured when the chain-carrying radical is unreactive.

An indirect mode of termination arises when the olefin has allylic hydrogens. Removal of these hydrogens is easy and the resulting radical is resonance stabilized. This stability favours combination and hence chain-breaking. The process is known as 'allylic termination' or (rather cryptically) 'degradative chain transfer'. The high yields of chloroform and dicyclohexenyl obtained in the carbon tetrachloride/cyclohexene reaction show the importance of this type of termination.

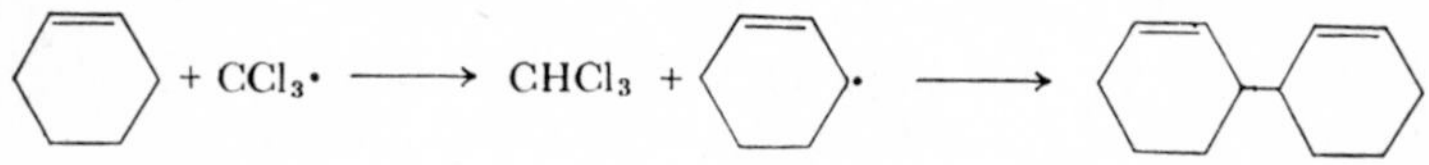

The absence of allylic hydrogen in t-butylethylene allows very long chain sequences, and no chloroform is obtained in the reaction with carbon tetrachloride. This last reaction is actually inhibited by the addition of allylbenzene which diverts the chain-carrying trichloromethyl radicals to allylic abstraction.

Allylic abstraction may, however, be the forerunner of chain-initiation. In the reaction between benzoyl peroxide and cyclohexene in carbon tetrachloride, benzene, benzoic acid, and 3-chlorocyclohexene are derived as follows:

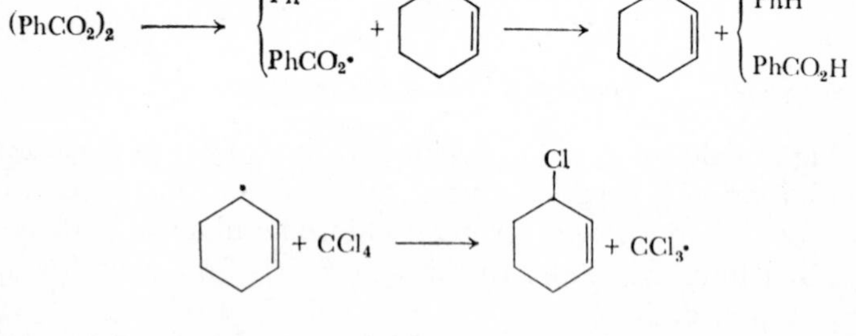

Trichloromethyl radicals produced in the second stage join the main stream of radicals produced in the two most important initiation reactions (6.6) and (6.7).

In general, the more reactive the olefin towards addition (Table 6.6), the less susceptible it is to allylic attack.

74

TYPES OF ADDENDA YIELDING SMALL MOLECULES

(a) Polyhalogeno-alkanes. Formation of a 1:1 adduct of an olefin with an alkyl polyhalide was first reported by Kharasch and his collaborators (1945). They showed that reaction between oct-1-ene and carbon tetrachloride, initiated by acetyl peroxide, gave 1,1,1,3-tetrachlorononane (85%):

$$CCl_4 + C_6H_{13}CH{=}CH_2 \longrightarrow C_6H_{13}CHClCH_2CCl_3$$

Many additions of simple alkyl polyhalides to a variety of olefins have since been accomplished, and the reactions are of great importance for the synthesis of polyhaloalkanes. Additions of polyhalogenomethanes have been most studied and the reactions are favoured by the exothermicity of both steps of the propagation sequence. This favourable energetic situation is the consequence of the cleavage of a relatively weak C—X bond to give a CX_3· radical which is resonance-stabilized (cf. p. 154). Recently, additions of polyfluoromethanes have been applied industrially; addenda such as CF_3I, CF_2Br_2 and so on have been used with a variety of olefins and fluoro-olefins. Walling and Huyser have given a list of reactions of this type reported up to 1962. Some examples are included in Table 6.4.

The reactivity of polyhalomethanes is determined by the strength of the carbon–halogen bond broken and by the stability of the radical produced by abstraction. As far as bond strength is concerned, the order of decreasing ease of abstraction is C—I > C—Br > C—Cl. In competitive additions with mixtures of CCl_4 and CCl_3Br, no addition of CCl_4 is observable, and among the trifluoromethyl halides, CF_3I is the only one to undergo radical addition to olefins. This sequence is also supported by polymerization chain transfer constants (next Chapter) which measure the ease of the reaction:

$$\text{\small\textasciitilde\textasciitilde\textasciitilde}P\cdot + X{-}R \longrightarrow \text{\small\textasciitilde\textasciitilde\textasciitilde}P{-}X + R\cdot$$

The transfer constant for the polystyrene/CCl_3Br system is 150 times that for CCl_4. When chloroform is used as an addendum, hydrogen and not chlorine is removed in the first propagation step. The situation is, however, finely balanced; replacement of protium by deuterium causes C—Cl cleavage to occur.

The second factor is the stability of the radical produced. The reactivity sequence $CX_3{-}X > CHX_2{-}X > CH_2X{-}X > CH_3{-}X$ can be ascribed to the decreasing stabilization, due to resonance, of the radical remaining when the halogen atom, X, is removed. CCl_4, for example, has a transfer constant in styrene polymerization which is 180 times larger

75

than that of chloroform, and halomethanes with less than three halogen atoms do not readily add to olefins. Replacement of halogen in a poly-halomethane by a substituent such as alkoxycarbonyl, however, allows π-orbital resonance to contribute to the stability of the radical, and olefin addition occurs readily (Table 6.4).

(b) Aldehydes, Ketones and Esters. Aldehyde addition has been very much more studied than that of ketones and esters. The reactions follow the sequence in which the acyl radical is the chain carrier:

$$RCHO + In\cdot \longrightarrow RCO\cdot$$

$$RCO\cdot + CH_2{=}CHR' \longrightarrow RCOCH_2\overset{\cdot}{C}HR'$$

$$RCOCH_2\overset{\cdot}{C}HR' + RCHO \longrightarrow RCOCH_2CH_2R' + RCO\cdot$$

The RCO—H bond strength is around 78 kcal/mole so that the transfer step for simple alkenes is exothermic by about 20 kcal/mole (Table 6.1). Many aldehydes have been successfully added to olefins and some examples are given in Table 6.4. As in most radical additions in which small molecule formation is desired, excess of the aldehyde is used to cut down telomer formation. For reasons that were mentioned earlier, telomers and polymers are obtained almost exclusively when styrene is used, but good yields of γ-keto esters and γ-diketones can be obtained from α,β-unsaturated esters and ketones. An example of the reaction with a ketone is given in Table 6.4, and recently Hey and his collaborators have examined the addition of malonic, cyanoacetic, and acetoacetic esters to olefins, using t-butyl and benzoyl peroxides for initiation. Note that in reactions with ketones and esters, hydrogen is removed from carbon adjacent to the carbonyl group. Formates, which are structurally analogous to aldehydes, lose the hydrogen attached to the carbonyl group. Conversions are good, provided that large excesses of addendum (50 moles) over olefin are used. Interestingly, addition of ethyl $(-)$-α-bromopropionate to oct-1-ene, initiated by acetyl peroxide, gives the adduct (*6.5*) which is slightly optically active. This shows that addition of the radical CH₃ĊHCO₂Et to the olefin can compete, if only to a minor extent, with its very rapid racemization:

$$CH_3CHBrCO_2Et + CH_2{=}CHC_6H_{13} \longrightarrow \begin{matrix} H_3C \\ EtOCO \end{matrix}\!\!\!\!\!\searrow\!\!\!\!\!\nearrow CHCH_2CHBrC_6H_{13}$$

(*6.5*)

(c) Amines, Alcohols and Thiols. Amines and alcohols behave similarly to esters in giving products which are derived from abstraction of hydrogen from the carbon adjacent to the hydroxyl or amino group (examples in Table 6.4).

76

Abstraction at C—H rather than O—H or N—H bonds is a consequence of the high bond strengths of the latter. Furthermore, the adjacent oxygen and nitrogen atoms render these C—H bonds vulnerable to attack by radicals (cf. p. 154). Large excesses of addenda are, however, needed to achieve reasonable conversions. Isopropanol is about three times as reactive as ethanol in additions to oct-1-ene, a result which fits well with reactivities of primary and secondary C—H bonds in halogenation. Abstraction of α-hydrogen in alcohols has been demonstrated directly by ESR methods. Irradiation of a mixture of propan-2-ol and hydrogen peroxide at 110°K in the cavity of an ESR spectrometer shows the formation of radicals and the absorption line is split into a septet. This indicates that 2-hydroxy-2-propyl radicals are produced:

$$Me_2CHOH + \cdot OH \longrightarrow Me_2\overset{\cdot}{C}OH + H_2O$$

The hydroxyl proton does not split the absorption line and this is evidently due to rapid proton exchange with other molecules.

Addition of thiols to olefins takes a different course. The S—H bond strength is much less than that of the O—H bond and abstraction of hydrogen attached to sulphur occurs exclusively. Both steps in the propagation sequence are exothermic and reactions proceed readily without appreciable telomer formation. Examples are given in Table 6.4. Thiol acids add in a similar way giving thiol esters, which provide a useful route to thiols:

$$RCOSH + CH_2 = CHR' \longrightarrow RCOSCH_2CH_2R' \longrightarrow HSCH_2CH_2R'$$

Hydrogen sulphide gives mixtures of thiol and dialkyl sulphide.

Because hydrogen attached to sulphur is so easily transferred, thiols are used in the control of polymer molecular weights; they alter the degree of competition between reactions (6.2) and (6.3) (see following chapter).

(d) **Halides and Hydrogen Halides.** In examples of olefin addition that have so far been discussed, there is little doubt of the homolytic nature of the reactions. [Note, however, that nucleophilic (base-catalysed) addition of thiols to α,β-unsaturated esters and nitriles yield the same type of products as homolytic addition.] Heterolytic addition of halides and hydrogen halides is well known, and in solution reactions, the difficulty of distinguishing heterolytic and homolytic processes arises. Most studies of homolytic halogen addition have been made on gas phase reactions—photo-initiated chlorination of ethylene, for example, gives a quantum yield of around 10^6 and shows oxygen inhibition. Both steps with chlorine are strongly exothermic but with bromine the addition and displacement steps have ΔH of -9 and of -21

Table 6.4. Addition to Olefins

Addendum	Olefin	Mole Ratio Addendum : Olefin	Initiator	1 : 1-Adduct	Yield (%)
CCl_4	hept-1-ene	3	Bz_2O_2	$CCl_3CH_2CHClC_5H_{11}$	72
CBr_4	styrene	6	$h\nu$	$CBr_3CH_2CHBrPh$	96
CCl_3Br	ethyl cinnamate	3·3	$h\nu$	$CCl_3CH(CO_2Et)CHBrPh$	60
CCl_3Br	vinyl acetate	2	Ac_2O_2	$CCl_3CH_2CHBrOAc$	90
CCl_3Br	allyl cyanide	4	$h\nu$	$CCl_3CH_2CHBrCH_2CN$	65
CCl_3Br	oct-1-yne	4	$h\nu$	$CCl_3CH{=}CBr(CH_2)_5CH_3$	80
CCl_3I	1,1,1-trifluoropropene	1·1	$h\nu$	$CCl_3CH_2CHICF_3$	57
CF_3I	ethylene	1·7	$h\nu$	$CF_3CH_2CH_2I$	82
$CHCl_3$	oct-1-ene	4	Bz_2O_2	$CCl_3CH_2CH_2C_6H_{13}$	22
$CF_2{=}CFI$	ethylene	1·5	$h\nu$	$CF_2{=}CFCH_2CH_2I$	67
$CHCl_2CO_2Me$	oct-1-ene	4·4	Ac_2O_2	$MeOCOCCl_2CH_2CH_2C_6H_{13}$	40
$CH_3(CH_2)_2CHO$	oct-1-ene	5·2	$h\nu$	$CH_3(CH_2)_2COCH_2CH_2CH(CH_2)_5CH_3$	57
CH_3CHO	diethyl maleate	3	Bz_2O_2	$CH_3COCH(CO_2Et)CH_2CO_2Et$	78
CH_3CHO	methyl undecylenate	20	Bz_2O_2	$CH_3CO(CH_2)_{10}CO_2CH_3$	30
$CH_3(CH_2)_2CHO$	perfluoropropene	1	Bz_2O_2	$CH_3(CH_2)_2COCF_2CHFCF_3$	70
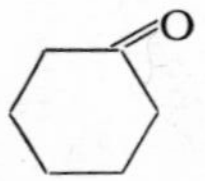 (cyclohexanone)	oct-1-ene	0·13	$h\nu$	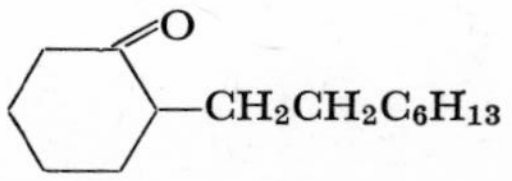 (cyclohexanone with $CH_2CH_2C_6H_{13}$)	26

Reagent	Olefin		Conditions	Product	Yield
HCO₂Me	cyclohexene	30	(t-BuO)₂	[cyclohexyl]—CO₂Me	36
CH₂(CO₂Et)₂	oct-1-ene	2 / 50	(t-BuO)₂	CH(CO₂Et)₂CH₂CH₂C₆H₁₃	{6 / 73}
[pyrrolidine] NH	allyl alcohol	13·5	(t-BuO)₂	[N-pyrrolidinyl]—CH₂CH₂CH₂OH	63
CH₃(CH₂)₂CH₂OH	oct-1-ene	30	(t-BuO)₂	CH₃(CH₂)₂CHOHCH₂CH₂C₆H₁₃	38
HBr	1-bromocyclohexene	2	*hv*	[cyclohexane with Br, Br]	86
H₂S	but-1-ene	2	*hv*	{ HSCH₂(CH₂)₂CH₃ / (CH₃(CH₂)₃)₂S }	12 / 70
PhSH	1-methylcyclohexene	1	*hv*	[cyclohexane with Me, SPh]	85
CH₃COSH	cyclohexene	1	*hv*	[cyclohexyl]—SCOMe	93
PCl₃	oct-1-ene	6	Ac₂O₂	Cl₂PCH₂CHClC₆H₁₃	47
SiHCl₃	oct-1-ene	6	Ac₂O₂	Cl₃SiCH₂CH₂C₆H₁₃	99

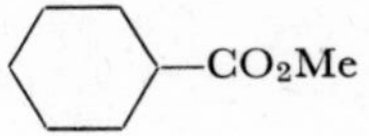

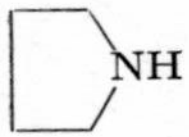

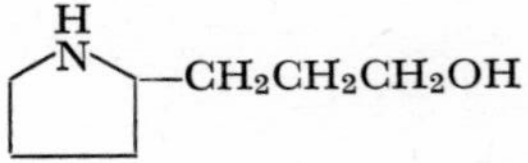

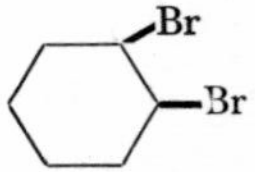

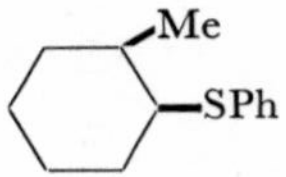

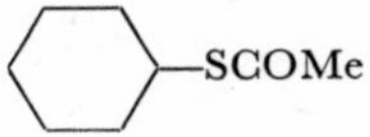

kcal/mole respectively. Furthermore, addition of bromine (and iodine) atoms tends to be reversible, with important consequences that are discussed in a later section (p. 85).

The intensive study of the addition of hydrogen bromide to olefins carried out by Kharasch and Mayo (1933) occupies an important place in the development of radical chemistry. At that time there was considerable confusion over the factors that determined the orientation of addition (these are discussed later, p. 83) but by very careful studies with allyl bromide, Kharasch and Mayo were able to distinguish two sets of conditions that consistently gave opposite orientations:

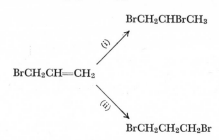

(i) Reactions carried out in the dark with carefully purified (i.e. peroxide-free) reagents and in the absence of oxygen, *slowly* gave 1,2-dibromopropane quantitatively. This orientation (Markovnikov) corresponded with other additions that were clearly heterolytic. (ii) Reactions under illumination and/or in the presence of peroxides gave 1,3-dibromopropane. These conditions will now be recognized as being likely to favour homolytic mechanisms. This work led to formulation of the generalized two-stage chain mechanism given at the start of the Chapter. Hydrogen bromide additions have been much investigated subsequently in connection with the stereochemistry of radical additions.

No other hydrogen halides add satisfactorily to olefins; transfer steps are endothermic with HF and HCl, and the addition step is endothermic for iodine atoms (but see p. 86).

Reactions with other addenda, particularly those which involve abstraction from elements other than carbon are mentioned in the accounts listed in the bibliography. Some have been included in Table 6.4.

REACTIVITY OF OLEFINS TOWARDS RADICAL ADDITION

We have seen earlier that direct determination of absolute rate constants and hence reactivities is not a simple matter when dealing with radical reactions. A few absolute rate constants have been obtained for simple reactions (cf. p. 99); these are given in Table 6.5:

Table 6.5. Rate Constants for the Propagation Steps in Additions of CCl₃Br to Cyclohexene and Vinyl Acetate

	Cyclohexene	Vinyl acetate
	(k in l. mole^{-1} sec^{-1})	
Addition step: CCl$_3$· + $>$C$=$C$<$	256	1120
Abstraction step: CCl$_3$C—C· + BrCCl$_3$	63·8	2740

The data of Table 6.5 have been obtained by Melville using the techniques involving intermittent irradiation that were developed for studies of polymerization rates (references at the end of following Chapter).

A simpler approach is the competitive method. Reactions are carried out with an equimolecular mixture of two olefins and a limited amount of addendum. The amount of adduct obtained from each olefin then gives a measure of their relative reactivities. For the results to be meaningful, yields of 1:1 adduct must be high and bromotrichloromethane is a suitable addendum on account of its high transfer constant.

Table 6.6. Relative Reactivities of Olefins towards Trichloromethyl and Dodecanethio Radicals

	Radical	
Olefin	CCl$_3$·	CH$_3$(CH$_2$)$_{10}$CH$_2$S·
α-Methylstyrene	420	—
Styrene	100	17
Butadiene	18	—
Cyclopentadiene	4·5	—
β-Methylstyrene	1·1	1·5
Oct-1-ene	1·0	1·0
2-Methylbut-1-ene	0·9	1·2
Ethyl cinnamate	0·8	—
Cyclopentene	0·8	0·6
Vinyl acetate	0·8	0·8
Allyl chloride	0·5	0·7
Allyl cyanide	0·3	0·4
Cyclohexene	0·24	0·25

Thiols are also suitable provided that allowance is made for reversibility, and values for both CCl$_3$· and CH$_3$(CH$_2$)$_{10}$CH$_2$S· additions are given in Table 6.6.

Values for the relative reactivities of vinyl acetate and cyclohexene obtained by direct and competitive methods agree quite well.

Three factors appear to be important in determining olefin reactivity:

(a) *Stability of the Intermediate Radical.* The lower the energy of the intermediate radical (*6.1*) the more readily one might expect radical addition to the olefin to occur.

$$A \cdot + CH_2 = CHR \longrightarrow ACH_2\dot{C}HR$$

$$(6.1)$$

The nature of R determines the stability of this radical; delocalization of the unpaired electron would be expected to favour olefin reactivity. This expectation is justified as styrene and butadiene are considerably more reactive than simple terminal olefins:

$$A \cdot + CH_2 = CHCH = CH_2 \longrightarrow ACH_2\dot{C}H \text{---} CH \text{---} CH_2$$

On the other hand, the attachment of conjugating groups stabilizes double bonds and should thus diminish reactivity in addition. Of these opposing effects, radical rather than olefin stabilization is known to be more important; this question is dealt with further in the following Chapter.

Similarly, by analogy with halogenation and autoxidation, an α-alkyl group in the intermediate radical would be expected to increase radical stability, and with it, olefin reactivity. The limited data on this point are indecisive; α-methylstyrene is more reactive than styrene but 2-methylbut-1-ene is less reactive (towards $CCl_3\cdot$) than oct-1-ene. The higher reactivity of cyclopentene relative to cyclohexene can be put down to the greater relief of angle strain in the former. A double bond is less well accommodated in a five- than in a six-membered ring, and the 'opening' energy of the double bond in the former is consequently lower.

(b) *Steric Effects.* The large reactivity difference between α- and β-methylstyrene (Table 6.6) has been attributed to steric interference in the β-derivative towards the approach of the attacking radical. This effect on reactivity seems too large to be explained by steric effects alone and the fact that trichloromethyl and dodecanethio radicals are affected to a similar extent does not fit well with a purely steric phenomenon. More convincing evidence for adverse steric effects on reactivity in addition reactions has been obtained from copolymerization studies (p. 110).

82

(c) *Polar Effects.* It has already been seen that polar effects may quite markedly influence the reactions of radicals, despite their electrical neutrality. The trichloromethyl radical has marked electron acceptor properties and prefers reaction sites of high electron density. In allyl chloride and allyl cyanide, inductive effects lower the electron density at the terminal carbon atom and reactivity *towards the* CCl_3 *radical* is reduced. Thio radicals behave in the same way; this is shown by the effects of nuclear substituents upon the reactivity of α-methylstyrene towards ·SCH_2CO_2H radicals (Table 6.7):

Table 6.7. Reactivities of α-Methylstyrenes towards ·SCH_2CO_2H Radicals

Substituent	Relative reactivity
p-OMe	100
p-Me	2·28
H	1·00
m-Br	0·96
p-Br	0·90
p-F	0·51

It must be emphasized that these effects apply to these specific electron acceptor radicals; the exceptionally high reactivity of *p*-methoxy-α-methylstyrene is hard to understand. Opposite effects are observed in different systems (Chapter 7).

ORIENTATION OF ADDITION

Addition to unsymmetrical olefins raises the question of the position of attachment of the adding radical. In instances involving terminal olefins we have seen (Table 6.4) that addition of the radical occurs at the terminal carbon atom. We might expect that the factors that control reactivity will also control orientation and much effort has been devoted to this aspect of the reactions.

Polar effects may be dismissed briefly. Haszeldine (1953) has found that bromine atoms and trifluoromethyl radicals, both of which should be sensitive to polar effects, add predominantly at the terminal carbon in the olefins $RCH = CH_2$, where R = Me, Cl, F, CO_2Me, CF_3 or CN. Cadogan (1962) has similarly found that the direction of addition of CCl_3Br to *trans*-stilbenes (Table 6.8) is little dependent upon the nature of nuclear substituents.

Table 6.8. Orientation in Addition of CCl₃Br to trans-Stilbenes

(%)		

	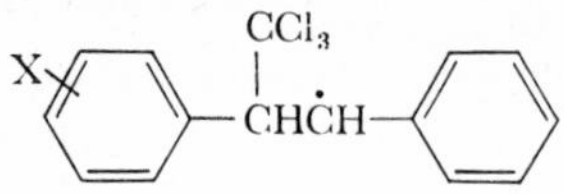	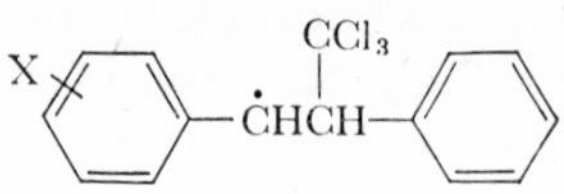
4-NO₂	40	60
4-Me	60	40
4-Br	47	53
3-NO₂	47	53
3-Me	55	44
3-Br	45	55
3-MeO	48	52

The opposing effects of 4-NO₂ and 4-Me substituents are significant in showing that the observed orientation cannot be solely due to a general stabilizing effect common to all substituents.

It appears, in fact, that orientation is chiefly decided by the energy difference between the two possible radicals and, to a lesser degree, by steric effects. We have seen in earlier chapters that most substituents are better able than hydrogen to stabilize radicals and that consequently in terminal olefins, terminal addition will be favoured. As all substituents are bulkier than hydrogen, steric considerations will also favour terminal addition. The situation for terminal and non-terminal olefins is nicely illustrated in the cyclization of the following nitrile esters:

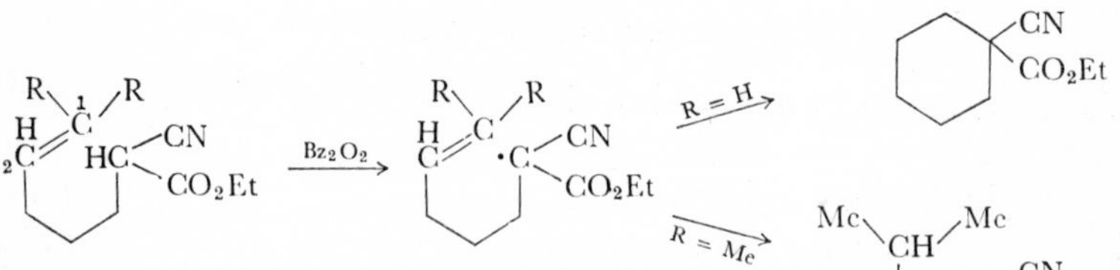

(6.6)

When R=Me, addition in the radical (6.6) at C_2 rather than at C_1 is encouraged by the steric effects of the methyl groups and by the resultant formation of the more stable tertiary radical. Stability and steric effects can, however, operate in opposite directions; addition of butanal to mesityl oxide (6.10) gives the adducts (6.7) and (6.8). The major product

(*6.7*) is derived from the mesomeric radical (*6.9*) showing the greater importance (in this instance) of radical stabilization:

$$CO(CH_2)_2CH_3$$
$$Me_2\overset{|}{C}CH_2COMe \qquad (90\%)$$
$$(6.7)$$

$$CH_3(CH_2)_2CO\cdot + Me_2C\!\!=\!\!CHCOMe$$
$$(6.10)$$

$$CO(CH_2)_2CH_3$$
$$Me_2CH\overset{|}{C}HCOMe \qquad (10\%)$$
$$(6.8)$$

$$\underset{\overset{|}{C}O(CH_2)_2CH_3}{Me_2\overset{\overset{O}{\|}}{C}\overset{\cdot}{C}HCMe} \quad \longleftrightarrow \quad \underset{\overset{|}{C}O(CH_2)_2CH_3}{Me_2\overset{\overset{O\cdot}{|}}{C}CH\!\!=\!\!CMe}$$
$$(6.9)$$

An important aspect of orientation in radical addition is that the observed direction is usually anti-Markovnikov. Many homolytic additions thus usefully complement their heterolytic analogues in which Markovnikov orientation is normal.

Reversibility. *Cis-trans* isomerization of olefins is frequently found to accompany radical addition. This is particularly true of reactions which involve addition of a bromine atom or an RS· radical as the first stage. Reaction of $^{82}Br_2$ with *cis*-1,2-dibromoethylene, for example, causes isomerization to the *trans* isomer *and* isotopic exchange, the latter process occurring about twice as fast as the former. It appears, then, that addition of a bromine atom (scheme, p. 86) gives a radical cf. (*6.11*) which re-eliminates bromine either before or after inversion occurs. The extent of isomerization is thus dependent upon how well inversion competes with elimination, and this is determined by the structure of the olefin. *cis*-2-Chlorobut-2-ene, for example, is isomerized by hydrogen bromide even at $-78°$ while *cis*-but-2-ene is unaffected by these conditions. Occurrence of *cis-trans* isomerization during allylic bromination with *N*-bromosuccinimide was mentioned earlier (p. 56) as evidence in support of the formation of bromine in the reactions. The sequence of addition and elimination constitutes a chain reaction and the photo-initiated, bromine-catalysed conversion of dimethyl maleate to dimethyl fumarate has a quantum yield of 600.

Addition of RS· radicals to olefins is also reversible. In the reaction of methanethiol with *cis*-but-2-ene at 60°, initiated by azoisobutyronitrile, the rate of formation of *trans*-but-2-ene from the intermediate radical is 80 times that of the subsequent transfer step which yields the final product. At lower temperatures olefin isomerization is not observed.

Radical catalysed isomerization of olefins has been put to good use by those concerned with synthesis. Procedures involved in the building up of polyene chains such as exist in β-carotene, for instance, are frequently non-specific as regards the geometric disposition of groups about the unsaturated centres. The result is that the products frequently contain disorderly sequences of *cis* and *trans* double bonds. The final stages of many polyene syntheses accordingly involve an ironing out procedure in which treatment with bromine or iodine causes 'stereomutation' and the formation of (predominantly) 'all *trans*' structures.

STEREOCHEMISTRY OF ADDITION

Addition to olefins bearing substituents attached to each end of the double bond raises the question of the steric course of the addition. Experimentally it is found that reactions may be completely non-stereospecific, as in the addition of CCl_3Br to the *cis* and *trans* but-2-enes; partially stereospecific (*trans* addition) as in the addition of thiolacetic

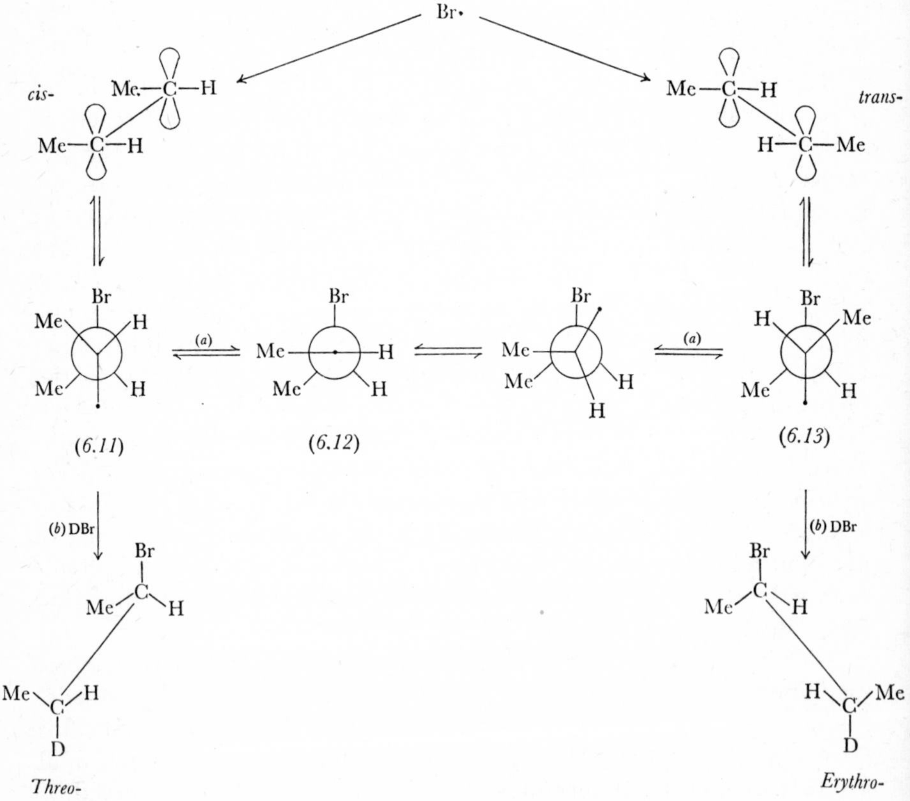

(6.11) (6.12) (6.13)

Threo- *Erythro-*

acid to 1-methylcyclohexene; or completely selective (*trans* addition) as in addition of DBr to the but-2-enes at $-70°$. This last reaction becomes non-specific at higher temperatures and illustrates well the factors that determine steric control.

The experimental observations are interpreted as follows: The attacking radical (in this case Br·) approaches perpendicularly to the plane of the olefin molecule. The resulting radical is probably pyramidal (*6.11*) and (*6.13*) rather than planar (*6.12*) as non-bonded interactions in (*6.12*) raise its energy relative to the pyramidal states. Rapid inter-conversions of (*6.11*) and (*6.13*) *via* (*6.12*) undoubtedly occur, however, as we have seen radicals to be unable to hold configuration in other reactions. Further, it seems likely that the intermediate radical would initially adopt a configuration (*6.11*) or (*6.13*) which can be taken up in the addition step without eclipsing of groups. The products from each olefin are then determined by the relative rates of inversion (*a*) and transfer (*b*). At low temperatures, the transfer reaction is considerably favoured with respect to inversion, and specific *trans* addition is the result. As the temperature is raised, inversion becomes better able to compete with transfer and stereo-selectivity diminishes until, at 25°, both olefins give the same product mixtures. At higher temperatures, addition of Br· is reversible so that re-elimination also competes with transfer. The fact that stereo-specificity is obtained at all in this reaction is due to the very high transfer constant of DBr (i.e. $k_b \gg k_a$ at $-78°$) and it is unlikely that complete specificity can be achieved with other addenda.

Abel and Piette (1962) have examined the ESR spectra obtained when mixtures of olefins and hydrogen bromide are irradiated at 77°K. *Cis* and *trans*-but-2-enes show identical seven-line patterns but with *different* splittings. These results indicate the formation of sym-metrical but not identical intermediate radicals from the two isomers. The symmetry may arise by bridging or by rapid oscillation of the bromine atom between the carbon atoms of the original double bond:

[The very weak interactions to be expected from the olefinic protons do not appear in the ESR spectra (cf. p. 10)].

Addition of methanethiol-(S-*D*) to the isomeric but-2-enes, even at low temperatures ($-78°$) is not stereospecific, in spite of the fact that *cis-trans* isomerization does not occur under these conditions. The abstraction step is evidently not sufficiently fast to exclude inversion of the radical. When a *mixture* of methanethiol-(S-*D*) and deuterium bromide is used, however, *stereospecific* addition of the *thiol* is observed at $-78°$. This suggests that addition of MeS· is followed by very rapid transfer with DBr, the rapidity of the second stage preserving stereospecificity. If this suggestion is correct, the rate of equilibration between bromine atoms and thiol must compare with that of the transfer step:

$$\text{MeSD} + \text{Br·} \rightleftharpoons \text{MeS·} + \text{DBr}$$

The steric course of homolytic addition to cyclic olefins has been studied by several groups using several addenda. Most reactions have been carried out with 1-substituted cyclohexenes using thiols and hydrogen bromide. The *cis* isomer, formed by *trans* addition predominates in the products to the extent of 75–95%.

In general, it seems reasonable that transfer should occur on the side of the molecule away from that at which the incoming radical entered. Formation of *cis* products by *trans* addition results. The situation may be pictured as follows:

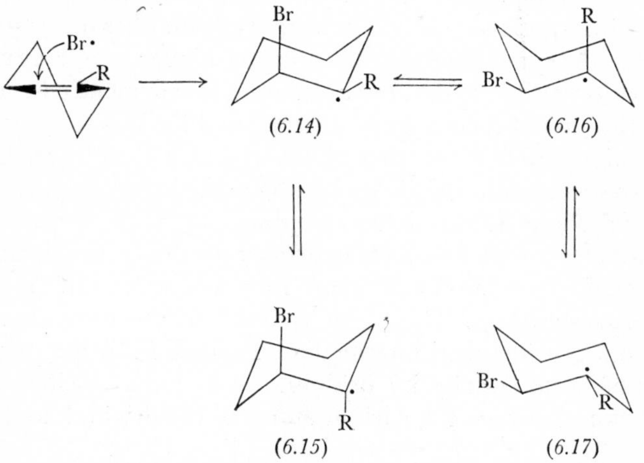

(6.14)   (6.16)

(6.15)   (6.17)

Radical attack probably occurs perpendicularly to the σ-bond with formation of radical (*6.14*) (R eq.) or (*6.15*) (R ax.). The relative energies of (*6.14*) and (*6.15*) are uncertain although (*6.14*) is probably the more stable and axial transfer in (*6.14*) away from the large axial bromine atom would certainly be preferred. Unless transfer is very rapid, ring inversion to (*6.16*) and hence (*6.17*) can occur, and axial transfer (in *6.17*) produces the *trans* isomer (*cis* addition). Stereoselectivity is usually greater in the cyclic olefins suggesting that equilibration processes are less well able to compete with transfer.

One would expect that any gross steric effects would interfere with this pattern of perpendicular addition and *trans* abstraction. In addition of hydrogen bromide to 2-bromo-2-norbornene (*6.18*), for example,

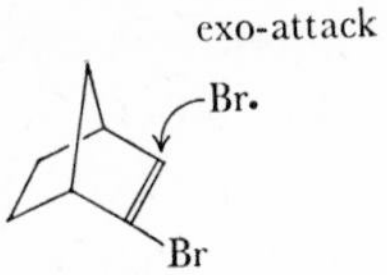

exo-attack

(*6.18*) 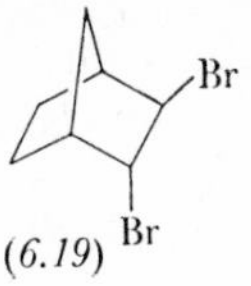   (*6.19*) 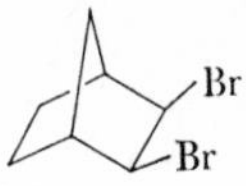   (*6.20*)

the *trans* (*cis* addition) (*6.19*) and *cis* (*trans* addition) (*6.20*) products are obtained in the ratio of 5:2. Addition of Br· undoubtedly occurs perpendicularly to the *exo-* face but transfer, which in *trans* addition must occur on the *endo-* side is slowed down to such an extent that inversion occurs, allowing transfer to occur more favourably from the *exo-* side. Similar behaviour has been observed in the addition of ethyl bromoacetate to norbornene:

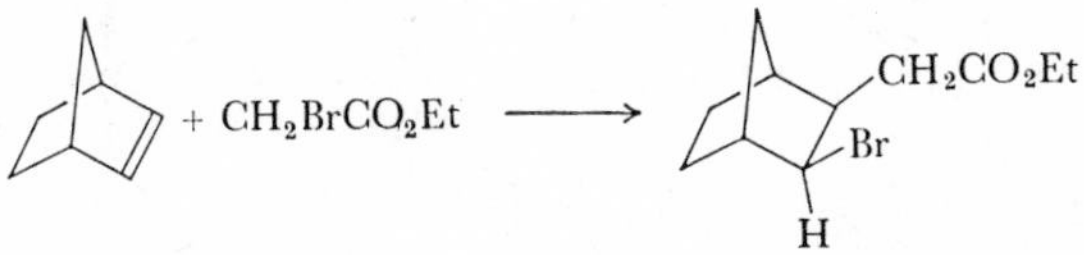

For further reading

BOHM and ABELL, 'Stereochemistry of Radical Additions to Olefins', *Chem. Rev.*, 1962, **62**, 599.

CADOGAN, *Roy. Inst. Chem. Lecture Series*, 1960, No. 5.

ELIEL, *Stereochemistry of Carbon Compounds*. McGraw Hill, 1962.

STACEY and HARRIS, *Org. React.*, 1963, **13**, 150.

WALLING and HUYSER, *Org. React.*, 1963, **13**, 91.

WILLIAMS, *Progress in Stereochemistry*, Chapter 2 (Ed. Klyne and de la Mare). Butterworths, London, 1961.

PROBLEMS

1. Discuss the following:

(*a*) Radical addition of thiophenol to phenylacetylene gives 95% of the adduct (1) when an excess of the acetylene is used. When an excess of thiol is present, a 20:80 mixture of the adducts (1) and (2) is obtained.

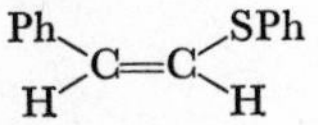

$PhSCH_2CH{=}CH_2$ $PhSC(CH_3){=}CH_2$

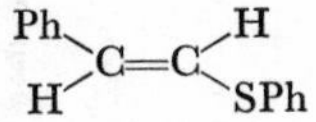

(1)   (2)   (3)   (4)

(*b*) Radical addition of thiophenol to allene gives the adducts (3) and (4) in a 2:1 ratio.

7

(c) Irradiation of phenylacetylene and thiophenol in the presence of oxygen gives the hemithioacetal (5):

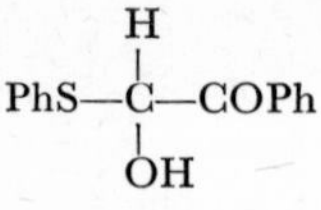

$$
\begin{array}{ccc}
\overset{\displaystyle H}{\underset{\displaystyle OH}{PhS—\overset{|}{\underset{|}{C}}—COPh}} &
\underset{\displaystyle HO_2C—\overset{\|}{C}—H}{C_6H_{11}S—C—CO_2H} &
C_6H_{11}S—\overset{\|}{C}—CO\diagdown \hspace{-0.5em} O \\
 & & H—\overset{\|}{C}—CO\diagup \\
(5) & (6) & (7)
\end{array}
$$

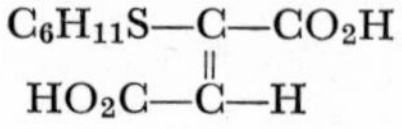

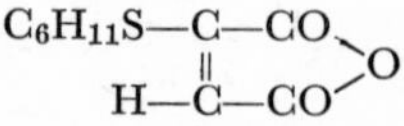

(d) Radical addition of cyclohexanethiol to acetylene dicarboxylic acid gives the products (6) and (7).

2. What compounds would you expect to obtain from the following compounds or mixtures of compounds by u.v. irradiation or treatment with catalytic quantities of benzoyl peroxide or t-butyl peroxide?

(a) $+ CCl_4$

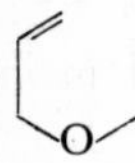

(b) $+ BrCCl_3$

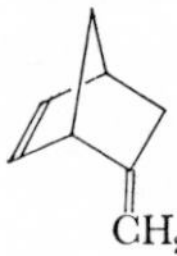

(c) $—(CH_2)_3CH(CN)CO_2Et$

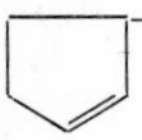

(d) $—(CH_2)_3CH(CN)CO_2Et$

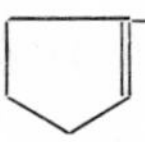

(e) $CH_3(CH_2)_5CHO +$ $—CH{=}CH_2$

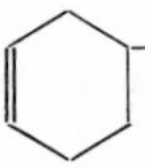

(f) $+ CH_2{=}CHCO_2H$

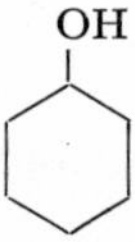

(g) $HSCH_2CH_2SH + AcOCH_2C{\equiv}CCH_2OAc$

(h) $PhSO_2I +$

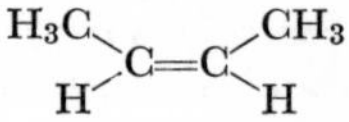

(i) $CH_3CH{=}CH_2 + Cl_2 + N_2O_4$

(j) $CH_3CH{=}CH_2 + I_2 + N_2O_4$

CHAPTER 7

POLYMERIZATION

It was seen at the beginning of the previous Chapter that the new radical produced by addition of a radical to an olefin could undergo two main alternative reactions:

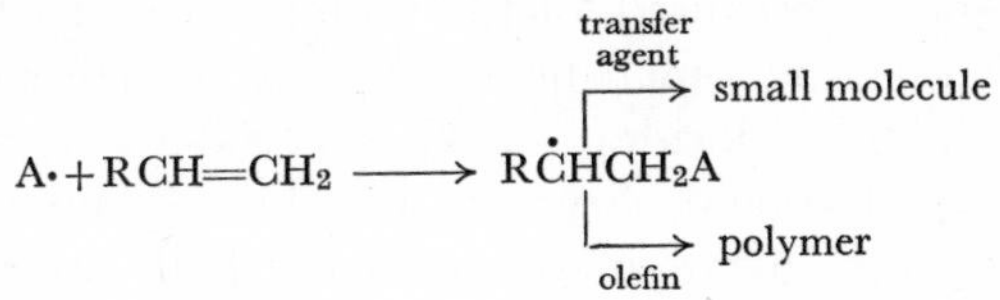

$$A\cdot + RCH{=}CH_2 \longrightarrow R\overset{\cdot}{C}HCH_2A \begin{array}{l} \xrightarrow{\text{transfer agent}} \text{small molecule} \\[2ex] \xrightarrow[\text{olefin}]{} \text{polymer} \end{array}$$

Reactions with molecules containing readily abstractable atoms (transfer agents) have been outlined in Chapter 6 and we now turn to the reaction of the 'intermediate radical' with successive olefin molecules; the process which leads eventually to the formation of *polymers*. Polymerization is of tremendous technical importance, and in this respect overshadows the remainder of radical chemistry. More work has been carried out on polymerization than on the rest of radical reactions put together and only a very superficial treatment can be given here. An attempt has been made in this Chapter to extract from the mass of data in this field those aspects which throw light on the behaviour and reactivity of radicals in general.

General Characteristics of Radical Polymerization. When radicals are generated in the presence of a polymerizable olefin (monomer), addition occurs (initiation) and the resulting radical adds to a further molecule of monomer. In principle this process continues stepwise (*propagation*) either until production of initiating radicals ceases, or the supply of monomer gives out. The individual polymer molecules continue growth until the unpaired electron of the most recently added monomer unit is paired by combination, disproportionation, or transfer with another component of the system. The chain lengths attained before termination may be very high—typical polymers have 10^5 monomer units in the chain. This number is estimated from molecular weight data obtained by viscometry, osmosis, or ultracentrifugation.

Formation of polymers from olefinic monomers is, of course, by no means restricted to systems in which radicals are produced. Cationic and anionic polymerization are both well known but the reactions that will be considered here are catalysed by light and by radical sources, and are subject to inhibition by compounds which have been seen to be retarders of other radical chain reactions. Absolute proof of radical participation in polymerization has been obtained by the detection of ESR signals from polymerizing styrene.

The number of olefins that readily undergo radical polymerization is fairly limited, the majority being terminal olefins ($RCH=CH_2$). We saw earlier that this type of olefin is generally the most reactive towards radical addition; monomers with allylic C—H bonds are usually as unsatisfactory in polymerization as in small molecule formation, and relatively few polysubstituted olefins polymerize at all. In general, the most widely used monomers bear 'negative' substituents such as —Cl (vinyl and vinylidene chloride) —CO_2R (acrylates and methacrylates), and —OCOR (vinyl esters). Styrene and butadiene are exceptional among hydrocarbons in polymerizing easily; high pressure conditions are required for the polymerization of simple olefins such as ethylene.

The successive steps in building up the polymer chain are extremely rapid, so that examination of a polymerizing system reveals only monomer and 'finished' high polymer. While the amount of polymer present in a system increases with time, its average molecular weight remains constant and successive steps are completed in a period which is very short compared with that required for the overall conversion of monomer into polymer.

The question of the orientation of successive additions arises in polymerization just as in small molecule formation. X-ray examination of polyvinylidene chloride shows the general 'head to tail' arrangement, cf. (7.1); this is the arrangement to be expected from considerations put forward in Chapter 6, but it is not invariable. Hydrolysis of polyvinyl

$$...—CHCH_2 \left[CHCH_2 \right]_n —CHCH_2—...$$
$$\quad\quad | \quad\quad | \quad\quad\quad |$$
$$\quad\quad R \quad\quad R \quad\quad\quad R$$

(7.1)

acetate, for example, gives polyvinyl alcohol whose molecular weight is lowered by treatment with periodate. This reagent specifically cleaves 1,2-diols and the reaction shows departure *(7.2)* from the 'head-to-tail' arrangement to the extent of 1–2%. It must be noted, however, that this 'head to head' arrangement also arises when termination of the chain sequence occurs by combination (p. 93).

$$\quad OAc(H) \quad\quad OAc(H) \left[OAc(H) \quad OAc(H) \right] \quad OAc(H)$$
$$\quad\quad | \quad\quad\quad\quad | \quad\quad | \quad\quad\quad | \quad\quad\quad\quad |$$
$$...CH_2CHCH_2——CHCH_2\_CH———CH——\_CH_2CHCH_2...$$

(7.2)

Kinetics of Polymerization. This aspect of polymerization is now considered so that the process may be broken down into the stages upon which quantitative studies have been made.

The chief steps of initiation, propagation, and termination may be expressed as follows (M = monomer):[†]

Initiation:

$$\text{Radical source} \longrightarrow \text{In} \cdot + RCH{=}CH_2 \xrightarrow{k_i} R\overset{\cdot}{C}HCH_2{-}In$$

or

$$\text{In} \cdot + M \xrightarrow{k_i} M \cdot \qquad \ldots(7.1)$$

Propagation:

$$R\overset{\cdot}{C}HCH_2{-}In + RCH{=}CH_2 \xrightarrow{k_p} In{-}CH_2\overset{\overset{R}{|}}{C}HCH_2\overset{\overset{R}{|}}{C}H\cdot$$

or

$$M_n\cdot + M \xrightarrow{k_p} M_{n+1}\cdot \qquad \ldots(7.2)$$

Termination (by combination):

$$2In{-}\left[CH_2\overset{\overset{R}{|}}{C}H\right]_n{-}CH_2\overset{\overset{R}{|}}{C}H\cdot \xrightarrow{k_{tc}}$$

$$In{-}\left[CH_2\overset{\overset{R}{|}}{C}H\right]_n{-}CH_2\overset{\overset{R}{|}}{C}H\overset{\overset{R}{|}}{C}HCH_2{-}\left[\overset{\overset{R}{|}}{C}HCH_2\right]_n{-}In$$

or

$$M_n\cdot + M_m\cdot \xrightarrow{k_{tc}} \sim\!\!\sim\!\!\sim P_{n+m} \qquad \ldots(7.3a)$$

Termination (by disproportionation):

$$2In{-}\left[CH_2\overset{\overset{R}{|}}{C}H\right]_n CH_2\overset{\overset{R}{|}}{C}H\cdot \longrightarrow$$

$$In{-}\left[CH_2\overset{\overset{R}{|}}{C}H\right]_n CH{=}\overset{\overset{R}{|}}{C}H + In{-}\left[CH_2\overset{\overset{R}{|}}{C}H\right]_n CH_2CH_2R$$

or

$$M_n\cdot + M_m\cdot \xrightarrow{k_{td}} \sim\!\!\sim\!\!\sim P_n + \sim\!\!\sim\!\!\sim P_m \qquad \ldots(7.3b)$$

Making the reasonable assumption that k_p and k_t are not dependent upon the size of the polymer radical, the rate of disappearance of monomer is equal to the sum of the initiation and propagation rates:

$$-d[M]/dt = k_i[In\cdot][M] + k_p[M\cdot][M] \qquad \ldots(7.4)$$

When chains are long, the rate of removal of monomer in the initiation step may be neglected when compared with consumption during propagation:

$$-d[M]/dt = k_p[M\cdot][M] \qquad \ldots(7.5)$$

[†] In the general expressions, the subscripts n and m denote the number of connected monomer units. $M_n\cdot$ thus indicates a polymer radical containing n units of monomer.

As the rate of change of concentration of polymer radicals M· is small when compared with their rates of formation and disappearance, steady state treatment may be applied:

$$k_i[\text{In·}][\text{M}] = k_t[\text{M·}]^2 \qquad \qquad \ldots(7.6)$$

or

$$[\text{M·}] = \left(k_i \frac{[\text{In·}][\text{M}]}{k_t}\right)$$

Substituting in equation (7.5)

$$-\frac{d[\text{M}]}{dt} = k_p \left(\frac{k_i}{k_t} \cdot [\text{M}][\text{In·}]\right)^{\frac{1}{2}} \cdot [\text{M}] \qquad \qquad \ldots(7.7)$$

Now the initiation rate, $k_i[\text{M}][\text{In·}]$, may be rewritten as $k_h.f.[\text{S}]$, where s represents a source of radicals giving one radical per molecule,† f, the fraction of these radicals which actually start chains (the initiator efficiency), and k_h, the rate constant for radical production from the initiator.

$$R_p \text{ (rate of polymerization)} = k_p \left(\frac{k_h}{k_t} \cdot f[\text{S}]\right)^{\frac{1}{2}} \cdot [\text{M}] \qquad \qquad \ldots(7.8)$$

As in many other systems, the rate of polymerization of vinyl acetate, initiated with benzoyl peroxide, is indeed found to be first order in monomer and half order in initiator; the same applies to photo-initiation.

Initiation. The role of the initiator is to provide radicals, which by addition to the monomer, start off polymerization. This is conclusively shown by the identification of fragments of the initiator in the polymer produced. Polystyrene obtained using *p*-bromobenzoyl peroxide as initiator contains bromine, and with radioactive azoisobutyronitrile (*7.3*) radioactive polymers are obtained.

$$(CH_3)_2C(^{14}CN)\text{---}N\text{==}N\text{---}C(^{14}CN)(CH_3)_2$$
$$(7.3)$$

Assuming that [M] is large, the factors which control the rate of initiation are the efficiency factor, f, and the specific rate, k_h, of radical production from the source.

$$R_i = f.k_h.[\text{S}][\text{M}] \qquad \qquad \ldots(7.9)$$

In the ideal situation, when all the radicals produced from the source start chains, $f = 1$. In practice, values of f are significantly lower than unity. The value of f may be determined in three ways:

† For simplicity. Most sources give two radicals per molecule.

(i) *Molecular Weight Determination*. Each radical from the initiator should, if $f = 1$, produce a polymer molecule of the average chain length. Measurement of the *amount* of polymer produced from a given amount of initiator together with an accurate knowledge of polymer molecular weight thus gives f directly. k_h can usually be obtained easily from non-polymer studies and, hence, R_i is directly calculable. This method involves assumptions about termination processes (later) but the benzoyl peroxide/styrene system gives f values of 0·6–1·0.

(ii) *Initiator Incorporation*. This is an absolute method in which the amount of initiator incorporated in the polymer is compared with the total amount of initiator reacted. The method assumes that no induced decomposition (see Chapter 8) occurs and that termination by combination with initiator radicals does not take place. Both assumptions are probably valid when azonitriles are used and with methyl methacrylate, for example, values of $f \simeq 0.5$ are obtained.

(iii) *Scavenger Technique*. A compound with a high reactivity towards radicals is added to the system and the rate of its consumption is measured. Diphenylpicrylhydrazyl, the violet 'long-life' radical is particularly suitable, and the rate of radical production is then related to the rate of colour fading. Ferric salts can be used in the same way, when the rate of ferrous ion production equals the rate of radical formation. Considerable

$$R \cdot + FeCl_3 \longrightarrow RCl + FeCl_2$$

assumptions are, however, involved in this method, notably that the scavenger reacts solely and quantitatively with the growing polymer chains.

Reactivity of Monomers in Initiation. When benzoyl peroxide is used for initiation, the benzoyloxy radicals produced survive long enough to escape from the solvent cage and their subsequent reactions occur in the bulk of the solution. The radicals may either attack monomer:

$$PhCO_2 \cdot + M \longrightarrow PhCO_2M \cdot \qquad \ldots(7.10)$$

or decompose with formation of carbon dioxide and phenyl radicals which then attack monomer:

$$PhCO_2 \cdot \longrightarrow Ph \cdot + CO_2 \qquad \ldots(7.11)$$

$$Ph \cdot + M \longrightarrow PhM \cdot \qquad \ldots(7.12)$$

The more reactive the monomer, the less reactions (7.11) and (7.12) will occur. The extent of capture of benzoyloxy radicals by the monomer has been determined by using peroxide labelled with ^{14}C in the carbonyl group. Determination of radioactivity in the polymer then gives a measure of the relative rates of reactions (7.10) and (7.11). Monomer reactivities determined in this way are given in Table 7.1.

Table 7.1. Monomer Reactivities (at 60°) towards Benzoyloxy Radicals

Monomer	$k_{rel.}$
2,5-Dimethylstyrene	2·0
Styrene	1·0
2,4,6-Trimethylstyrene	0·67
Vinyl acetate	0·36
Methyl methacrylate	0·12
Acrylonitrile	0·05

The spread of reactivity is rather less than that observed with tri-chloromethyl radicals (p. 81) but the benzoyloxy radical, like the trichloromethyl radical, is clearly an electron acceptor: acrylonitrile is less reactive than vinyl acetate even though the intermediate radical is considerably stabilized.

Propagation. Once a radical from the initiator attacks monomer, the chain process of propagation continues until the polymer radical is destroyed. Statistically, termination occurs most frequently when the polymer reaches the average molecular weight or degree of polymeriza-tion, $\bar{P}$. (Polymer chains may, of course, terminate at *any* molecular weight and a spread of chain lengths is always obtained.) The propaga-tion step is usually repeated hundreds of times for every act of initiation, and the mechanism (p. 93) explains not only why a small amount of a radical source suffices to produce large quantities of polymer, but also why small amounts of inhibitors (chain breakers) can prevent its forma-tion.

The kinetic chain length, ν, or the number of propagation steps before termination, is related to the relative rates of propagation and termination:

$$\nu = R_p/R_t \qquad \dots (7.13)$$

and as we have seen from the steady state assumption (p. 94), $R_i = R_t$, so

$$\nu = R_p/R_i \qquad \dots (7.14)$$

These relationships reveal an important fact about propagation and polymer formation. Increase in the amount of initiator increases the concentration of polymer radicals and, as $R_p = k_p$ [M·] [M], raises the polymerization rate. The rate of termination $R_t = k_t$ [M·]^2, however,

96

increases more rapidly, being dependent upon the square of the radical concentration; the kinetic chain length, v, consequently decreases.

Termination and Inhibition. Growth of a polymer molecule ceases when the odd electron is paired. If another polymer radical is involved, termination is by combination or disproportionation, the former usually being preferred. In styrene polymerization, initiated by radio-active azobisisobutyronitrile, the product contains two initiator fragments in each molecule:

$$\text{In*—P·} + \text{·P—In*} \longrightarrow \text{In*—P—P—In*}$$

Lower proportions of initiator incorporation have, however, been detected, indicating the simultaneous operation of termination by disproportionation.

Growth is also terminated by electron-pairing with radicals other than those derived from the polymer. Good examples of this type are the long-life radicals such as triphenylmethyl and diphenylpicrylhydrazyl. Use of the latter as a scavenger in initiation studies was mentioned earlier. The structure of the combination product with DPPH is uncertain but with triphenylmethyl the structure is as expected:

$$\text{\textasciitilde P·} + \text{·CPh}_3 \longrightarrow \text{\textasciitilde P—CPh}_3 \qquad \ldots(7.15)$$

Inorganic ions which will undergo one-electron transfer also break the polymer chain:

$$\text{\textasciitilde P·} + \text{FeCl}_3 \longrightarrow \text{\textasciitilde PCl} + \text{FeCl}_2 \qquad \ldots(7.16)$$

These energetically favourable processes inhibit polymerization because *each* step of the propagation sequence has to compete with them, and $k_p \ll k_{\text{combination}}$. The effect of this type of inhibitor is shown in Fig. 7.1. Polymerization is completely prevented during the induction period in which the inhibitor is used up. Thereafter, polymerization resumes at its normal rate.

More commonly, compounds can adversely affect polymerization by reaction with the growing polymer radical to give a new but unreactive radical. This radical does not carry on the chain process efficiently because it is diverted to side reactions such as combination. Inhibition of this type is often not complete; some of the new radicals do continue propagation and the process is frequently referred to as *retardation*. The situation for a typical system is illustrated in Fig. 7.1. Increase in the concentration of inhibitor causes a proportional increase in the period before the normal rate of polymerization is established. The inhibitory action of quinones probably involves addition at oxygen giving a

97

stabilized phenoxy radical (*7.4*). Coupling (cf. Chapter 10) with a similar radical or combination with a polymer radical follows:

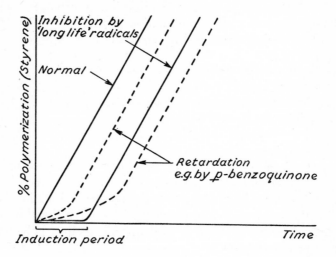

(7.4)

Analysis gives a number of quinone molecules incorporated into polystyrene varying between 0·5 and 1·8.

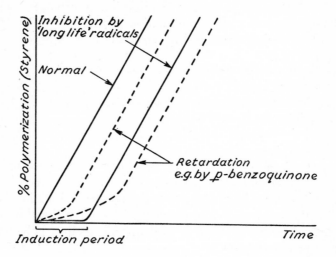

Fig. 7.1

Nitro-compounds and oxygen are also important polymerization inhibitors. The mechanism of inhibition by nitro-compounds is uncertain, but with oxygen, unreactive alkylperoxy radicals are produced:

$$\text{wwP·} + O_2 \longrightarrow \text{wwP—OO·}$$

This reaction is very rapid; for styrene it is 2×10^5 times as fast as the propagation step and, consequently, degassing of systems for kinetic measurements is essential.

98

Individual Rate Coefficients. Knowledge of the magnitudes of the rate coefficients k_i, k_p, and k_t is obviously of interest in relation to the understanding of radical reactivity. We have seen (eqn. 7.8) that the rate of polymerization is given by:

$$R_p = k_p \left(\frac{k_h}{k_t} f.[\text{S}]\right)^{1/2}.[\text{M}]$$

Where R_i, the initiation rate $= k_h' f.[\text{S}]$. Measurement of R_i has been outlined, and as R_p and [M] may be measured directly, k_p and k_t remain. Rearrangement of equation (7.8) gives:

$$k_p^2/k_t = (R_p/[\text{M}])^2/R_i \qquad \qquad \ldots(7.8a)$$

The ratio of these important rate constants can thus be determined for any polymerization system following these kinetics and the magnitude of this ratio may be compared for different monomers (provided that a constant rate of initiation obtains and that termination is by coupling). The ratio broadly expresses the rate of polymerization and it is found that values of k_p^2/k_t decrease in the order vinyl acetate > methyl methacrylate > styrene. Differences between systems may be due either to high polymer radical reactivity or to high monomer reactivity. As we shall see later, radical reactivity is the dominant effect.

The determination of k_p and k_t separately has, however, been accomplished. The determination depends upon the examination of kinetics under non-steady state conditions and has been described in detail by Walling and by Bamford. Some values of k_p and k_t for various polymer systems are given in Table 7.2 together with activation energies.

Table 7.2. Rate Constants (1. mole^{-1} sec^{-1}) and Activation Energies (kcal/mole) for Propagation and Termination (at 25°)

Monomer	k_p	E_p	$k_t(\times 10^{-6})$	E_t
Styrene	19	6·5	3	2
Methyl methacrylate	310	4·4	3	2
Methyl acrylate	720	7·1	4·3	5·3
Vinyl acetate	1000	5	100	0

Chain Transfer. Propagation of polymerization has to compete not only with combination and disproportionation but also with another reaction that brings the growth of the polymer radical to an end, namely *transfer*. In this reaction, the polymer radical abstracts an atom (or very occasionally a group of atoms) from a component of the system:

$$\text{\small$\sim\!\sim\!\sim$}\text{P}\cdot + \text{A—B} \longrightarrow \text{\small$\sim\!\sim\!\sim$}\text{P—B} + \text{A}\cdot \qquad \ldots(7.18)$$

Polymerization

The process differs from combination and termination in that the total number of radicals in the system is unaffected by it. The atom B, reaction (7.18), as we saw in the previous chapter, is nearly always hydrogen or halogen. Examination of transfer in polymer systems has yielded much information on radical reactivity and on this account will be considered in some detail.

Transfer with Solvent. In the term "solvent" will be included all the components in the system other than initiator, monomer, and polymer. The degree of polymerization $\bar{P}$, in many systems is less than would be expected from a knowledge of polymerization rates. This is understandable if the polymer chain is cut short by transfer before it can reach the statistical average molecular weight. The new radical A·, produced by transfer, is often able to start a new chain (*re-initiation*) so that while the *rate* of polymerization is unaffected, the polymer produced has shorter

$$A· + M \longrightarrow A—M· \longrightarrow A—P· \qquad \qquad \ldots(7.19)$$

chains, i.e. $\bar{P}$ is smaller than in the absence of the transfer agent. An example is the polymerization of styrene in carbon tetrachloride:

$$\underset{}{\sim\!\!\wedge\!\!\wedge CH_2\overset{\overset{\displaystyle Ph}{|}}{C}H·} \quad \xrightarrow{\text{polymerization}} \quad \sim\!\!\wedge\!\!\wedge CH_2\overset{\overset{\displaystyle Ph}{|}}{C}HCH_2\overset{\overset{\displaystyle Ph}{|}}{C}H· \qquad \ldots(7.20)$$

$$\sim\!\!\wedge\!\!\wedge CH_2\overset{\overset{\displaystyle Ph}{|}}{C}H· + CCl_4 \quad \xrightarrow{\text{transfer}} \quad \sim\!\!\wedge\!\!\wedge CH_2\overset{\overset{\displaystyle Ph}{|}}{C}HCl + CCl_3· \qquad \ldots(7.21)$$

$$CCl_3· + CH_2{=}\overset{\overset{\displaystyle Ph}{|}}{C}H \quad \xrightarrow{\text{re-initiation}} \quad CCl_3CH_2\overset{\overset{\displaystyle Ph}{|}}{C}H·$$

The extent of transfer expresses the relative importance of reactions (7.20) and (7.21). If (7.21) occurs very readily, the degree of polymerization decreases in the limit to the formation of 1:1-adducts between monomer and transfer agent; the system then yields small molecules.

The ease of transfer may be assessed both by analysis of the polymer for fragments of the transfer agent and by measuring the change in the average degree of polymerization that the transfer agent produces. It can be shown (references at the end of the Chapter) that

$$1/\bar{P} = 1/\bar{P}_0 + c[T]/[M] \qquad \ldots(7.22)$$

where $\bar{P}_0$ is the degree of polymerization obtained in the absence of a transfer agent, [T] is the concentration of transfer agent, and c is the *transfer constant* which expresses the ease of abstraction from the transfer agent for a *particular polymer radical*. c is simply obtained by a plot of [T]/[M] against $1/\bar{P}$. Some plots for styrene polymerization are given in

100

Fig. 7.2.† Note that there is rectilinear dependence on [T]/[M] and that the same value of $1/P_0$ is obtained by extrapolation in each case. Values of some transfer constants are given in Table 7.3.

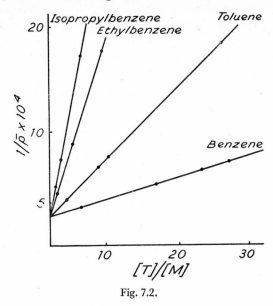

Fig. 7.2.

The value of the transfer constant for carbon tetrachloride shows that the styrene polymer radical abstracts chlorine about one-fiftieth as readily as it adds to a new monomer molecule.

Table 7.3. **Transfer Constants ($\times 10^4$) for Styrene Polymerization**

Cyclohexane	0·024	n-Butyl chloride	0·04
Benzene	0·018	n-Butyl bromide	0·06
Toluene	0·125	n-Butyl iodide	1·85
Ethylbenzene	0·67	Chloroform	0·5
Isopropylbenzene	0·82	Carbon tetrachloride	90
t-Butylbenzene	0·06	Carbon tetrabromide	13,600
Pentaphenylethane	20,000		
Propionic acid	0·05	2-Methylpropane-2-thiol	36,000
Phenylacetic acid	6	Dodecane-1-thiol	190,000
n-Butanol	0·06	Ethyl thioglycollate	580,000
Butyraldehyde	5·7	Di-n-butyl disulphide	125
Triethylamine	7·1		
Dioxan	2·8		

The results in Table 7.3 extend the knowledge of the ease of homolytic bond fission that has been obtained in the consideration of other types of

† Reproduced by permission of Dr. F. R. Mayo and the Faraday Society.

radical reaction. Cyclohexane and benzene, with strong C—H bonds, have low transfer constants and the low values for alkyl halides suggest that abstraction of hydrogen occurs. Alkyl iodides are exceptional; the low C—I bond strength favours halogen abstraction. The polyhalogeno-methanes, which readily give 1:1-adducts, have the high transfer constants that would be expected. In the series of alkylbenzenes, the order $PhCH_3 < PhEt < Ph.i-Pr > Ph.t-Bu$ agrees well with the extents of side-chain abstraction found during homolytic phenylation (p. 37).

Amines and alcohols have low transfer constants; hydrogen is abstracted from the α-carbon; O—H and N—H bonds are too strong for cleavage. The series

$$\underset{N-C}{\overset{H}{|}} > \underset{O-C}{\overset{H}{|}} > \underset{C-C}{\overset{H}{|}}$$

fits well with recent experiments (Henbest, 1961) in which t-butoxy radicals were found to remove hydrogen with decreasing ease in the series $ArNMe_2 > ArOMe > ArCMe_3$.

Thiols have particularly high constants and transfer occurs at the S—H bond in contrast with alcohols and amines. Because of their large constants, thiols are used to control polymer molecular weights, $\bar{P}$ being proportional to $1/c$. Disulphides are particularly interesting, as transfer occurs at the S—S bond

$$\sim\!\!\sim\!P\cdot + RSSR \longrightarrow \sim\!\!\sim\!P-SR + RS\cdot \qquad \ldots(7.23)$$

The course of transfer has been established by product analysis and is one of the rare examples of displacement reactions (Chapter 8).

Table 7.4. Variation in Transfer Constant with Polymer System

$(c \times 10^4)$

Transfer agent	Styrene	Methyl methacrylate	Acrylonitrile	Vinyl acetate
Benzene	0·018	0·075	2·46	3
Toluene	0·0125	0·525	5·83	21
Ethylbenzene	0·67	1·35	35·7	55
Triethylamine	7·1	8·3	5,900	3,700
Carbon tetrachloride	90	2·4	0·85	10,000
Carbon tetrabromide	13,600	3,300	1,900	39,000
Butane-1-thiol	220,000	67,000	—	480,000

It must be emphasized that the magnitude of the transfer constant of a compound varies with the polymer system. In Table 7.4, transfer constants for different systems are compared.

The results show clearly that transfer constants vary widely with the system and that for hydrocarbon transfer agents, they decrease in the order vinyl acetate > acrylonitrile > methyl methacrylate > styrene. The polymer radical in styrene is stabilized and weakly reactive, but the monomer is readily attacked by radicals. Transfer, accordingly, is not well favoured. In vinyl acetate, on the other hand, the polymer radical is unstabilized and highly reactive, while the monomer is much less susceptible to addition. Transfer consequently is much more probable.

The magnitude of the transfer constant of a given transfer agent is not, however, solely a function of polymer radical and monomer reactivities. The data for thiols and polyhalogenomethanes show that polar effects must also be taken into account. Walling has suggested that radicals from acrylonitrile and methyl methacrylate are electron acceptors, while those from styrene are donor radicals. The latter may stabilize the transition state for transfer:

$$\underset{\text{Ph}}{\text{wwCH}_2\dot{\text{C}}\text{H}\cdot}\ \text{Cl—CCl}_3 \longleftrightarrow \underset{\text{Ph}}{\text{wwCH}_2\overset{\oplus}{\text{C}}\text{H}}\dots\overset{\cdot}{\text{Cl}}\dots\overset{\ominus}{\text{CCl}_3}$$

In this situation, the residual portion of the transfer agent develops the anionic character particularly favourable in the cases of thiols and polyhalogenomethanes. Polymer radical and monomer reactivity will be discussed again in the section on copolymerization.

When a transfer agent yields a very poorly reactive radical, this new radical may be unable to reinitiate polymerization efficiently and the rate of polymerization consequently falls. Transfer agents of this type are termed *retarders* and are distinct from inhibitors in that polymerization does not cease (cf. p. 98). Compounds such as diphenylpicrylhydrazine and triphenylmethane have this effect; the new radicals produced are diphenylpicrylhydrazyl and triphenylmethyl respectively. Their effect on polymerization is greater with vinyl acetate than with styrene because of the higher transfer constants in the former system.

Transfer to Polymer. Transfer may occur not only with extraneous components of the polymerization system but also with the essential ones—polymer and monomer. The importance of transfer to polymer naturally increases with the degree of polymerization and its chief effect is to cause chain branching. Abstraction (nearly always of hydrogen) may occur at any position in the polymer chain and the resulting radical re-initiates, producing a branch at the abstraction site:

$$\underset{\text{H}}{\text{ww}\,|}\,+\,\text{wwP}\cdot \longrightarrow \underset{\cdot}{\text{ww}\,|}\,+\,\text{wwPH}$$

$$\underset{\cdot}{\text{ww}\,|}\,+\,\text{M} \longrightarrow \{\text{wwP}\cdot$$

This reaction would be expected to occur least in styrene polymerization as the unreactive polymer radical very much prefers propagation to transfer. The transfer constant of isopropylbenzene, which closely resembles the polymer structure in polystyrene, gives a rough value for this type of transfer. Bevington has calculated that at a degree of polymerization of 10^3, in a system containing 10% of polystyrene, branches are produced at one-hundredth of the rate that chains are propagated. The rare occurrence of transfer to polymer in polystyrene is shown by the observation that α-deuterated styrene gives polymer with the same properties as the isotopically normal monomer. If transfer to polymer were significant, the deuterated polymer would have a higher $\bar{P}$ because transfer is harder at C—D than at C—H bonds.

The situation with polyvinyl acetate, however, is quite different. The polymer radical is highly reactive and although hydrogen atoms in the polymer are less readily removable, branching is common. The extent of branching can be assessed from the solution properties of the polymer and, in the case of PVA, hydrolysis detaches many branches from the main chain. This demonstrates that C—H bonds of the acetyl group are involved:

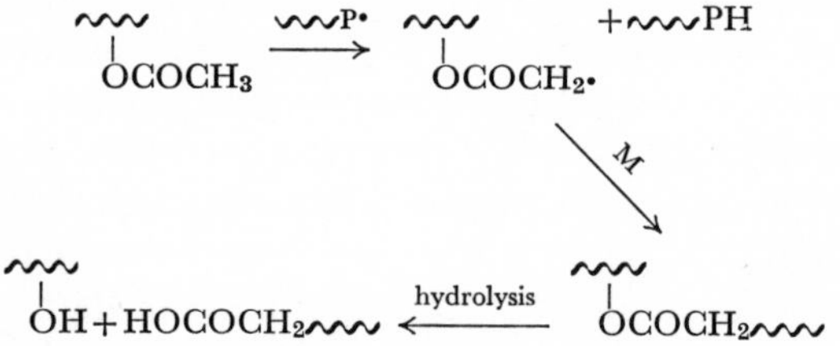

Chain transfer in ethylene polymerization, in which the polymer radicals are again very reactive, is very important because of its effect on the mechanical properties of the polymer. Many short branches of about four carbon atoms can be detected in polythene and these are believed to arise by 'back-biting' or intramolecular chain transfer:

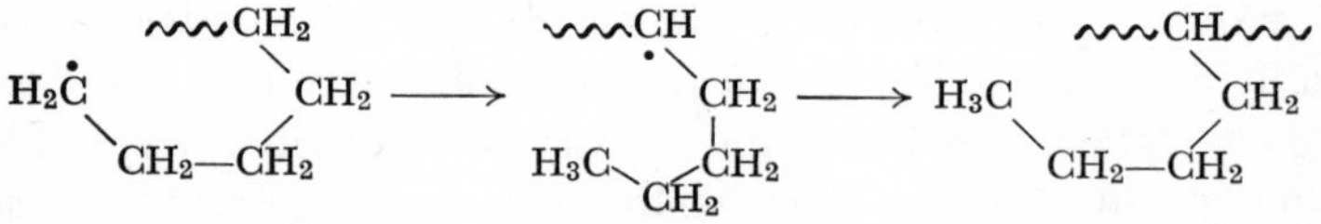

The number of atoms in the branch is decided by the optimum ring size of the transition state for abstraction. As five- and six-membered rings are favoured, three- and four-membered branches are formed.

Transfer to Monomer. Monomer is another inevitable component of the polymerization system and its transfer reactions likewise have an important influence on the characteristics of polymerization. Transfer to monomer will be most serious when the polymer radical is reactive and when the monomer has readily abstractable atoms. Values of self-transfer are given in Table 7.5; details of their measurement are given by Bamford.

Table 7.5. Self-transfer Constants

Monomer	$c_M \times 10^4$ at 60°
Styrene	0·60
Methyl acrylate	0·4
Methyl methacrylate	0·5
Vinyl chloride	0·2
Vinyl acetate	20
Allyl acetate	175
Allyl chloride	400

These values express the joint effect of polymer radical reactivity and atom abstractability in the monomer. The low value for styrene is expected; the polymer radical is weakly reactive and the monomer contains only aromatic and vinylic C—H bonds. In vinyl acetate, the reactive polymer radical removes hydrogen fairly easily from the acetyl group and, accordingly, c_M has a much higher value. The most favourable case for transfer to monomer is found in allylic monomers. The polymer radical is reactive and allylic hydrogen in the monomer is readily abstracted:

$$\text{wwCH}_2\text{—CH·} + \underset{\text{CH}_2\text{OAc}}{\overset{}{\underset{|}{\text{CH=CH}_2}}} \underset{\text{CH}_2\text{OAc}}{\overset{}{\underset{|}{\;}}} \longrightarrow \text{wwCH}_2\text{CH}_2 + \overset{\cdot}{\text{CH}_2\text{=-CH---CHOAc}}$$

The stabilized allylic radical produced can re-initiate only very inefficiently and for this reason allylic monomers show little tendency to polymerize.

The correctness of this scheme for allylic monomers has been confirmed by Bartlett (1953) who used the deuterated monomer: $CH_2\text{=CHCD}_2\text{OCOCH}_3$. This polymerizes about twice as fast as the isotopically normal monomer and gives about twice the degree of polymerization. The stronger C—D bonds cut down the extent of allylic attack on monomer.

Methyl methacrylate is interesting in this connection because it polymerizes very well in spite of having vulnerable C—H bonds at the allylic position:

$$\underset{CH_2\text{=CCO}_2\text{Me}}{\overset{\text{Me} \longleftarrow}{\underset{|}{\;}}} \qquad \underset{\text{wwCH}_2\overset{\cdot}{\text{C}}\text{C}}{\overset{\text{Me}}{\underset{|}{\;}}}\overset{O}{\underset{\text{OMe}}{\diagdown}} \longleftrightarrow \underset{\text{wwCH}_2\text{C=C}}{\overset{\text{Me}}{\underset{|}{\;}}}\overset{O·}{\underset{\text{OMe}}{\diagdown}}$$

$$(7.5)$$

The polymer radical (7·5), however, is stabilized and unreactive (cf. transfer constants in Table 7.4); transfer to monomer is, consequently, less serious.

COPOLYMERIZATION

When a mixture of two or more monomers is polymerized, a polymer is formed which incorporates each monomer to a greater or lesser extent. The product is termed a *copolymer* and the process of copolymerization is of great technical importance because the properties of copolymers may have great advantages for specific applications over those obtained from single monomers. The production of synthetic rubbers by diene copolymerization is the most important contemporary application of the process; more than 600,000 tons of the synthetic rubber GR–S, obtained by copolymerizing styrene and butadiene, was produced in the U.S.A. in 1952.

Technical aspects aside, copolymerization yields much significant information on radical and olefin reactivity which is not available from simple polymerizations. We have seen, for example (p. 99), that while values of k_p may be obtained from single monomer systems, it is not possible to separate the differential effects on k_p of radical and monomer reactivity. Quantitative data from copolymerization supply this information and strengthen the conclusions that were reached on this question in Chapter 6.

Monomer Reactivity Ratios. Propagation in the copolymerization of two monomers involves four reactions [$\sim M_1\cdot$ denotes a polymer radical ending in a unit of monomer (1)]:

$$\sim\!\!\sim\!\!M_1\cdot + M_1 \xrightarrow{\ k_a\ } \sim\!\!\sim\!\!M_1 - M_1\cdot \qquad \dots(7.24)$$

$$\sim\!\!\sim\!\!M_1\cdot + M_2 \xrightarrow{\ k_b\ } \sim\!\!\sim\!\!M_1 - M_2\cdot \qquad \dots(7.25)$$

$$\sim\!\!\sim\!\!M_2\cdot + M_2 \xrightarrow{\ k_c\ } \sim\!\!\sim\!\!M_2 - M_2\cdot \qquad \dots(7.26)$$

$$\sim\!\!\sim\!\!M_2\cdot + M_1 \xrightarrow{\ k_d\ } \sim\!\!\sim\!\!M_2 - M_1\cdot \qquad \dots(7.27)$$

The ratio k_a/k_b expresses the tendency of the polymer radical ending in a monomer unit M_1 to attack its own type of monomer (M_1) compared with attack on the other monomer (M_2). Similarly, the ratio k_c/k_d expresses the same tendency for the polymer radical ending in a unit M_2. (As previously, it is assumed that the behaviour of a polymer radical is determined only by its terminal unit.) These ratios, k_a/k_b and k_c/k_d are known as the *monomer reactivity ratios*, r_1 and r_2 respectively.

In two-monomer copolymerization, the rates of removal of each monomer are given by equations (7.28) and (7.29):

$$-dM_1/dt = k_a[M_1\cdot][M_1] + k_d[M_2\cdot][M_1] \qquad \ldots(7.28)$$

$$-dM_2/dt = k_b[M_1\cdot][M_2] + k_c[M_2\cdot][M_2] \qquad \ldots(7.29)$$

Assuming steady state concentrations of each polymer radical:

$$dM_1\cdot/dt = k_d[M_2\cdot][M_1] - k_b[M_1\cdot][M_2] = 0. \qquad \ldots(7.30)$$

Dividing (7.28) by (7.29) and eliminating radical concentrations by (7.30) gives:

$$\frac{d[M_1]}{d[M_2]} = \frac{[M_1]}{[M_2]} \cdot \frac{r_1[M_1] + [M_2]}{[M_1] + r_2[M_2]} \qquad \ldots(7.31)$$

Reactivity ratios, r, are measured by determining the composition of the copolymer for two or more different monomer mixtures (feeds), and values of r_1 and r_2 are selected to give the best fit of equation (7.31), the 'Copolymerization Equation'. Other methods of determining r are discussed by Walling and by Alfrey.

A large value of r implies that the polymer radical is much better able to add the same monomer unit than to change to the other monomer. When r is small the opposite situation applies. In practice it is generally found either that both r's (for a binary monomer system) are less than unity or that r_1 is greater than unity and r_2 is very small. Some values are given in Table 7.6.

Table 7.6. Monomer Reactivity Ratios (at 60°)

Monomer 1	Monomer 2	r_1	r_2
Styrene	Butadiene	0·78	1·4
Styrene	1,1-Dichloroethylene	10	0
Styrene	Maleic anhydride	0·05	0
Styrene	Vinyl chloride	17	0·02
Styrene	Acrylonitrile	0·40	0·05
Styrene	Methyl methacrylate	0·52	0·46
Butadiene	Isoprene	0·75	0·85
Butadiene	Acrylonitrile	0·28	0·02
Acrylonitrile	Vinyl acetate	5	0·1
Acrylonitrile	Vinyl chloride	3·3	0.04
Methyl methacrylate	Vinyl acetate	20	0·03

When r's are of the same order of magnitude and less than unity, there is a strong tendency towards 'alternacy' in the copolymer, each type of radical preferring to attack the other monomer. The methyl methacrylate-styrene system exemplifies this behaviour. When r's are very different, the component with the large r value will be used up preferentially. The initial polymer produced from a 1:1 mixture of styrene and vinyl chloride is nearly pure polystyrene.

Significance of Reactivity Ratios. *Olefin and Radical Reactivity.* The monomer reactivity ratio gives a direct measure of the relative reactivity of an olefin towards radical addition. The greater the value of r for a given monomer, the lower is the reactivity of the other monomer. Consequently, for a given monomer M_1 in a binary system, $1/r_1$ expresses the reactivity of the other monomer towards the polymer radical $\sim\!M_1$. Values of $1/r$, collected chiefly by Walling, are given in Table 7.7 for a number of polymer radicals.

Table 7.7. Relative Reactivities ($1/r$) of Olefins (at 60°)

Monomer	Polymer Radical					
	S	VA	VC	MeM	VCl	A
2,5-Dichlorostyrene	5·0	—	—	2·3	—	5
2-Vinylpyridine	1·8	100	—	2·5	—	—
Butadiene	1·3	—	—	4·0	20	20
Styrene	1·0	50	30	2·2	12	20
Methyl methacrylate	1·9	70	—	1·0	4	5·5
Methyl vinyl ketone	3·5	20	—	—	—	1·6
Acrylonitrile	2·4	18	15	0·74	2·7	1·0
Vinylidene chloride	0·54	30	5	0·4	1·0	1·1
2-Methylpropene	—	—	0·5	0·7	—	—
Vinyl chloride	0·05	3·5	1·0	0·07	0·5	0·30
Allyl chloride	0·03	1·4	0·5	0·05	0·26	0·20
Vinyl acetate	0·02	1·0	0·5	0·05	0·25	0·20
Maleic anhydride	20	18	3·5	0·15	0·1	0·16
Trichloroethylene	0·06	1·5	—	0·01	—	0·015
cis-Dichloroethylene	0·005	0·17	—	—	—	—
trans-Dichloroethylene	0·03	1·0	—	—	—	—
Tetrachloroethylene	0·005	0·16	—	—	—	—

S = Styrene; VA = vinyl acetate; VC = vinyl chloride; MeM = methyl methacrylate; VCl = vinylidene chloride; A = acrylonitrile.

Monomers are arranged in the Table so that they fall (roughly) in decreasing order of reactivity towards radicals. The values for the polystyrene radical, for example, show that 2,5-dichlorostyrene is five times as reactive as styrene towards the polystyrene radical.

The orders of reactivity are more or less self-consistent, i.e. a particular monomer is not, in general, highly reactive towards one type of polymer radical and poorly reactive towards another. The chief exceptions are found when polar effects operate in the radical or olefin; these are discussed later. Table 7.7 gives the broad picture of substituent effects on reactivity and these may be put in the order:

$$Ph- \simeq CH_2{=}CH- > CH_3CO- > CN- > ROCO- > Cl- > XCH_2- > RCOO-$$

The most important factor in determining olefin reactivity is the stability of the intermediate radical that is produced; the greater the extent to which the unpaired electron may be delocalised, the greater the reactivity of the olefin is found to be. It has, however, been pointed out that substituents which stabilise the intermediate radical should also stabilize the olefin and hence reduce its susceptibility to radical attack. Comparison of the heat of hydrogenation (giving olefin stabilization) and bond dissociation energies (giving radical stabilization) shows that the latter is much more important. For styrene, olefin stabilization amounts to 3–4 kcal/mole, while radical stabilization is about 25 kcal/mole.

Similar conclusions about the effect of radical stabilization on the reactivity of olefins had been reached in the previous Chapter. Polymerization data also yield information on *radical reactivity* about which we could gain only rather superficial knowledge from the extents of telomerization observed with different olefins (Chapter 6). The propagation rates are known for a number of monomers (Table 7.2); as copolymerization analysis gives the reactivity ratio of two monomers towards a given polymer radical, rate constants for the addition of a number of radicals to a variety of olefins may be calculated from values of k_p and r. Some values are given in Table 7.8.

Table 7.8. Velocity Constants for Radical Addition to Olefins

(k in l. mole^{-1} sec^{-1} at 60°)

	Olefin			
Radical	S	MeM	VC	VA
Polystyrene	176	338	7	3·2
Polymethyl methacrylate	1600	734	49	37
Polyvinyl chloride	$3·7 \times 10^5$	—	$12·3 \times 10^3$	6150
Polyvinyl acetate	$3·7 \times 10^5$	$2·47 \times 10^5$	8000	3000

Table 7.8 shows the usual inverse relationship between olefin and radical reactivity. The more reactive the monomer, the less reactive is the polymer radical. The polystyrene radical gives the lowest rates of addition and, as with other radicals, these decrease sharply on going across the table from left to right, the order of decreasing olefin reactivity.

109

Polymerization

The unstabilized vinyl acetate radical has very large velocity constants but its monomer has the lowest reactivity towards addition. Thus for a single monomer, these effects on propagation rate are opposed. This has the effect of making the propagation rate in polystyrene only a factor of about fifty less than in polyvinyl acetate, in spite of the fact that the polymer radical in the latter system is about a thousand times as reactive in additions as the polystyrene radical.

Table 7.9. Relative Reactivities of Chloroethylenes towards Radicals

Olefin	Polymer radical	
	Vinyl acetate	*Styrene*
Vinyl chloride	1·0	1·0
1,1-Dichloroethylene	10	9·2
cis-1,2-Dichloroethylene	0·05	0·08
trans-1,2-Dichloroethylene	0·3	0·46
Trichloroethylene	0·45	1·0
Tetrachloroethylene	0·04	0·09

Steric Effects. In Chapter 6 it was seen that 1,2-disubstituted olefins have reduced susceptibilities to radical attack; β-methylstyrene, for example, is about ninety times less reactive than styrene towards the trichloromethyl radical. Copolymerization results reveal similar tendencies in halo-olefins (Table 7.9) and unsaturated acids (Table 7.10).

Table 7.10. Relative Reactivities of α,β-Unsaturated Acids and Esters

Olefin		Polymer radical		
		S	VA	VCl
Acrylic acid	$CH_2{=}CHCO_2H$	3·5	2	—
Methacrylic acid	$CH_2{=}C(Me)CO_2H$	5·2	20	6·7
Crotonic acid	$CH_3CH{=}CHCO_2H$	0·04	0·6	0·03
Methyl acrylate	$CH_2{=}CHCO_2Me$	1	1	1
Methyl methacrylate	$CH_2{=}C(Me)CO_2Me$	1·5	14	4

The data of Table 7.9 show that introduction of a further substituent on the *non-terminal* carbon atom increases olefin reactivity; substituents contribute to radical stability better than hydrogen. Reactivity in the isomeric 1,2-dichloroethylenes, however, is markedly depressed. The *trans*-isomer in this instance (as in many others) is the more reactive. The introduction of a third substituent, as in trichloroethylene, raises reactivity again but not nearly to the level of the 1,1-disubstituted compound. The radical stabilizing effect of the third chlorine atom is unable to compensate for the adverse steric effect of the second, and hence tetrachloroethylene is the least reactive of the series. Similarly, crotonic acid is much *less* reactive than its isomer, methacrylic acid, which is *more* reactive than acrylic acid. (Cf. the series β-methylstyrene– α-methylstyrene–styrene, Chapter 6, Table 6.6.)

These findings lend support to the rather sparse evidence for steric effects on olefin reactivity that was discussed in Chapter 6, and accounts for the fact that disubstituted ethylenes generally show little tendency to polymerize alone, although they frequently copolymerize with vinyl monomers. Neither maleic anhydride nor stilbene, for example, poly-merize alone but both readily copolymerize with styrene.

Polar Effects. The general principle that a reactive monomer gives a weakly reactive radical and *vice versa* was discussed earlier. This principle implies that r_1 should be greater than unity and r_2 less than unity except for the special case where $r_1 \simeq r_2 \simeq 1$. There are many cases, however, when r_1 and r_2 are *both* less than unity (Table 7.6), and this suggests that polar effects are overlaid on the simple relationship between radical stabilization and olefin reactivity. $r_1 < 1 > r_2$ indicates a tendency for alternation of monomer units in the chain, and this occurs most frequently when one monomer possesses an electron withdrawing group and the other an electron acceding group. The monomer pair, styrene and methacrylonitrile, for example, have $r_1 = r_2 = 0.25$.

Monomer reactivity ratios are little affected by change of solvent dielectric so that dipolar attraction between polymer and monomer is not responsible for alternacy. Contribution of polar structures in the transition state appears more probable:

$$[\text{\small\textbf{$\sim$}}M_1 \cdot \ldots M_2] \longleftrightarrow [\text{\small\textbf{$\sim$}}\overset{\oplus}{M_1} \ldots \overset{\ominus}{M_2}] \longleftrightarrow [\text{\small\textbf{$\sim$}}\overset{\ominus}{M_1} \ldots \overset{\oplus}{M_2}]$$

The degree of alternacy in copolymerization can be expressed as the product of r_1 and r_2; values of this product for some monomer pairs are given in Table 7.11. Monomers fall into a polarity series. The greater the separation in this series, the greater is the likelihood of alternacy and hence the extent to which the polarities of the monomers are opposed.

Quantitative studies of the magnitudes of polar effects in radical addition have been made on copolymerizations with nuclear substituted styrenes. This system allows direct comparison of substituent effects with those encountered in heterolytic reactions. Data are given in Table 7.12 for the polystyrene and the methyl methacrylate radicals which have opposite polarities.

111

Table 7.11. Products of Monomer Reactivity Ratios

Butadiene	Styrene	Vinyl acetate	Vinyl chloride	2,5-Dichlorostyrene	Methyl methacrylate	Methacrylonitrile	Acrylonitrile	Diethyl fumarate	Maleic anhydride
Butadiene									
1·0	**Styrene**								
—	0·55	**Vinyl acetate**							
—	0·34	0·63	**Vinyl chloride**						
0·2	0·16	—	—	**2,5-Dichlorostyrene**					
0·19	0·24	0·30	1·0	—	**Methyl methacrylate**				
0·01	0·06	0·24	—	—	0·43	**Methacrylonitrile**			
0·02	0·02	0·25	0·13	—	0·24	—	**Acrylonitrile**		
—	0·02	0·004	0·06	—	—	—	8	**Diethyl fumarate**	
—	very small	2×10^{-4}	0·002	—	0·13	—	6	—	**Maleic anhydride**

Data for the polystyrene radical give a rectilinear plot of log k/k_0 against σ. The positive slope ($\rho = 0.5$) indicates that the radical is an electron donor and that attack on the olefin is encouraged by electron

Table 7.12. Substituent Effects in Radical Addition to Styrene

Substituent in styrene	Relative reactivities	
	Polystyrene radical	Methyl methacrylate radical
p-MeO	0·86	1·59
p-Me₂N	0·98	2·24
p-Me	—	1·14
None	1	1
p-Cl	1·35	1·11
p-Br	1·44	1·16
m-Cl	1·56	0·98
m-NO₂	2·22	1·3
p-CN	3·57	2·09
p-NO₂	5·26	—

withdrawing groups. In the more strongly alternant styrene–methyl methacrylate system (cf. Table 7.11), however, correlation between reactivity and σ is poor. The question has been discussed by Walling but it is hard to obtain a clear picture, on the evidence available at present, of a transition state in which opposing polar influences both cause activation.

For further reading

ALFREY, BOHRER and MARK, *Copolymerization*. Interscience, 1952.
BAMFORD, BARB, JENKINS and ONYON, *The Kinetics of Vinyl Polymerization by Radical Mechanisms*. Butterworths, London, 1958.

BEVINGTON, *Radical Polymerization*. Academic Press, 1961.
BILLMEYER, *Textbook of Polymer Science*. Interscience, New York, 1962.
MARVEL, *An Introduction to the Organic Chemistry of High Polymers*. Wiley, New York, 1959.
SORENSON and CAMPBELL, *Preparative Methods of Polymer Chemistry*. Interscience, 1961.
  (A valuable survey of practical procedures including emulsion polymerization in aqueous systems.)
STILLE, *Introduction to Polymer Chemistry*. Wiley, NewYork, 1962.
WALLING, *Free Radicals in Solution*, Chapters 3, 4 and 5. Wiley, New York, 1957.

PROBLEMS

1. The following monomer reactivity ratios have been determined:

M_1	M_2	r_1	r_2
Vinyl acetate	*cis*-dichloroethylene	6·3	0·18
,,	*trans*-dichloroethylene	1·0	0·86
,,	diethyl fumarate	0·01	0·44
,,	diethyl maleate	0·17	0·04

Trans-dichloroethylene and diethyl maleate are the less thermodynamically stable isomers in each pair: suggest an explanation for the results.

2. What do you conclude from the following information?

(*a*) copolymerization data for vinyl ethers and sulphides:

M_1	M_2	r_1	r_2
Styrene	methyl vinyl ether	90	0
Styrene	methyl vinyl sulphide	5·1	0·11

b) $Ph—X—CH_3 + (t\text{-}BuO)_2 \xrightarrow{140°} Ph—X—CH_2CH_2—X—Ph$

(1)

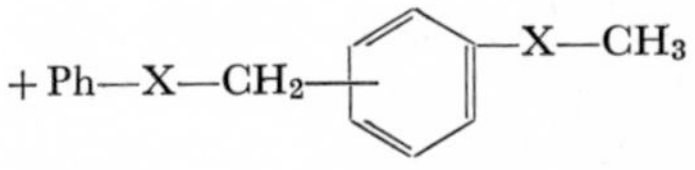

$+ Ph—X—CH_2$ ⬡ $—X—CH_3$

(2)

When X = O, (2) and not (1) is obtained.
When X = S, (1) and not (2) is obtained.

3. The following efficiencies of re-initiation in transfer reactions with 2,6-dimethylocta-2,6-diene have been reported:

acrylonitrile, 25%; vinyl acetate, 48%; styrene, 100%; methyl methacrylate, 100%.

Comment on these figures. Arrange the monomers in order of increasing transfer constant with this transfer agent.

CHAPTER 8

FRAGMENTATION, REARRANGEMENT, AND DISPLACEMENT

In this Chapter we take up three of the rather less common types of radical reaction that were outlined in Chapter 1.

FRAGMENTATION

Although radicals may have widely differing degrees of reactivity, they do not generally break up before entering into reaction. The most frequent exceptions to this rule are radicals which possess the unpaired electron either on oxygen or on carbon adjacent to oxygen. These radicals are of four main types:

(a) Alkoxy Radicals. Fragmentation of alkoxy radicals occurs so that a carbonyl function is produced; it is evidently the formation of the carbonyl group that provides the driving force for cleavage. The general case is given in reaction (8.1):

$$R_1R_2R_3C—O\cdot \longrightarrow R_1COR_2 + R_3\cdot \qquad \dots(8.1)$$

When the radical is primary ($R_1 = R_2 = H$) or secondary ($R_1 = H$), fragmentation can occur by loss either of an alkyl radical or of a hydrogen atom. Primary and secondary alkoxy radicals have been studied mainly in the gas phase and under these conditions the predominant reaction is loss of an alkyl radical. Primary alkoxy radicals thus chiefly yield formaldehyde while secondary radicals give higher aldehydes.

Tertiary alkoxy radicals have been very much more widely studied. At temperatures above about 120°, breakdown of the t-butoxy radical, for example, becomes appreciable. Acetone and methyl radicals are produced:

$$Me_3CO\cdot \longrightarrow MeCOMe + Me\cdot$$

This reaction competes with other reactions of the t-butoxy radical, notably hydrogen transfer. As the product of hydrogen transfer is t-butanol, the ratio of t-butanol to acetone produced in a reaction with t-butoxy radicals gives a measure of the ease of hydrogen abstraction from the substrate. Thus for isopropylbenzene and t-butylbenzene at

125°, the t-butanol/acetone ratios are 4·1 and 0·6 respectively. The high ratio with isopropylbenzene is due to the presence of readily removable benzylic hydrogens. These results fit well with the extent of side chain abstraction in homolytic phenylation (p. 37).

When the groups R_1, R_2, and R_3, in a tertiary radical are not all identical, different products may be formed by fragmentation according to which group is lost as an alkyl radical. Aryl radicals are never produced in this way; alkyl radicals are lost preferentially, as resonance between the carbonyl group and the aromatic nucleus is possible in the ketonic product. The cumyloxy radical (*8.1*) accordingly gives acetophenone and methyl radicals:

$$PhC(Me)_2O\cdot \longrightarrow PhCOMe + Me\cdot$$
(*8.1*)

In triarylmethoxy radicals, $Ar_3C{-}O\cdot$, rearrangement and not cleavage occurs (following section).

Alkyl groups are lost from tertiary alkoxy radicals in the sequence $Me \ll Et > n\text{-}Pr > n\text{-}Bu$. In cyclic tertiary alkoxy radicals, ring cleavage occurs:

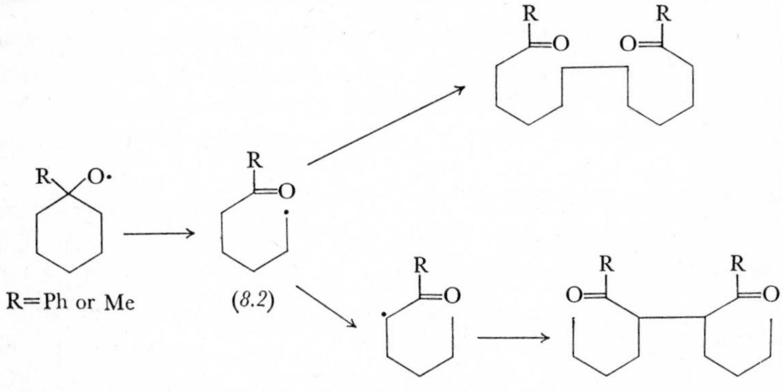

R=Ph or Me   (*8.2*)

(*8.3*)

Formation of dimers both from the resulting radical (*8.2*) and the rearranged radical (*8.3*) is observed. The latter radical probably arises from a 1,5-hydrogen shift (below).

(b) α-Alkoxyalkyl Radicals. Reaction of radicals with ethers usually involves transfer of hydrogen from carbon adjacent to oxygen. Although the α-alkoxyalkyl radicals may participate in other reactions (p. 126), fragmentation frequently intervenes. Decomposition of t-butyl peroxide in tetrahydrofuran gives the radical (*8.4*) in which C—O bond fission subsequently occurs. Again, the driving force is formation of the carbonyl group.

115

Rearrangement involving intramolecular hydrogen transfer is found in this case also. The products from acyclic ethers can be accounted for in a similar way.

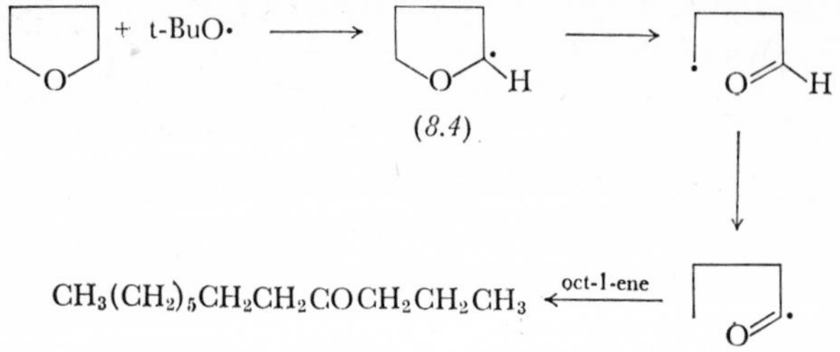

+ t-BuO·
H
H
oct-1-ene
CH3(CH2)5CH2CH2COCH2CH2CH3

(*8.4*)

(c) Acyloxy Radicals. Formation of acyloxy radicals by oxygen–oxygen homolysis of diacyl peroxides and electron transfer from carboxylate ions was mentioned in Chapter 1. These radicals are stabilized by electron delocalization but loss of carbon dioxide (carbonyl group formation again) readily occurs:

$$\left. R{-}C\begin{matrix}O\\O\end{matrix}\right\}\cdot \longrightarrow R\cdot + CO_2 \qquad \ldots(8.2)$$

Acetyloxy radicals decarboxylate much more easily than benzoyloxy radicals; when R=Me, reaction (8.2) is exothermic by 12–14 kcal/mole but when R=Ph the reaction is *endo*thermic by 4 kcal/mole. This indicates a substantial degree of resonance interaction with the nucleus in the latter.

Decarboxylation of acyloxy radicals is a valuable route from acids, which are usually readily available, to alkyl and aryl radicals. Anodic synthesis (Chapter 10) depends upon the reaction. Decarboxylation, particularly of aroyloxy radicals, competes with other reactions; in phenylation (Chapter 3) with benzoyl peroxide, aryl esters, which are always produced in addition to biphenyls, arise from substitution effected by the benzoyloxy radical.

Decomposition of apocamphoyl peroxide (*8.5*) in carbon tetrachloride gives the chloride (*8.7*). The course of the reaction outlined below seems very likely and shows that the radical (*8.6*) *can* adopt a pyramidal conformation which in this case is imposed by the molecular geometry.

COO⁻
COO·
Cl
CCl4
+ CCl3·

(*8.5*) (*8.6*) (*8.7*)

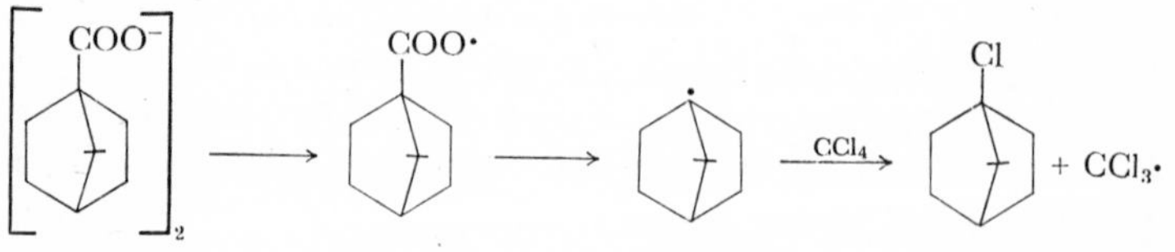

(d) Acyl Radicals. The initiation step of radical addition of aldehydes to olefins (Chapter 6), involves hydrogen transfer from the aldehyde and formation of an acyl radical:

$$R'\cdot + RCHO \longrightarrow R'H + R\overset{\cdot}{C}{=}O$$

Additions are usually run at around 80° but in reactions carried out above 100° or when α-branched aldehydes are used, decarbonylation intervenes, producing carbon monoxide and alkyl (though not aryl) radicals:

$$R\overset{\cdot}{C}{=}O \longrightarrow R\cdot + CO$$

Carbon monoxide is produced in the peroxide initiated addition of heptanal to oct-1-ene even when the reaction is carried out at 65°. Decarbonylation also occurs during the high-temperature autoxidation of certain aldehydes; hydrocarbons and not acids are then produced.

Decarbonylation constitutes another convenient method for generating alkyl radicals and is particularly useful when the appropriate acyl peroxides are not readily accessible. Rearrangement studies (following section) have frequently depended upon the generation of radicals by this means.

The reversal of radical addition to olefins is also an example of fragmentation; β-bromoalkyl radicals were mentioned in this connection earlier (p. 56).

REARRANGEMENT

Radical rearrangements may be broadly divided into two types; migrations involving hydrogen, halogen, or aryl groups, and skeletal rearrangements. The latter usually occur in strained ring systems. Radical rearrangements are not very common and often have quite strict structural requirements.

Hydrogen Migration. Migrations involving hydrogen can be regarded as intramolecular abstractions. The simplest possible case, that of 1,2 hydrogen migration, has not been observed in spite of the

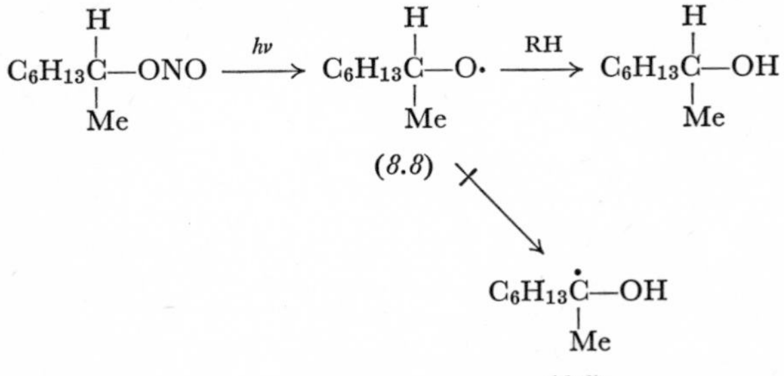

117

study of favourable instances. The 2-octyloxy radical (*8.8*), obtained from optically active 2-octyl nitrite, removes hydrogen from a suitable donor to give octan-2-ol with full activity. If C→O hydrogen migration had occurred, giving radical (*8.9*), racemization would have resulted.

1,3-Hydrogen migration, is, however, observed in the 1-propyl radical. Generation of this radical from α-^{14}C-butyryl peroxide (*8.10*) gives 4% of products derived from rearrangement:

$$(CH_3CH_2{}^{14}CH_2CO_2)_2 \xrightarrow{CCl_4} CH_3CH_2{}^{14}CH_2CO_2\cdot \longrightarrow CH_3CH_2{}^{14}CH_2\cdot$$
(*8.10*)

$$CH_3CH_2{}^{14}CH_2Cl \qquad {}^{14}CH_3CH_2CH_2Cl$$
$$(4\%)$$

The most reasonable assumption is that intramolecular hydrogen transfer occurs via a 4-membered transition state:

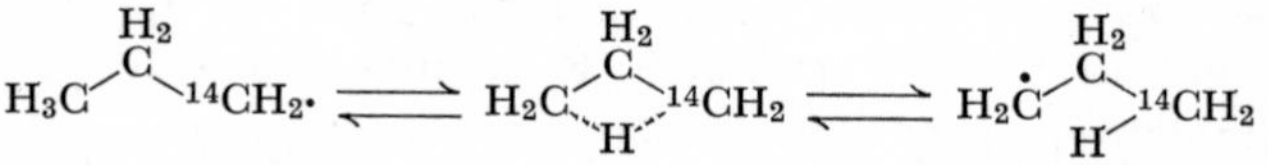

Formation of a non-classical radical or two-stage migration from the α-position can be excluded as no ^{14}C is found at position 2.

1,5-Hydrogen transfer has likewise been detected in the 5-phenyl-pentyl radical (*8.11*). Decomposition of 6-phenylhexanoyl peroxide gives 5,6-diphenyldecane (*8.12*) in addition to unrearranged products from abstraction and dimerization.

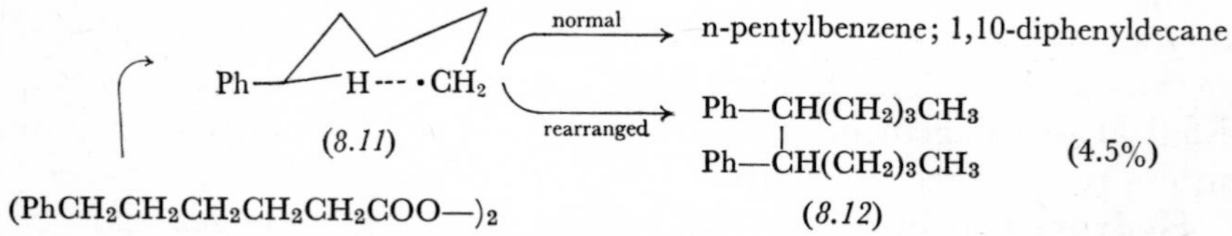

n-pentylbenzene; 1,10-diphenyldecane

$$Ph-CH(CH_2)_3CH_3$$
$$Ph-CH(CH_2)_3CH_3 \qquad (4.5\%)$$
(*8.12*)

$(PhCH_2CH_2CH_2CH_2CH_2COO-)_2$

As the yield of rearranged dimer is unaffected by the hydrogen donating capability of the solvent, the shift is *intra*- and not *inter*-molecular. Another 1,5-hydrogen shift of particular interest involves a nuclear hydrogen atom:

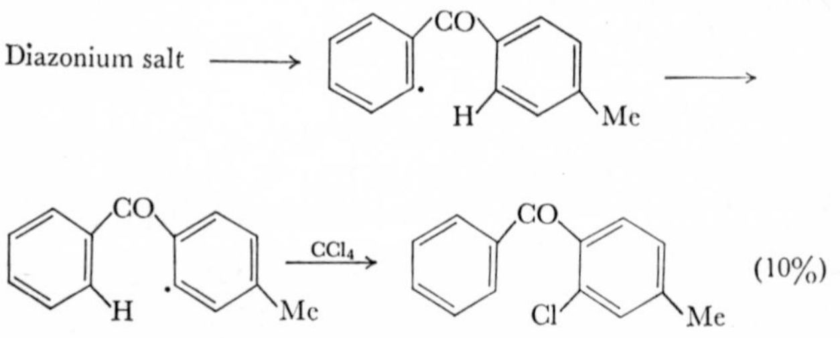

Intramolecular hydrogen transfer in growing polymer chains (p. 104) has already been mentioned.

Aryl Migration. Radical rearrangement was first observed by Kharasch and Urry (1944) during studies of the neophyl radical (*8.14*). This radical was found to rearrange to a significant extent before undergoing the familiar reactions of dimerization, disproportionation, and abstraction. Reactions of this radical have been outlined earlier (p. 13) as an illustration of the diversity of reaction types; it is one of a series of β-arylalkyl radicals in which rearrangement has been observed:

$$
\underset{\text{Me}}{\overset{\text{Me}}{>}}\!\!\underset{}{\overset{\text{Ph}}{\underset{|}{C}}}\!-\!\overset{\bullet}{\underset{}{C}}\!\!\underset{\text{H}}{\overset{\text{H}}{<}} \quad \xrightarrow{\text{RH}} \quad \underset{\text{Me}}{\overset{\text{Me}}{>}}\!\!\underset{}{\overset{\text{Ph}}{\underset{|}{C}}}\!-\!\underset{}{\overset{\text{H}}{\underset{|}{C}}}\!\!\underset{\text{H}}{\overset{\text{H}}{<}} \quad \text{(normal)}
$$

(*8.14*)

$$\downarrow$$

$$
\underset{\text{Me}}{\overset{\text{Me}}{>}}\!\!\overset{\bullet}{\underset{}{C}}\!-\!\underset{}{\overset{\text{Ph}}{\underset{|}{C}}}\!\!\underset{\text{H}}{\overset{\text{H}}{<}} \quad \xrightarrow{\text{RH}} \quad \underset{\text{Me}}{\overset{\text{Me}}{>}}\!\!\underset{}{\overset{\text{H}}{\underset{|}{C}}}\!-\!\underset{}{\overset{\text{Ph}}{\underset{|}{C}}}\!\!\underset{\text{H}}{\overset{\text{H}}{<}} \quad \text{(rearranged)}
$$

Results of rearrangement studies on a number of radicals of this type are given in Table 8.1; the radicals were obtained from aldehydes by decarbonylation (p. 117)

Table 8.1. Rearrangement of β-Arylalkyl Radicals

Radical	Migrating group	Product† type	Rearrangement (%)
(*8.13*) $PhCH_2{}^{14}CH_2\cdot$	Ph	abs. disp.	3.3
(*8.14*) $PhC(Me)_2CH_2\cdot$	Ph	abs. disp.	57
(*8.15*) $PhCH_2\overset{\bullet}{C}(Me)_2$	Ph	abs.	0
(*8.16*) ⬡$<^{Ph}_{CH_2\cdot}$	Ph	abs.	89
(*8.17*) ▢$<^{Ph}_{CH_2\cdot}$	Ph	abs.	63
(*8.18*) $Ph_2C(Me)CH_2\cdot$	Ph	dim.	100
(*8.19*) $Ph_3CCH_2\cdot$	Ph	abs. disp.	96
(*8.20*) $p\text{-}MeOC_6H_4CD(Ph)CH_2\cdot$	$\begin{cases} p\text{-}MeOC_6H_4 \\ \text{or} \quad Ph \end{cases}$	abs.	0
(*8.21*) $p\text{-}NO_2C_6H_4C(Ph)_2CH_2\cdot$	$p\text{-}NO_2C_6H_4$	disp.	80

† abs. = abstraction; disp. = disproportionation; dim. = dimerization.

The extent of rearrangement of the neophyl radical decreases with increase in concentration of the aldehyde. There is, therefore, competition between rearrangement of the radical and hydrogen transfer from the aldehyde. Decrease in the extent of rearrangement is even greater when better hydrogen donors such as thiols are present.

Rearrangement is also observed when β-arylalkyl radicals are produced by radical addition to olefins. Addition of butanethiol (a very good transfer agent) to 3,3-diphenylbut-1-ene (*8.22*) gives an unrearranged adduct (*8.23*). Addition of butyraldehyde, on the other hand, gives the rearranged product (*8.24*). In this case, rearrangement is faster than the relatively slow transfer with aldehyde.

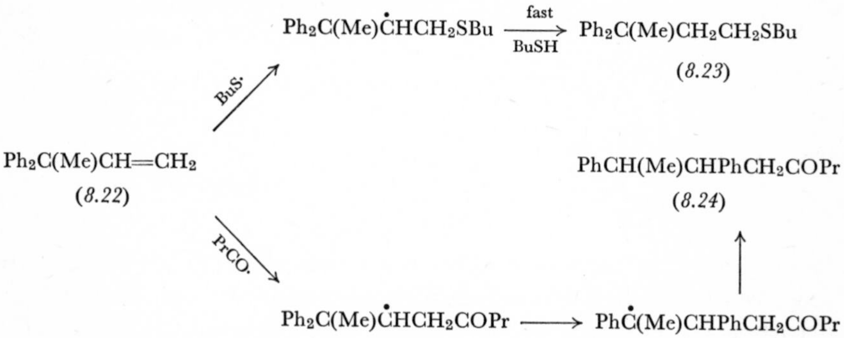

$$Ph_2C(Me)\overset{\bullet}{C}HCH_2SBu \xrightarrow[BuSH]{fast} Ph_2C(Me)CH_2CH_2SBu$$

$$(8.23)$$

$$Ph_2C(Me)CH{=}CH_2$$
$$(8.22)$$

$$PhCH(Me)CHPhCH_2COPr$$
$$(8.24)$$

$$Ph_2C(Me)\overset{\bullet}{C}HCH_2COPr \longrightarrow Ph\overset{\bullet}{C}(Me)CHPhCH_2COPr$$

Aryl migrations are not reversible: radical (*8.15*) does not rearrange and in every case migration occurs so as to give a radical of equal or lower energy. Rearrangement of the neophyl radical gives a tertiary radical in preference to a primary radical (cf. Chapter 4), and radicals (*8.18*) and (*8.19*) give benzylic radicals. Formation of the more stable radical provides part of the driving force for the reaction; rearrangements to benzylic radicals are nearly complete, while radical (*8.13*), which lacks this incentive, rearranges only to a slight extent.

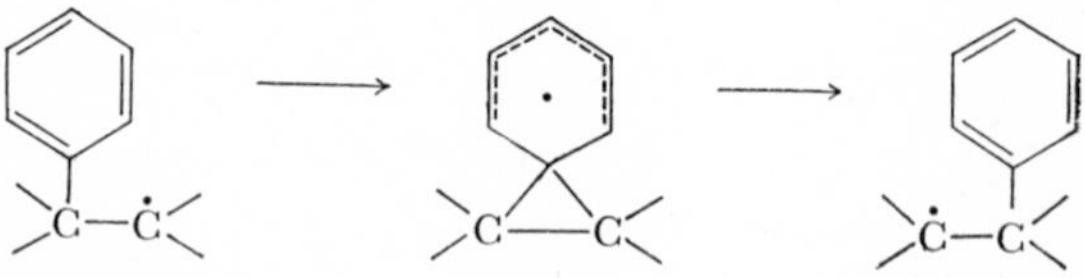

$$(8.25)$$

Aryl migration is considered to occur by way of a bridged transition state (*8.25*). This is analogous to the 'phenonium' ion formulated for carbonium ion rearrangements involving aryl migration. Formation of such a bridged structure appears to be essential for

120

rearrangement; methyl migration in the neophyl radical would be an energetically favourable process producing a benzylic radical, but yet does not occur. The optimum situation for migration involves maximum orbital overlap between the aryl nucleus and the unpaired electron. This occurs with the plane of the nucleus perpendicular to the plane in which C_α and C_β lie. The (1-phenylcyclopentyl)methyl radical (*8.26*) rearranges less readily than the (1-phenylcyclohexyl)methyl radical (*8.27*). In the former, there is considerably greater restriction on the attainment of the appropriate geometry.

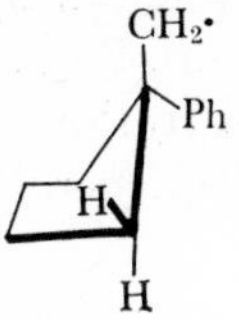

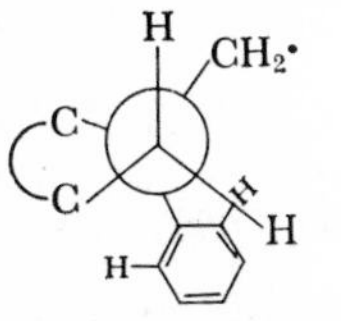

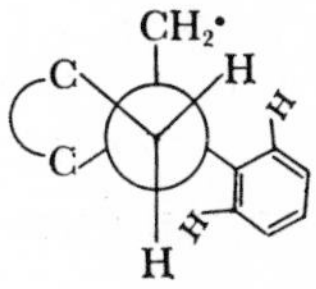

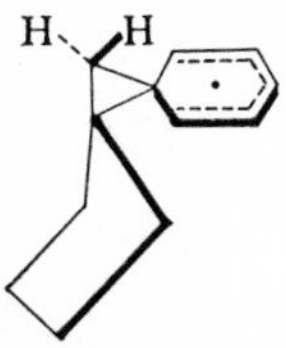

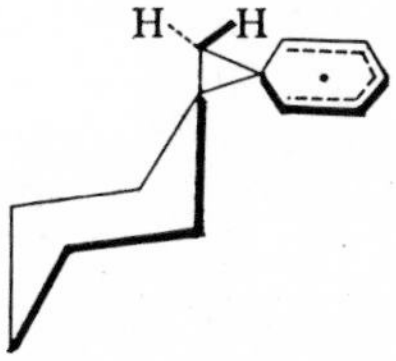

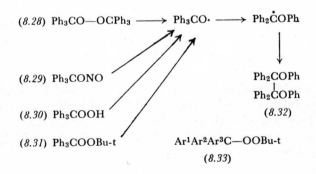

Aryl migration from carbon to oxygen has also been observed. When triphenylmethoxy radicals are generated from compounds (*8.28*) to (*8.31*), benzopinacol diphenyl ether (*8.32*) is produced. The relative

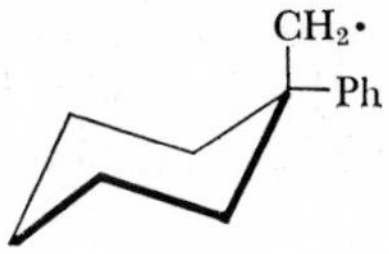

(*8.28*) Ph₃CO—OCPh₃ ⟶ Ph₃CO· ⟶ Ph₂ĊOPh

(*8.29*) Ph₃CONO

(*8.30*) Ph₃COOH

(*8.31*) Ph₃COOBu-t

Ph₂COPh
Ph₂COPh
(*8.32*)

Ar¹Ar²Ar³C—OOBu-t
(*8.33*)

9

121

tendencies of groups to migrate (migratory aptitudes) have been measured by using appropriately substituted triarylmethyl t-butyl peroxides (*8.33*). Phenyl and *p*-tolyl groups show nearly equal migratory aptitudes, but α-naphthyl and *p*-biphenylyl groups migrate about six times as readily as phenyl. Migration can be regarded as an internal aromatic substitution and we have already seen (Chapter 3) that biphenyl and naphthalene are more susceptible to radical substitution than benzene and toluene. Similarly, thermal decomposition of the hydroperoxide (*8.34*) in benzene, gives three times as much *p*-nitrophenol, resulting from *p*-nitrophenyl migration, as phenol. By contrast, *heterolytic* rearrangement occurs under acid conditions, and *only* phenyl migrates. In this instance, internal *electrophilic* substitution occurs and *p*-nitrophenyl is, understandably, much less inclined to migrate than phenyl.

$$p\text{-}NO_2C_6H_4C(Ph)_2\text{---}OOH \xrightarrow{H^{\oplus}} p\text{-}NO_2C_6H_4C(Ph)_2\text{---}\overset{\oplus}{O}$$
$$(8.34)$$

$$\begin{array}{c} \text{OH} \\ | \\ p\text{-}NO_2C_6H_4C(Ph)OPh \end{array} \xleftarrow{H_2O} p\text{-}NO_2C_6H_4\overset{\oplus}{C}(Ph)OPh$$

Intramolecular aromatic substitution likewise accounts for rearrangement of the 4-methyl-4-phenyl-1-pentyl radical (*8.35*).

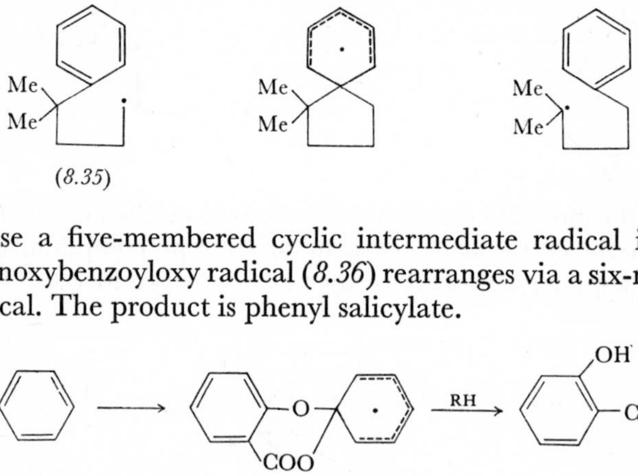

$$(8.35)$$

In this case a five-membered cyclic intermediate radical is formed. The 2-phenoxybenzoyloxy radical (*8.36*) rearranges via a six-membered cyclic radical. The product is phenyl salicylate.

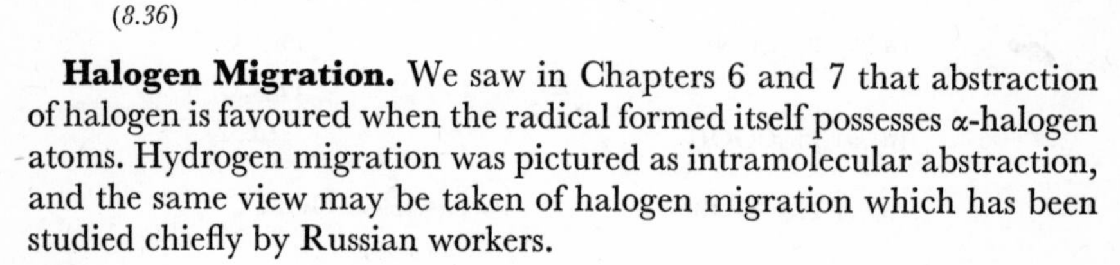

$$(8.36)$$

Halogen Migration. We saw in Chapters 6 and 7 that abstraction of halogen is favoured when the radical formed itself possesses α-halogen atoms. Hydrogen migration was pictured as intramolecular abstraction, and the same view may be taken of halogen migration which has been studied chiefly by Russian workers.

122

When bromine, hydrogen bromide, bromotrichloromethane, or thiophenol is added homolytically to 3-substituted propenes *(8.37)* part of the product is derived from migration of chlorine from C_3 to C_2. The general sequence is as follows:

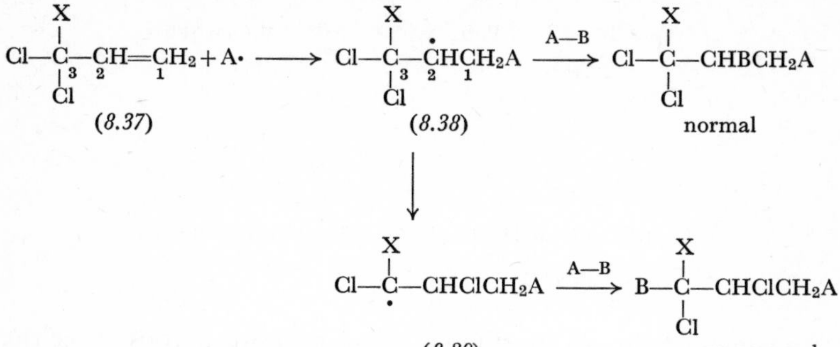

$$Cl-\underset{\underset{Cl}{|}}{\overset{\overset{X}{|}}{C}}-\underset{3}{CH}=\underset{2}{CH}\underset{1}{CH_2} + A\cdot \longrightarrow Cl-\underset{\underset{Cl}{|}}{\overset{\overset{X}{|}}{\overset{\cdot}{C}}}-\underset{3}{CH}\underset{2}{CH_2}\underset{1}{A} \xrightarrow{A-B} Cl-\underset{\underset{Cl}{|}}{\overset{\overset{X}{|}}{C}}-CHBCH_2A$$

(8.37) (8.38) normal

$$\downarrow$$

$$Cl-\underset{\overset{\cdot}{}}{\overset{\overset{X}{|}}{C}}-CHClCH_2A \xrightarrow{A-B} B-\underset{\underset{Cl}{|}}{\overset{\overset{X}{|}}{C}}-CHClCH_2A$$

(8.39) rearranged

For thiophenol A = PhS; B = H
For hydrogen bromide A = Br; B = H
For bromotrichloromethane A = CCl$_3$; B = Br
  X = H, Cl, F, Me

Rearrangement in additions of hydrogen bromide to *(8.37)* is very dependent on the nature of X. Only rearranged products are obtained when X=Cl and Me. When X=H, the extent of rearrangement falls to 90%, and to 30% when X=F. The ease of rearrangement is, presumably, determined by the relative stabilities of the radicals *(8.38)* and *(8.39)*, and it is significant in this connection, that rearrangement of radical *(8.38; X=Cl)* is still complete when hydrogen on C_2 is replaced by methyl. Radicals fall in the following order of stability according to their ease of formation by halogen migration:

$$Cl_2\overset{\cdot}{C}-C > Cl\overset{\cdot}{C}H-C > C-\underset{\underset{C}{|}}{\overset{\cdot}{C}}-C > Cl\overset{\cdot}{C}F-C > C-\overset{\cdot}{C}H-C$$

Unsaturated products usually accompany the 1:1-adducts obtained from the above reactions. These result from the elimination of a chlorine atom from the intermediate radical:

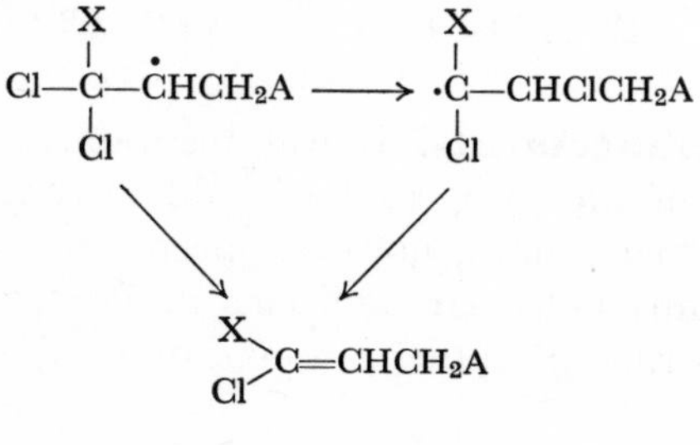

$$Cl-\underset{\underset{Cl}{|}}{\overset{\overset{X}{|}}{C}}-\overset{\cdot}{C}HCH_2A \longrightarrow \cdot\underset{\underset{Cl}{|}}{\overset{\overset{X}{|}}{C}}-CHClCH_2A$$

$$\underset{Cl}{\overset{X}{\diagdown}}C=CHCH_2A$$

123

Bromine atoms are particularly prone to elimination from β-bromoalkyl radicals (Chapter 6) and homolytic addition of thiophenol to 2-bromo-3,3,3-trichloropropene (*8.40*), for example, gives only the rearranged olefin (*8.42*).

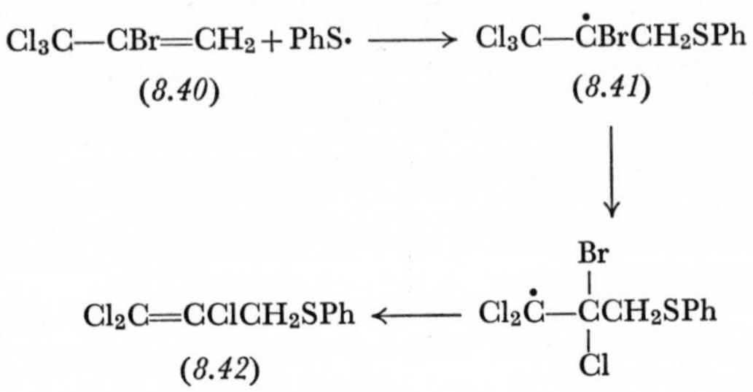

$$Cl_3C-CBr=CH_2 + PhS\cdot \longrightarrow Cl_3C-\overset{\cdot}{C}BrCH_2SPh$$

$$(8.40) \qquad\qquad\qquad (8.41)$$

$$Cl_2C=CClCH_2SPh \longleftarrow Cl_2\overset{\cdot}{C}-\overset{\overset{\displaystyle Br}{|}}{\underset{\underset{\displaystyle Cl}{|}}{C}}CH_2SPh$$

$$(8.42)$$

Rearrangement followed by elimination of bromine is thus faster than either direct elimination of chlorine from radical (*8.41*) or its transfer reaction with thiophenol.

Photo-isomerization of the propene (*8.43*) to (*8.44*) is explained in a similar way:

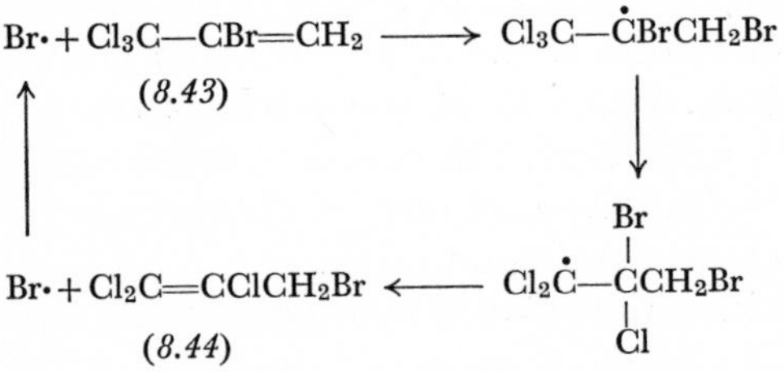

$$Br\cdot + Cl_3C-CBr=CH_2 \longrightarrow Cl_3C-\overset{\cdot}{C}BrCH_2Br$$

$$(8.43)$$

$$Br\cdot + Cl_2C=CClCH_2Br \longleftarrow Cl_2\overset{\cdot}{C}-\overset{\overset{\displaystyle Br}{|}}{\underset{\underset{\displaystyle Cl}{|}}{C}}CH_2Br$$

$$(8.44)$$

This homolytic process is quite different from the heterolytic rearrangement of the same olefin which is catalysed by antimony pentachloride and probably involves carbonium ions:

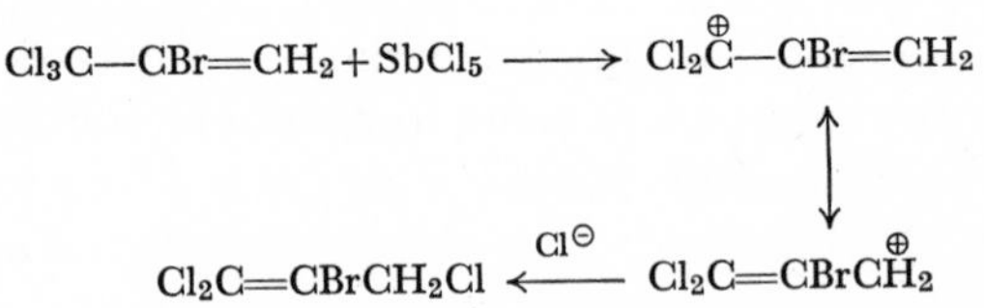

$$Cl_3C-CBr=CH_2 + SbCl_5 \longrightarrow Cl_2\overset{\oplus}{C}-CBr=CH_2$$

$$Cl_2C=CBrCH_2Cl \overset{Cl^{\ominus}}{\longleftarrow} Cl_2C=CBr\overset{\oplus}{C}H_2$$

Skeletal Rearrangements. It was mentioned earlier that alkyl groups do not migrate even in favourable circumstances. Certain skeletal rearrangements have, however, been observed and these can be regarded as intramolecular additions and/or eliminations. These examples will illustrate this rather rare type of reaction:

(*a*) *Elimination:*

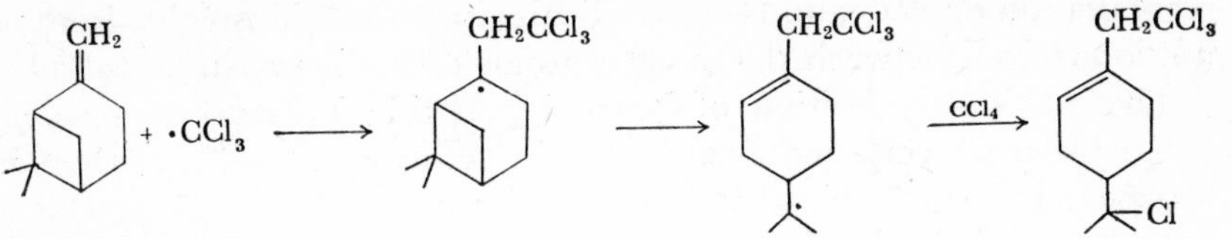

(*b*) *Addition:*

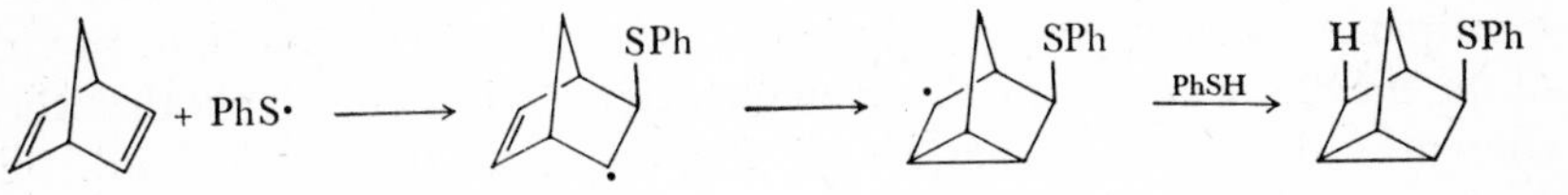

(*c*) *Elimination-addition:*

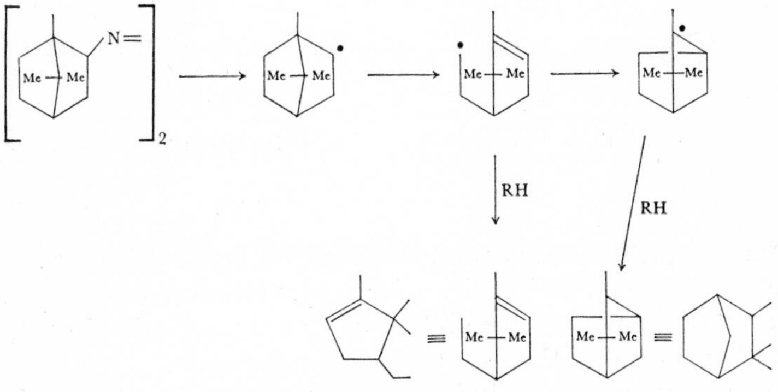

DISPLACEMENT

In Chapter 1, the process designated by reaction (8.3) was termed substitution or displacement:

$$R\cdot + R'Y \longrightarrow RR' + Y\cdot \qquad \ldots(8.3)$$

This expresses the overall reaction that occurs in homolytic aromatic substitution (R' = aryl; R = alkyl, aryl, etc.). This expression is, however, also a general statement of a rare type of radical reaction in which R' is not aryl and Y, instead of being hydrogen or halogen, is a group of atoms. It is the homolytic analogue of the $S_N 2$ reaction and can be designated S_R. The reaction is rarely met with and the best authenticated examples involve displacement at oxygen or sulphur.

Displacement at oxygen is involved in reactions of radicals with diacyl peroxides. Benzoyl peroxide reacts with triphenylmethyl radicals to give triphenylmethyl benzoate:

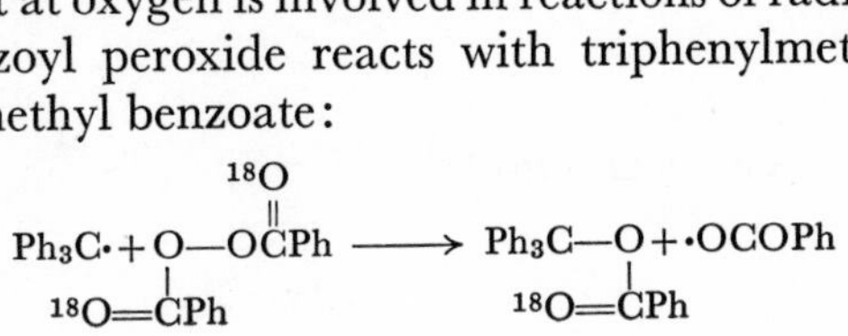

125

^{18}O-labelling shows that displacement at oxygen is involved and not combination of Ph$_3$C· and PhCO$_2$· radicals (which would involve isotopic randomization between the oxygen atoms of the benzoate).

Thermal decomposition of benzoyl peroxide is found to be very much faster in certain solvents, such as ethers and amines, than in benzene. It is probable that in 'fast solvents', radicals are produced from the solvent by hydrogen abstraction. These solvent radicals subsequently attack the peroxide causing an 'induced' decomposition to be superimposed upon the simple unimolecular decomposition. In view of the mechanism of the Ph$_3$C·/(PhCO$_2$)$_2$ reaction, it seems likely that these solvent radicals also react by displacement at the O—O bond. The reaction of benzoyl peroxide with diethyl ether, for example, gives 2-ethoxy-ethyl benzoate (*8.45*):

$$(PhCO_2)_2 \longrightarrow \begin{cases} PhCO_2· \\ Ph· \end{cases} + CH_3CH_2OEt \longrightarrow CH_3\overset{\bullet}{C}HOEt$$

$$CH_3\overset{\bullet}{C}HOEt + \underset{\underset{COPh}{|}}{O}{-}OCOPh \longrightarrow CH_3\overset{\overset{OCOPh}{|}}{C}HOEt + PhCO_2·$$

$$(8.45)$$

Solvent radicals are not produced in benzene (cf. Chapter 3) so that in this solvent decomposition is not induced. Solvent radicals are certainly produced in 'slow' solvents such as carbon tetrachloride but these are evidently too weakly reactive to attack the peroxide.

A recent example of displacement at a peroxide linkage involves intramolecular reaction in the tertiary alkyl peroxide (*8.46*). Decomposition of the peroxide gives the expected fragmentation product acetone,

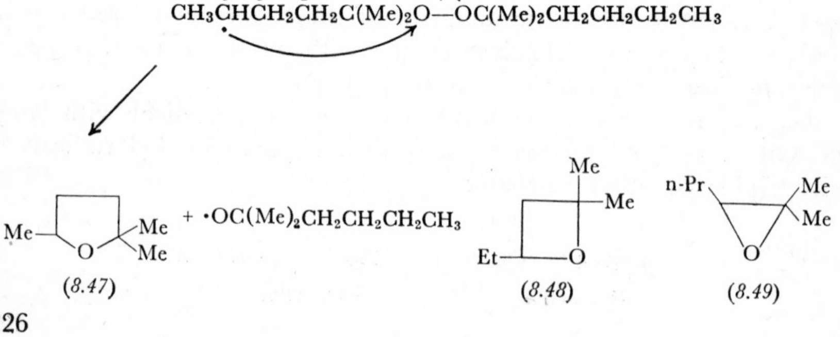

$$[CH_3CH_2CH_2CH_2C(Me)_2O{-}]_2 \longrightarrow CH_3CH_2CH_2CH_2C(Me)_2O·$$

$$(8.46)$$

R·

$$CH_3CH_2CH_2CH_2C(Me)_2OH \qquad CH_3COCH_3$$

$$\overset{4}{CH_3}\overset{3}{\underset{\bullet}{C}H}CH_2\overset{2}{C}H_2C(Me)_2O{-}OC(Me)_2CH_2CH_2CH_2CH_3$$

(*8.47*) $+ ·OC(Me)_2CH_2CH_2CH_2CH_3$ (*8.48*)   (*8.49*)

126

and 2-methylhexan-2-ol together with the cyclic ethers (8.47), (8.48) and (8.49). These ethers are formed by intramolecular reaction of the radicals produced by abstraction at C_4, C_3, and C_2, respectively, in the intact peroxide.

The ether (8.47), whose formation involves a five-membered cyclic transition state, is formed in greatest amount.

Displacement in disulphides is closely analogous to the peroxide reactions; disulphides behave as transfer agents in polymerization (p. 102), and formation of polymers with —SR groups as terminal residues indicates displacement at the S—S link.

Finally, cleavage of C—C bonds in displacement has occasionally been observed. Alkyl radicals react with α-diketones giving a monoketone and an acyl radical:

$$CH_3\cdot + CH_3COCOCH_3 \longrightarrow CH_3COCH_3 + CH_3CO\cdot$$

For further reading

FREIDLINA, KOST and KHORLINA, 'Rearrangement of Radicals in Solution', *Russian Chem. Rev.*, 1962, **31**, 1.

GRAY and WILLIAMS, 'The Thermochemistry and Reactivity of Alkoxyl Radicals', *Chem. Rev.*, 1959, **59**, 239.

WALLING, 'Free Radical Rearrangements', in *Molecular Rearrangements* (ed. de Mayo). Wiley, New York, 1963.

PROBLEMS

Discuss the following:

(*a*) Treatment of the ether (1) with t-butyl peroxide at 110° gave *p*-chlorotoluene (12%), benzaldehyde (14%), and *p*-chlorobenzaldehyde (51%):

$$p\ ClC_6H_4CH_2OCH_2Ph$$

(1)   (2) 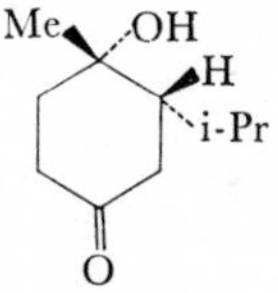   (3) 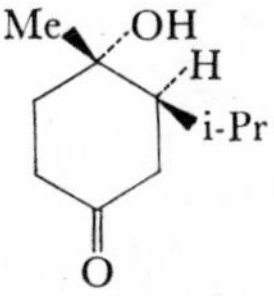   (4)

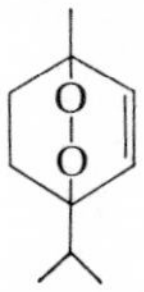

(*b*) Treatment of ascaridole (2) with saturated aqueous ferrous sulphate gave propane and the diastereoisomeric ketones (3) and (4).

(*c*) The following data are obtained for the decomposition of benzoyl peroxide in cyclohexane with added styrene:

			Yields (*moles/mole peroxide*)	
$[(PhCO_2)_2]$	[Styrene]	$t_{1/2}(min)$	PhH	$PhCO_2H$
0·003	0·000	65	1·11	0·523
0·003	0·015	110	1·28	0·528
0·003	0·12	107	1·07	0·524

(*d*) Decomposition of optically pure (+)-β-phenylisobutyryl peroxide in carbon tetrachloride gave (±)-2-chloro-1-phenylpropane and 1-phenyl-2-propyl β-phenylisobutyrate. The latter, on hydrolysis, gave (+)-1-phenylpropan-2-ol of 75% optical purity.

(*e*) Decomposition of t-butyl peroxide at 130° in a mixture of acetophenone and butan-2-ol gave butanone, t-butyl alcohol, and a mixture of *meso*- and racemic 2,3-diphenylbutan-2,3-diols.

Chapter 9

CARBENES AND NITRENES

We have already seen that the behaviour of certain molecules is best explained by the supposition that they possess *two* unpaired electrons. The oxygen molecule (Chapter 5) and certain bis-triarylmethyls (Chapter 2) are examples of this type. These diradicals are 'long-lived'. We now turn to a series of diradicals of short life and high reactivity in which the two electrons which participate in radical-type reactions are located on a single atom. These are the carbenes $R—\ddot{C}—R'$, and nitrenes $R—\ddot{N}:$

CARBENES

Dichlorocarbene, $:CCl_2$, was postulated as an intermediate in the alkaline hydrolysis of chloroform more than a century ago. Many reactions, especially those requiring the presence of strong bases, whose courses are best explained by the incursion of these reactive intermediates, have since been investigated. Systematic study of them, however, was not taken up until comparatively recently, notably by Hine, Doering and Closs.

Two distinct types of method are available for the generation of carbenes.

Preparation by Pyrolytic and Photolytic Methods. Diazomethane and ketene both yield carbene, $:CH_2$, on photolysis or pyrolysis:

$$\left.\begin{array}{r} CH_2N_2 \\ CH_2{=}C{=}O \end{array}\right\} \xrightarrow[\text{or } h\nu]{500°} CH_2: + \left\{\begin{array}{l} N_2 \\ CO \end{array}\right.$$

Carbene produced by photolysis of either compound was shown to be capable of removing mirrors of selenium and tellurium with formation of the paraformaldehyde analogues $(CH_2Se)_x$ and $(CH_2Te)_x$. Photolysis is usually the more convenient method for solution studies, and carbene is usually obtained from diazomethane in this way. Many other diazoalkanes yield carbenes on photolysis; a selection of these is listed in Table 9.1.

Carbenes are also produced when tosylhydrazones of aldehydes and ketones are treated with bases at temperatures around 170°. The first

129

stage involves a 1,1 elimination (cf. following section) with formation of a diazoalkane which subsequently decomposes:

$$R_1R_2C{=}N{-}NHSO_2p\text{-tolyl} \xrightarrow{\text{B:}} R_1R_2C{=}N{-}\overset{\ominus}{N}SO_2p\text{-tolyl}$$

$$R_1R_2C{:}{+}N_2 \longleftarrow R_1R_2CN_2 + \overset{\ominus}{S}O_2p\text{-tolyl} \longleftarrow$$

Preparation by 1,1-Elimination. In principle, carbenes can be generated by the removal of a cation and an anion from a single carbon atom. In practice the cation is nearly always a proton and the reaction may be expressed† thus:

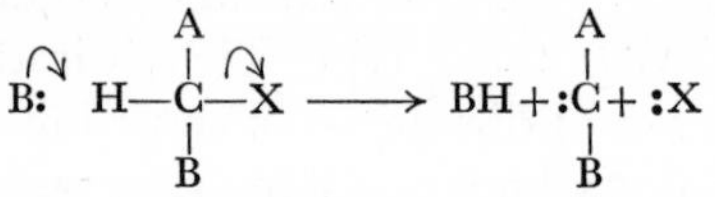

$$\text{B:} \quad H{-}\overset{\displaystyle A}{\underset{\displaystyle B}{C}}{-}X \longrightarrow BH + :\overset{\displaystyle A}{\underset{\displaystyle B}{C}} + :X$$

The leaving group, X, is of the type familiar in 1,2-eliminations and is most often halogen.

Alkyl Halides. Alkaline hydrolysis of chloroform is very much faster than that of methylene chloride or carbon tetrachloride. Further, deuterium-hydrogen exchange in chloroform is much faster than hydrolysis, which is itself retarded by halide ion but not by nitrate or perchlorate. While neither thiophenoxide nor iodide alone reacts with chloroform, rapid reaction ensues in the presence of hydroxyl ion, and $CHCl_2I$ has been obtained from base-promoted reactions with iodide. The following scheme accounts for these observations:

$$B: + CHCl_3 \longrightarrow BH + \overset{\ominus}{C}Cl_3 \qquad \qquad \ldots(9.1)$$

$$\overset{\ominus}{C}Cl_3 \longrightarrow :CCl_2 + \overset{\ominus}{C}l \qquad \qquad \ldots(9.2)$$

$$:CCl_2 + H_2O + \overset{\ominus}{O}H \xrightarrow[\text{steps}]{\text{several}} CO + HCO_2{}^{\ominus}, \text{ etc.}$$

A strong base is needed in reaction (9.1) to produce an appreciable concentration of trichloromethyl carbanion, and retardation by halide ions is accounted for by the mass law effect on reaction (9.2). $CHCl_2I$ is produced by the reversal of the reactions (9.2) and (9.1). Factors which determine the ease of halocarbene formation from haloforms have been discussed by Hine (see p. 142). Dichloro, dibromo, and di-iodocarbenes are conveniently obtained in homogenous systems by treatment of the appropriate haloform with potassium t-butoxide.

† For simplicity the reaction is presented as concerted, but may well involve a discrete carbanion.

Haloforms undergo 1,1-elimination much more readily than other alkyl halides because the α-proton is much more acidic. If, however, sufficiently strong bases are used, carbenes can be produced from alkyl mono-halides and *gem.*-di-halides. Treatment of neopentyl chloride with the very strong base, phenyl sodium, gives t-butylcarbene:

$$\text{t-BuCH}_2\text{Cl} + \overset{\ominus}{\text{Ph}}\overset{\oplus}{\text{Na}} \longrightarrow \text{t-BuCH:} + \text{PhH} + \overset{\ominus}{\text{Cl}}$$

Carbene itself has been produced in the same way from methyl chloride, and deuterium labelling studies show that, under these conditions, 94% of 1,1-elimination occurs in n-butyl chloride. Methylene halides are more acidic; butyl lithium suffices to produce chlorocarbene from methylene chloride:

$$\text{CH}_2\text{Cl}_2 + \text{n-Bu}\overset{\ominus}{\text{L}}\overset{\oplus}{\text{i}} \longrightarrow \text{:CHCl} + \text{n-BuH} + \overset{\ominus}{\text{Cl}}$$

Hydrolysis of haloforms was seen to involve loss of halide ion from a trihalocarbanion. Any method for producing these ions should therefore be a potential method for generating dihalocarbenes. Two such reactions are the decarboxylation of trihaloacetate ions and the reaction of hexahalogenoacetones with bases:

$$\text{CCl}_3\text{CO}_2{}^{\ominus} \overset{100°}{\longrightarrow} \text{CO}_2 + \overset{\ominus}{\text{C}}\text{Cl}_3 \longrightarrow \text{:CCl}_2 + \overset{\ominus}{\text{Cl}}$$

$$\text{CCl}_3\text{COCCl}_3 + \overset{\ominus}{\text{O}}\text{H} \longrightarrow \text{CCl}_3\text{C}\overset{\ominus}{\text{O}}_2 + \overset{\ominus}{\text{C}}\text{Cl}_3 \longrightarrow \text{:CCl}_2 + \overset{\ominus}{\text{Cl}}$$

'*Onium Salts.* Dialkyl sulphides and trialkylamines are familiar as leaving groups in 1,2-Hofmann eliminations, and the related 1,1-eliminations can be made to go provided that a strong enough base is used. Carbenes have been obtained in this way from both ammonium and sulphonium salts:

$$\text{Me}_4\overset{\oplus}{\text{N}} + \overset{\ominus}{\text{Ph}}\overset{\oplus}{\text{Na}} \longrightarrow \text{PhH} + \overset{\ominus}{\text{C}}\text{H}_2 - \overset{\oplus}{\text{N}}\text{Me}_3 \longrightarrow \text{:CH}_2 + \text{NMe}_3$$

$$\text{Ph}_2\overset{\oplus}{\text{S}}\text{CH}_2\text{n-Pr} + \text{n-Bu}\overset{\ominus}{\text{L}}\overset{\oplus}{\text{i}} \longrightarrow \text{Ph}_2\overset{\oplus}{\text{S}} - \overset{\ominus}{\text{C}}\text{Hn-Pr} \longrightarrow \text{n-BuH} + \text{Ph}_2\text{S} + \text{:CHn-Pr}$$

A brief survey of carbenes and their methods of formation (other than examples already given) is presented in Table 9.1.

Structure of Carbenes. These derivatives of divalent carbon possess a sextet of electrons, two of which are unshared. The question arises as to whether these electrons are paired (singlet state) or unpaired (triplet state). The vacuum ultraviolet spectrum of carbene has been obtained near 1400 Å during the flash photolysis of diazomethane, and

Table 9.1. Formation of Carbenes

Carbene	*Reaction*
$:CH_2$	$(CH_3)_2\overset{\oplus}{S}OCH_3 + NaH \longrightarrow (CH_3)_2SO + :CH_2$ $CH_2Br_2 + Na \longrightarrow :CH_2 + 2NaBr$ $CH_3OCH_2MgCl \longrightarrow :CH_2 + CH_3OMgCl$
$:CF_2$	$PhSO_2CHF_2 + Me\overset{\ominus}{O}\overset{\oplus}{Na} \longrightarrow PhS\overset{\ominus}{O_2} + MeOH + :CF_2$ $CHClF_2 + i\text{-}Pr\overset{\ominus}{O}\overset{\oplus}{K} \longrightarrow \overset{\ominus}{Cl} + i\text{-}PrOH + :CF_2$
$:CCl_2$	$PhHgCCl_3 \xrightarrow{100°} PhHgCl + :CCl_2$ $CCl_3CO_2Et + Me\overset{\ominus}{O}\overset{\oplus}{Na} \longrightarrow \overset{\ominus}{Cl} + EtOCOOMe + :CCl_2$
$:CClBr$	$PhHgCClBr_2 \xrightarrow{100°} PhHgBr + :CClBr$
$:CBr_2$	$PhHgCBr_3 \longrightarrow PhHgBr + :CBr_2$
$:CHCO_2R$	N_2CHCO_2R photolysis
$:C(CO_2R)_2$	$N_2C(CO_2R)_2$ photolysis
$:CHPh$	N_2CHPh photolysis $PhCH_2OPh + \overset{\ominus}{Bu}\overset{\oplus}{Li} \longrightarrow BuH + Ph\overset{\ominus}{O} + :CHPh$
$:CHC{\equiv}CMe$	$N_2CHC{\equiv}CMe$ photolysis
$:CHC{\equiv}CH$	$BrCH_2C{\equiv}CH + t\text{-}Bu\overset{\ominus}{O}\overset{\oplus}{K} \longrightarrow t\text{-}BuOH + \overset{\ominus}{Br} + :CHC{\equiv}CH$
$:CHOPh$	$PhOCH_2Cl + \overset{\ominus}{Bu}\overset{\oplus}{Li} \longrightarrow BuH + \overset{\ominus}{Cl} + :CHOPh$
	photolysis
	photolysis
	photolysis

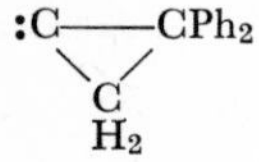

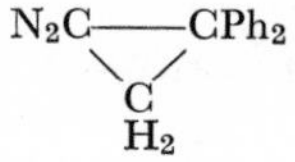

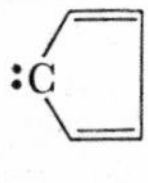

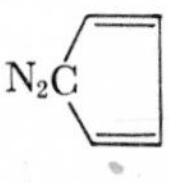

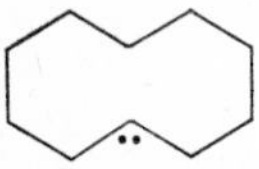

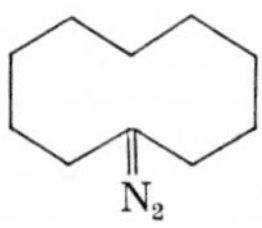

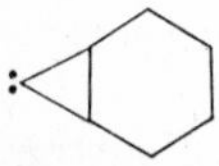

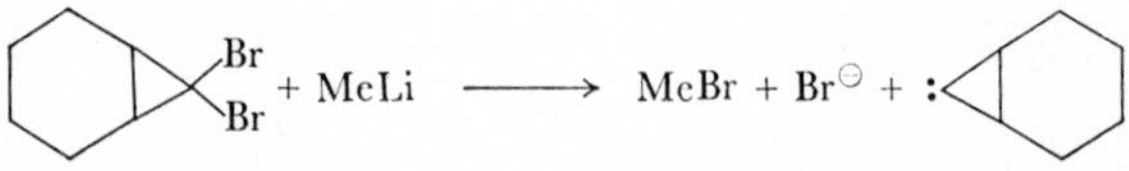

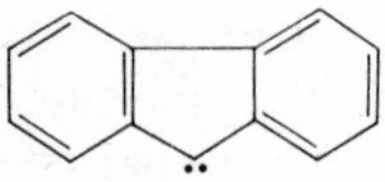

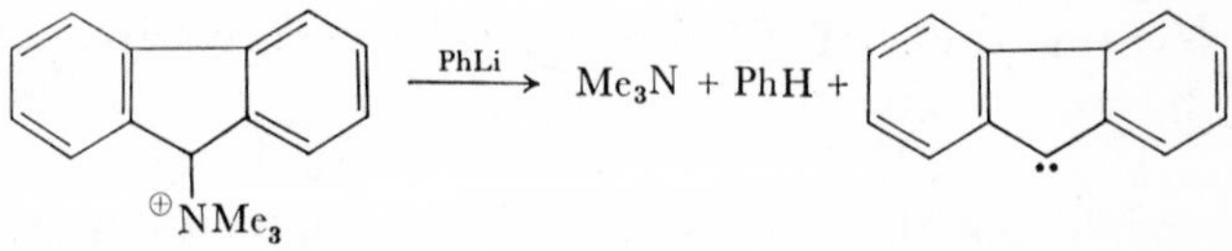

shows that carbene is produced initially in the excited singlet state which is rapidly converted to the lower energy triplet state. The triplet state is linear, with two sp bonding orbitals and an unpaired electron in each of the remaining p-orbitals. The singlet state has one empty p-orbital and three other orbitals one of which has largely s character and contains the unshared electrons. The other two orbitals have largely p character and participate in bonding.

The state of carbene at the instant of reaction is important in determining the product distribution in certain of the reactions which are discussed below. In general, it appears that carbene produced photolytically, is in the singlet state. Conversion to the triplet state before reaction is much more likely to occur in the gas phase than in solution, because collision (and reaction) with other molecules is less likely in the former. Less is known about the electronic state of other carbenes, but the triplet state of diphenylcarbene produced by the photolysis of diazodiphenylmethane at 77°K has been observed by electron spin resonance spectroscopy, and adds non-stereospecifically to olefins (below).

Strictly speaking, of course, the singlet states of carbenes, which do not possess unpaired electrons, lie outside the scope of this book. Their inclusion is justified by the radical-like characteristics of their reactions.

Reactions. As might be expected, carbenes show considerable differences from mono-radicals both in reaction type and reactivity. Carbene itself is exceedingly reactive; Doering has described it as 'the most indiscriminate reagent in organic chemistry'.

(i) *Addition to Carbon–Carbon Multiple Bonds*. This is the most characteristic and widely studied of the reactions of carbenes; it is given by all members of the series that have so far been described. The products, initially at any rate, are cyclopropanes:

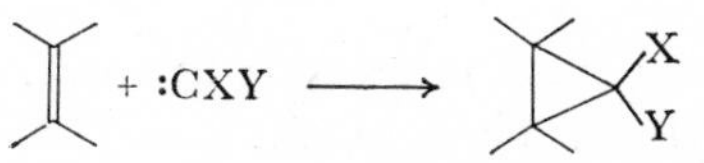

Cyclohexene is often used to trap carbenes when their formation is suspected. Norcarane derivatives bearing 7-substituents are obtained: e.g.

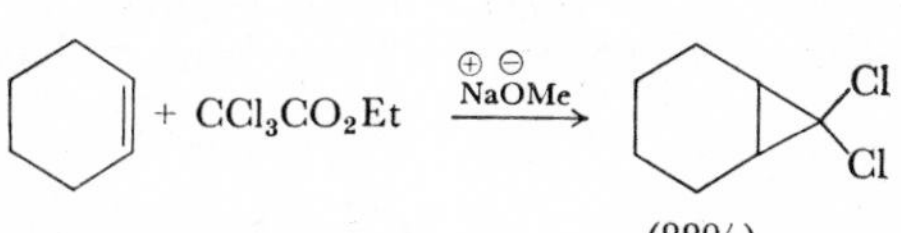

(88%)

Formation of cyclopropanes, however, is not proof that carbenes are involved. A general synthesis of cyclopropanes from olefins, using

133

methylene iodide and copper–zinc couple, is probably not a carbene reaction.

Carbene and chlorocarbene are sufficiently reactive to add to benzene. The norcaradienes formed either isomerize or react further:

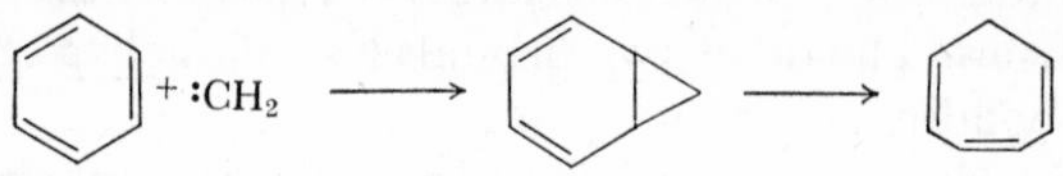

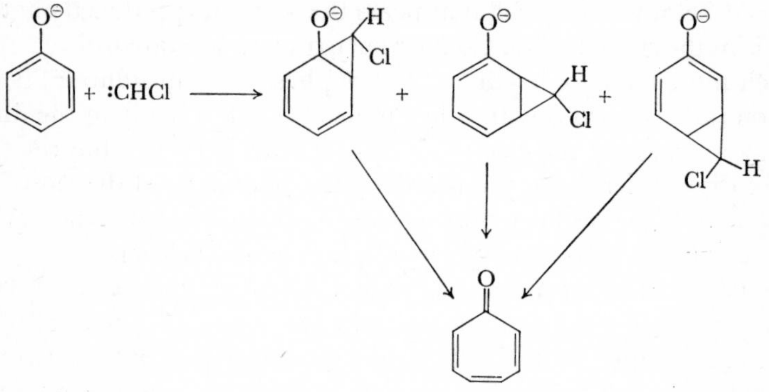

Dichloro- and dibromocarbene are not sufficiently reactive to add to the aromatic nucleus but with pyrroles and indoles, for example, addition occurs, and is followed by ring expansion:

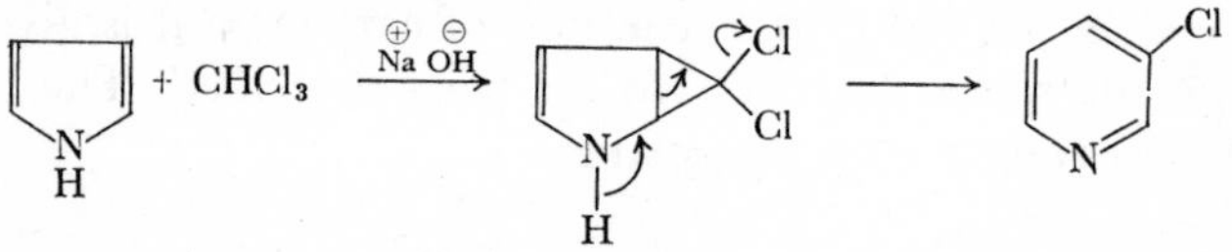

Many other additions have interesting features. Addition of carbene to allene yields methylenecyclopropane:

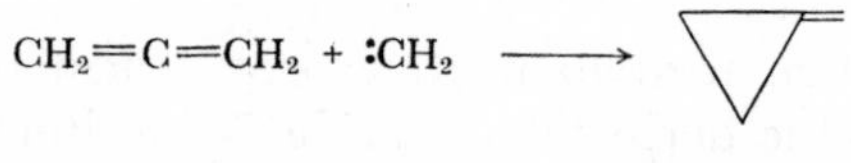

$$CH_2{=}C{=}CH_2 \;+\; {:}CH_2 \;\longrightarrow\;$$

Treatment of the dibromide (*9.1*) with methyl lithium at $-78°$ yields the unusual spiro-biscyclopropane (*9.2*) by intramolecular addition:

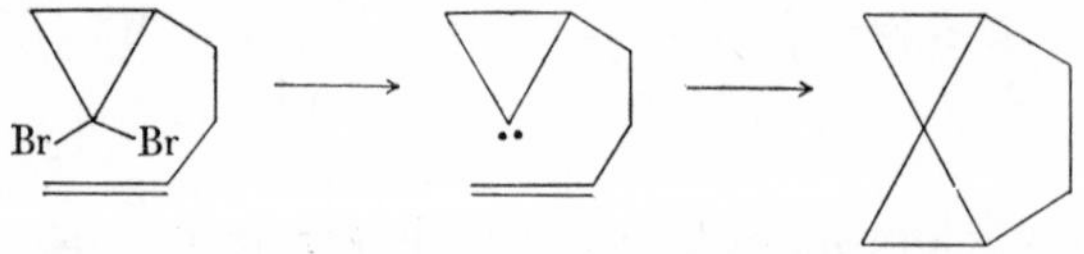

(*9.1*)   (*9.2*)

Addition of carbenes to acetylenes also occurs readily, and the products are cyclopropenes. An important example of this reaction is involved in the formation of cyclopropenium ions (Breslow, 1961):

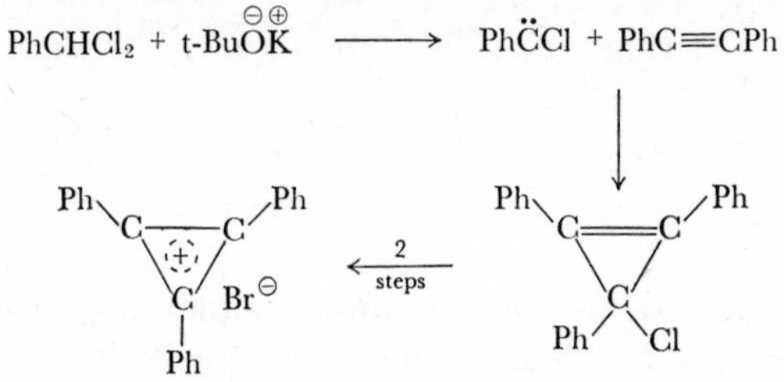

$$PhCHCl_2 + \text{t-BuO}\overset{\ominus}{\text{K}}\overset{\oplus}{} \longrightarrow Ph\overset{..}{C}Cl + PhC\equiv CPh$$

Relative reactivities of olefins towards halo-carbenes have been determined in competition experiments. Results are shown in Table 9.2. Olefin reactivity decreases with decrease in the extent of alkyl substitution at the double bond. This suggests that the halocarbenes are electrophilic, and it is noticeable that the increase in olefin reactivity due to electron accession by the alkyl groups, outweighs the unfavourable steric situation that they give rise to. The orders of reactivity for carbenes may be compared with that of an electrophilic reagent such as bromine. Chlorocarbene is much less discriminating than dichlorocarbene on account of its higher reactivity and lower electrophilicity.

Table 9.2. Relative Reactivities of Olefins towards Halocarbenes

Olefin	:CHCl	:CCl$_2$	:CBr$_2$	Br$^{\oplus}$
Me$_2$C=CMe$_2$	2·81	6·5	3·5	2·5
Me$_2$C=CHMe	1·78	2·8	3·2	1·9
Me$_2$C=CH$_2$	1	1	1	1
MeCH=CHMe (*cis*)	0·91	—	—	—
MeCH=CHMe (*trans*)	0·45	—	—	—
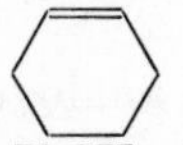 ⬡	0·6	0·12	0·4	—
PhCH=CH$_2$	—	—	0·4	0·59
n-PrCH=CH$_2$	0·23	—	—	—
n-BuCH=CH$_2$	—	0·02	0·07	0·36
CH$_2$=CHBr	—	—	< 0·01	0·01

Carbene-olefin reactions are generally stereospecific and give *cis* addition. Dichlorocarbene and *trans*-but-2-ene give *trans*-1,2-dimethyl-3,3-dichlorocyclopropane (*9.3*).

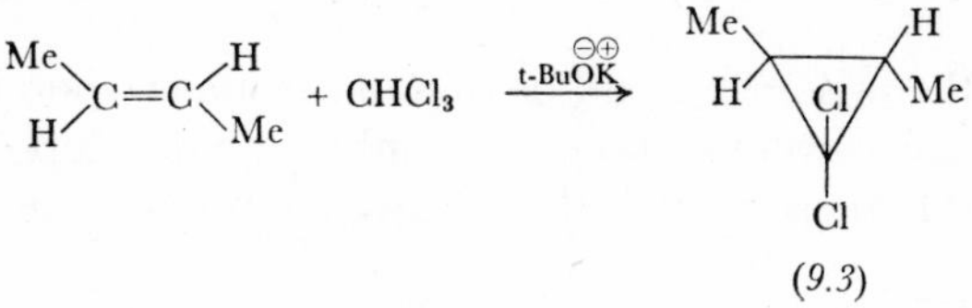

(*9.3*)

Chlorocarbene also adds stereospecifically to olefins but isomer mixtures are obtained with appropriate olefins:

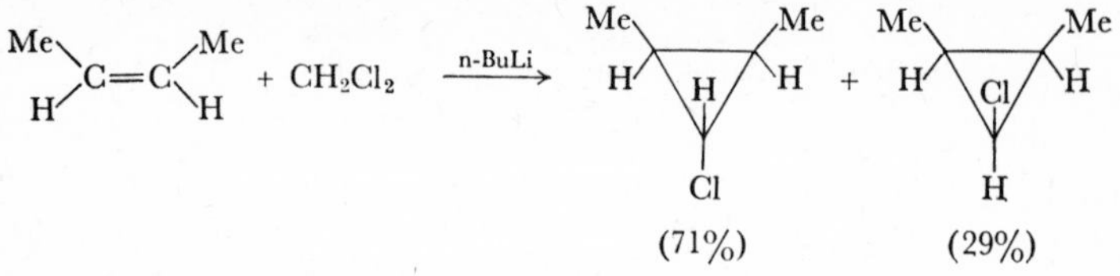

(71%)   (29%)

As would be expected, the predominant isomer is that in which non-bonded interactions are least. The stereospecificity of the additions implies either that both bonds are made simultaneously, or that the diradical (*9.4*), if formed, cyclizes in a period less than that required for rotation about the C_1—C_2 bond. This period is of the order of 10^{-13} sec.

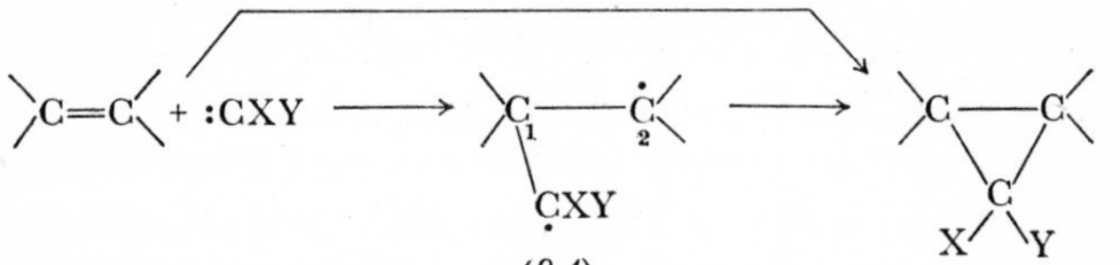

(9.4)

Non-specific addition is, however, observed in gas phase reactions with carbene when the reactants are diluted with large amounts of inert gas. It is concluded, therefore, that specificity is associated with the singlet state and that collision with inert molecules degrades the singlet to the triplet. The triplet state is considered to give the diradical (*9.4*), itself a triplet with the unshared electrons having unpaired spins. The diradical can cyclize only after sufficient collisions for triplet-singlet transition and this delay allows rotation about the C_1—C_2 bond, with consequent loss of stereospecificity.

(ii) *Insertion.* This important reaction, which does not have analogues in the reactions of monoradicals, involves insertion of carbene into a carbon–hydrogen bond:

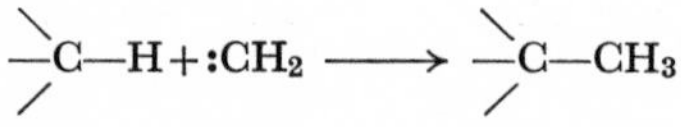

Propane, for example, gives butane and isobutane:

$$CH_3CH_2CH_3 + :CH_2 \longrightarrow CH_3CH_2CH_2CH_3 + CH_3CH(CH_3)CH_3$$

Formation of the n-isomer could be due to carbon–carbon insertion but this is unlikely since cyclopentane gives only methylcyclopentane and no cyclohexane. There is very little selectivity in insertion reactions of carbene in solution; isomer distributions for 2,3-dimethylbutane and cyclohexene (Table 9.3) illustrate this point.

Table 9.3. Insertion† of Carbene

Substrate		Found (%)	Statistical (%)
$(CH_3)_2CHCH(CH_3)_2$	Primary insertion	83	85·7
	Tertiary insertion	17	14·3
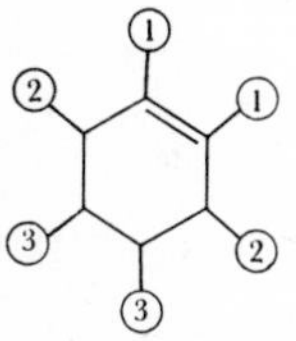	(1) Vinylic	16·6	20
	(2) Allylic	41·7	40
	(3) β-Methylene	41·7	40

† Cyclohexene also gives addition.

The figures for cyclohexene are to be contrasted with the attack of mono-radicals on this compound (cf. p. 73).

Indiscriminate reaction in solution appears to be due to the singlet state of carbene. In the gas phase, conversion to the triplet state before reaction is much more likely, particularly when inert gas is present. The triplet state is less reactive and selectivity consequently increases.

Insertion occurs in two ways, the major path being direct and not involving the formation of intermediate radicals. Thus carbene reacts with 1-^{14}C-2-methylpropene (9.5) giving 2-methylbut-1-ene in which 92% of the label is at the terminal position:

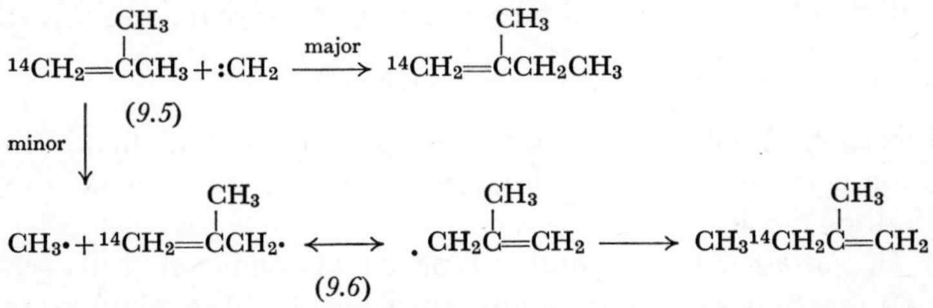

$$^{14}CH_2{=}\overset{\overset{\displaystyle CH_3}{|}}{C}CH_3 + :CH_2 \xrightarrow{\text{major}} {}^{14}CH_2{=}\overset{\overset{\displaystyle CH_3}{|}}{C}CH_2CH_3$$

(9.5)

minor ↓

$$CH_3{\cdot} + {}^{14}CH_2{=}\overset{\overset{\displaystyle CH_3}{|}}{C}CH_2{\cdot} \longleftrightarrow {\cdot}CH_2\overset{\overset{\displaystyle CH_3}{|}}{C}{=}CH_2 \longrightarrow CH_3{}^{14}CH_2\overset{\overset{\displaystyle CH_3}{|}}{C}{=}CH_2$$

(9.6)

The abstraction pathway involves removal of a hydrogen atom with formation of a methyl radical and the mesomeric butenyl radical (9.6).

10

C_1 and C_3 in this radical are equivalent so that this pathway must yield 50% of each isotope isomer. The abstraction–combination mechanism has also been implicated in gas phase reactions by the isolation of dimers of the radicals involved. Propane gives, as by-products of insertion reactions, hexane, 2-methylpentane, and 2,3-dimethylbutane by combinations of n- and isopropyl radicals.

Intramolecular insertions lead to some interesting ring closures:

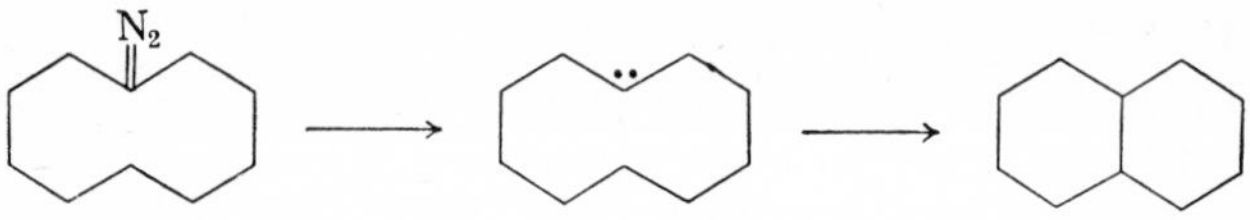

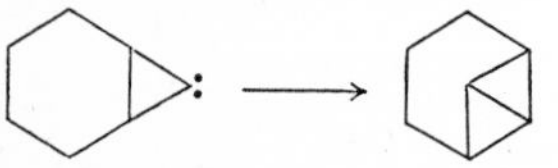

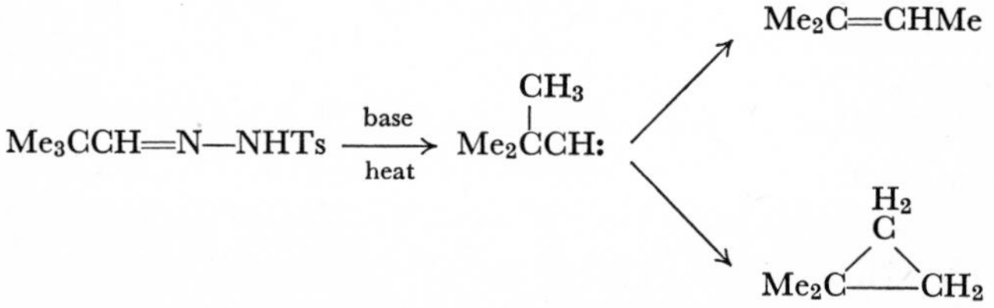

$$Me_3CCH = N - NHTs \xrightarrow[heat]{base} Me_2\overset{\overset{\displaystyle CH_3}{|}}{C}CH:$$

with products:

$$Me_2C = CHMe$$

$$\underset{Me_2C \diagdown CH_2}{\overset{\overset{\displaystyle H_2}{\overset{\displaystyle C}{\diagup \diagdown}}}{}}$$

In the last example, the ratio of cyclopropane to olefin formed by isomerization (next section), is very similar to that obtained by α-dehydrohalogenation of neopentyl chloride. This suggests that the reactions have t-butylcarbene as a common intermediate.

Insertion in O—H bonds is also known; isopropanol and carbene yield isopropyl methyl ether as well as C—H insertion products.

(iii) *Isomerization.* Isomerization of carbenes with hydrogen on an adjacent carbon atom is very favourable energetically. A new C—C bond and a new C—H bond are formed by isomerization, and for carbenes of the appropriate structure, this is a major reaction pathway:

e.g. $$CH_3CH: \longrightarrow CH_2 = CH_2$$

Isomerization also appears to occur by alkyl migration when hydrogen migration is impossible. t-Butyl carbene, for example, was seen to give 2-methylbut-2-ene.

(iv) *Displacement.* This is another type of reaction peculiar to carbenes, in which reaction with ethers causes displacement of *O*-alkyl groups. A new ether and an olefin result:

$$PhOEt + :CHCO_2Et \longrightarrow PhOCH_2CO_2Et + CH_2 = CH_2$$

Aryl groups are not displaced; unsymmetrical dialkyl ethers give mixtures of products resulting from the displacement of either alkyl group.

The Reimer–Tiemann Reaction. This classical and familiar reaction has recently been shown by Hine to involve dichlorocarbene. It had been widely (albeit unreasonably) held that the mechanism was one of C-alkylation in an S_N reaction with chloroform. Chloroform and sodium phenoxide alone, however, give salicylaldehyde only very slowly, while reaction is rapid in the presence of sodium hydroxide. Hine showed that the rate of reaction decreased with increasing ionic strength and that therefore attack of phenoxide ion upon trichloromethyl carbanion could be ruled out. A possible mechanism is as follows:

$$CHCl_3 + \overset{\ominus}{O}H \longrightarrow \overset{\ominus}{C}Cl_3 \longrightarrow \overset{\ominus}{C}l + :CCl_2$$

$$\text{(phenoxide)} + :CCl_2 \longrightarrow \text{(cyclohexadienone-}\overset{\ominus}{C}Cl_2) \longrightarrow \text{(o-HO-C}_6H_4\text{-CHCl}_2) \longrightarrow \text{(o-HO-C}_6H_4\text{-CHO)}$$

A clear distinction between the subsequent (heterolytic) steps, however, has not so far been made.

It should be emphasized that for many reactions which appear to involve carbenes, good evidence for their formation is lacking. Information about these reactive intermediates is rapidly being collected and many rationalizations now current will doubtless be subject to future modification.

NITRENES

Nitrogen analogues of carbenes, the nitrenes $R—\ddot{\overset{..}{N}}:$, appear to be involved in a number of closely related reactions. Among the simplest is the photolysis of hydrazoic acid in aromatic solvents which produces small amounts of primary aromatic amines:

$$HN_3 \xrightarrow{h\nu} N_2 + H\ddot{\overset{..}{N}}: + PhCH_3 \longrightarrow NH_2C_6H_4CH_3$$

Photolysis of aliphatic azides in benzene similarly gives N-alkylanilines; n-butyl and n-octyl azides, for instance, give the N-alkylarylamines in yields of 22 and 31% respectively. Many reactions which appear to involve nitrenes, however, are intramolecular and involve ring closures either on to aromatic nuclei or ring formation in aliphatic systems.

139

Ring Closures in Aromatic Systems. Photolysis of *o*-azido-biphenyl (*9.7*) yields carbazole in high yield:

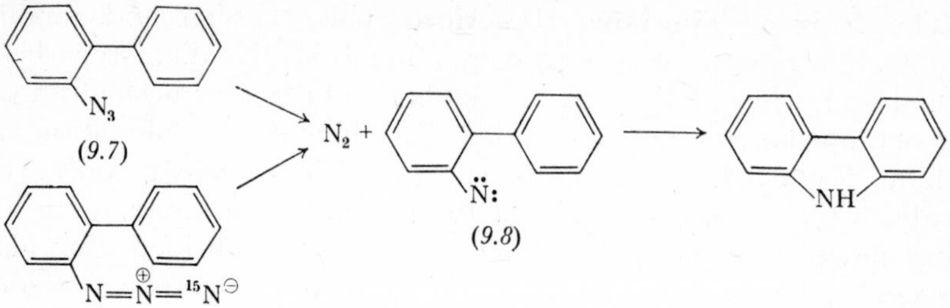

Ring closures of this type have also been carried out by pyrolysing azides and by deoxygenation of *o*-nitroso and *o*-nitrobiphenyls, with trialkyl phosphites. All of these reactions probably involve a nitrene (cf. *9.8*) and this view is supported by the observation that in the photolysis of the azide (*9.7a*), all of the heavy isotope appears in the gas. This shows that it is the nitrogen linked to carbon that becomes part of the ring. Furthermore, photolysis of phenylazide at 77°K gives an ESR signal indicating that the nitrene produced is in the triplet state.

Related ring closures can be achieved by photolysis of arylalkyl azides, cyclization occurring either from side chain to nucleus or nucleus to side chain:

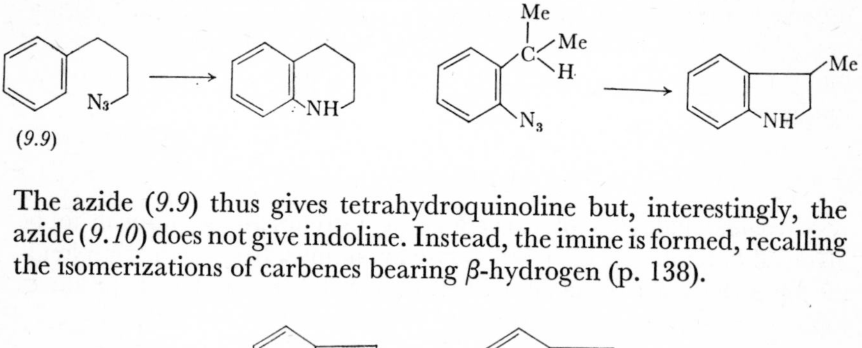

The azide (*9.9*) thus gives tetrahydroquinoline but, interestingly, the azide (*9.10*) does not give indoline. Instead, the imine is formed, recalling the isomerizations of carbenes bearing β-hydrogen (p. 138).

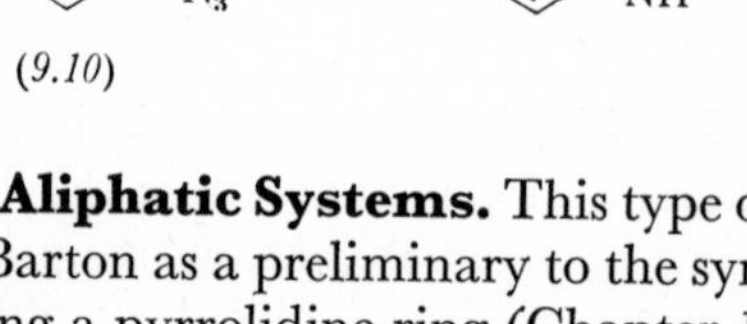

Ring Closure in Aliphatic Systems. This type of reaction has been studied in detail by Barton as a preliminary to the synthesis of biological compounds containing a pyrrolidine ring (Chapter 10). In the simplest example, photolysis of n-butyl azide (*9.11;* R=H) gives pyrrolidine itself together with the imine (*9.12*, R=H). When longer-chain azides, e.g. n-octyl azide (*9.11;* R=n-Bu) are used, only five-membered rings are formed and acyclic amines and imines are obtained as by-products.

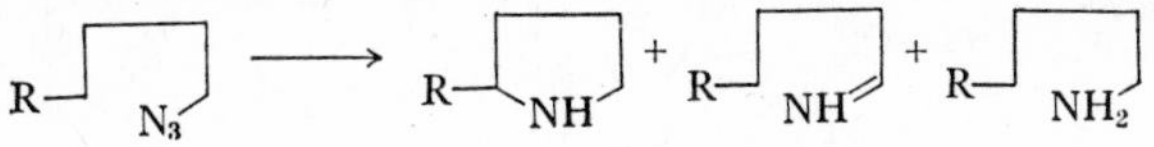

(*9.11*)   (*9.12*)

Imines and amines clearly result from isomerization and hydrogen abstraction, respectively. Cyclization, however, could occur either by insertion, as found with singlet carbene, or by abstraction–combination shown by triplet carbene. Barton has provided evidence for the abstraction–combination route in that the optically active azide (*9.13*) yields the inactive pyrrolidine (*9.15*):

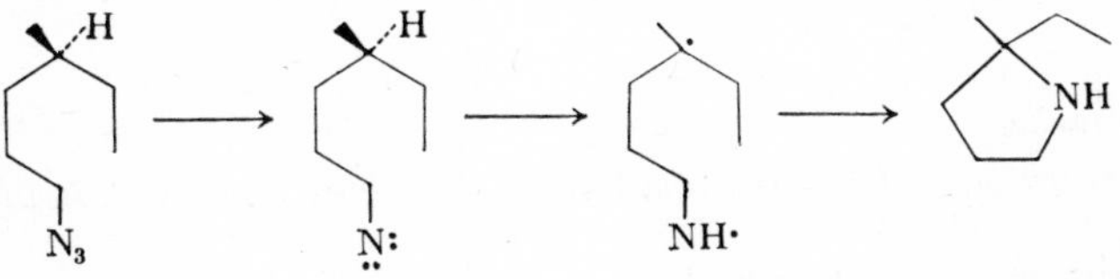

(*9.13*)   (*9.14*)   (*9.15*)

The intermediate diradical (*9.14*) is unable to hold its configuration.

Direct insertion may, however, be involved in the photolysis of t-butyl azide:

Formation of the three-membered ring is analogous to the behaviour of t-butylcarbene (p. 138).

Sulphonamidation. Thermal decomposition of benzenesulphonyl-azide in aromatic solvents yields *N*-arylbenzenesulphonamides:

$$PhSO_2N_3 + ArH \longrightarrow PhSO_2NHAr + N_2$$

The reaction resembles homolytic aromatic substitution and has been examined quantitatively in the same way. Results are presented in Table 9.4.

The results show an interesting ambiguity in that while the orientation is characteristic of electrophilic substitution, the small effects of substituents on activation recall homolytic processes. There is little doubt

141

Table 9.4. Sulphonamidation

Substrate	Isomer ratio (%)			Rate ratio $\left(\frac{X}{H}K\right)$	Partial rate factor		
	o-	*m-*	*p-*		k_{o-}	k_{m-}	k_{p-}
$PhCH_3$	61	1	38	1·0	1·8	0·03	2·3
PhOMe	71	2	27	0·96	2·0	0·06	1·6
PhCl	46	2	52	0·69	0·95	0·04	2·2
PhH	—	—	—	1·0	1·0	1·0	1·0
$PhCO_2Me$	43	54	3	0·38	0·49	0·62	0·07

that the intermediate has radical character, as sulphonyl azides can initiate vinyl polymerization. Benzenesulphonylnitrene, $PhSO_2\ddot{N}$:, appears to be the reactive species involved and its electrophilic character can be accounted for by the powerful $-I$ effect of the adjacent sulphonyl group.

For further reading

Addition Reactions of Halocarbenes: PARHAM and SCHWEIZER, *Org. React.*, 1963, **13**, 55.

CHINOPOROS, 'Reactive Intermediates Containing Divalent Carbon', *Chem. Rev.*, 1963, **63**, 235.

HINE, *Physical Organic Chemistry*, 2nd edition, Chapter 24. McGraw Hill, 1962.

HORNER and CHRISTMANN, 'Nitrenes', *Angew. Chem. Int. Ed.*, 1963, **2**, 599.

PROBLEMS

Suggest mechanisms for the following reactions:

(*a*) 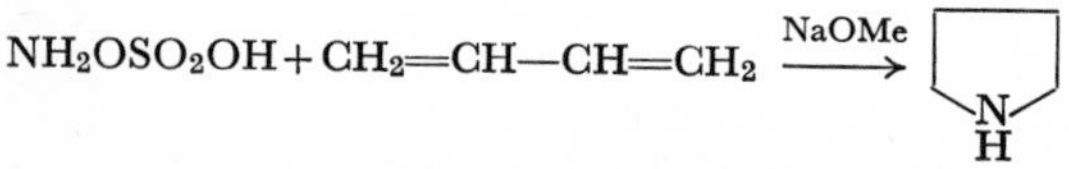
NH₂OSO₂OH + CH₂=CH—CH=CH₂
NaOMe
N
H

(*b*) 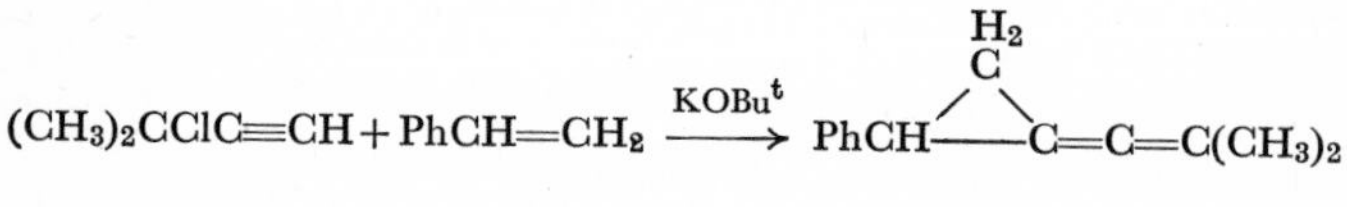
(CH₃)₂CClC≡CH + PhCH=CH₂
KOBuᵗ
H₂
C
PhCH—C=C=C(CH₃)₂

(*c*) 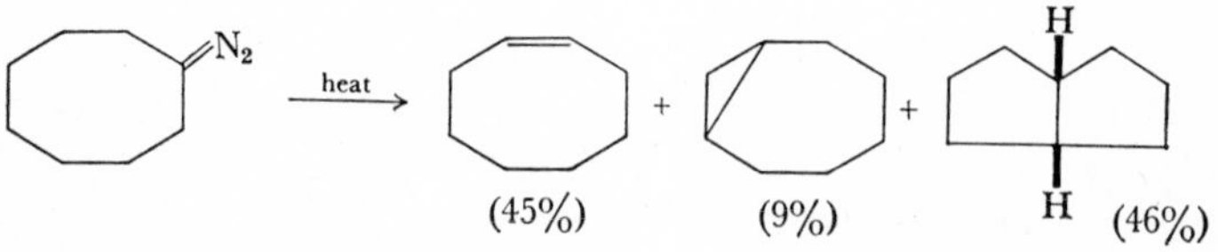
N₂
heat
+
+
H
H
(45%)
(9%)
(46%)

(*d*) 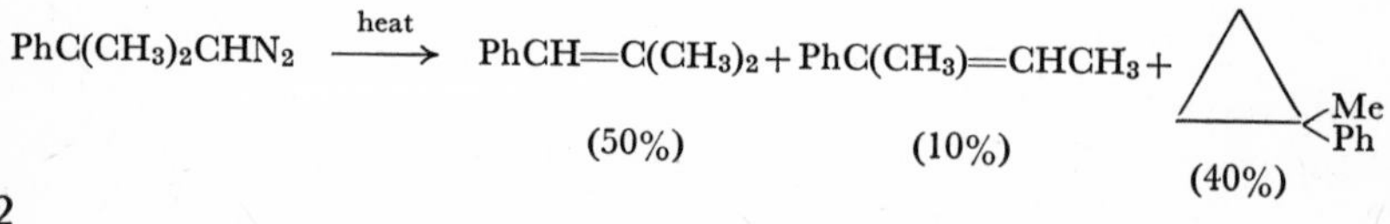
PhC(CH₃)₂CHN₂
heat
PhCH=C(CH₃)₂ + PhC(CH₃)=CHCH₃ +
Me
Ph
(50%)
(10%)
(40%)

(e)

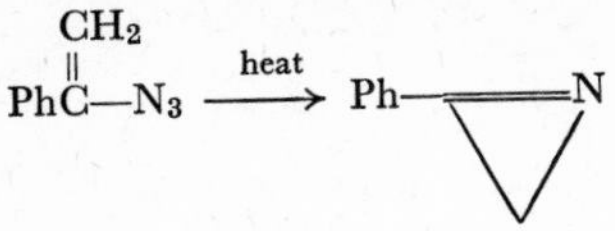

$$\underset{\substack{CH_2 \\ \parallel}}{PhC}-N_3 \xrightarrow{\text{heat}} Ph-\triangle\!\!=\!\!N$$

(f)

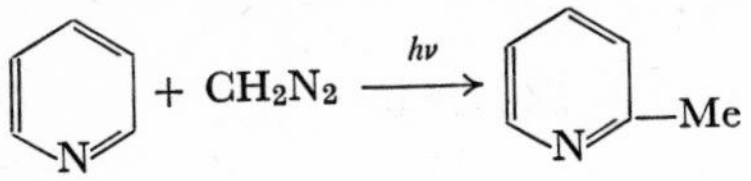

+ CH$_2$N$_2$ $\xrightarrow{h\nu}$ —Me

(g) CH$_2$=CH—CH=CH$_2$ + CH$_2$N$_2$ $\xrightarrow[\text{gas phase}]{h\nu}$

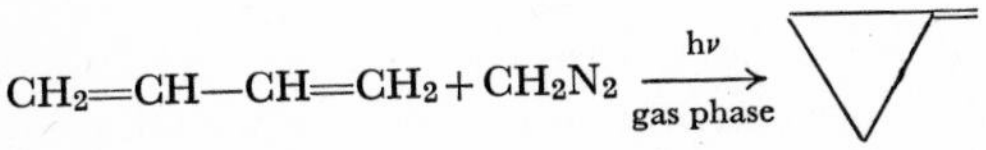

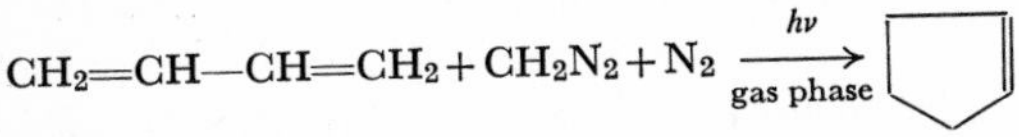

(h) CH$_2$=CH—CH=CH$_2$ + CH$_2$N$_2$ + N$_2$ $\xrightarrow[\text{gas phase}]{h\nu}$

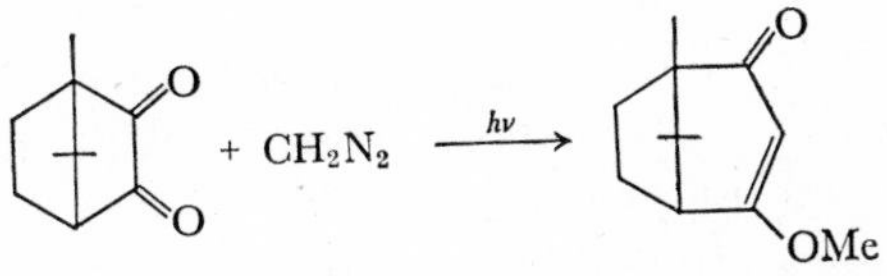

(i) + CH$_2$N$_2$ $\xrightarrow{h\nu}$

(j) CH$_3$COCH$_3$ + N$_2$CHCO$_2$Et $\xrightarrow[90°]{\text{Cu}}$ CH$_2$=C(Me)—OCH$_2$CO$_2$Et +

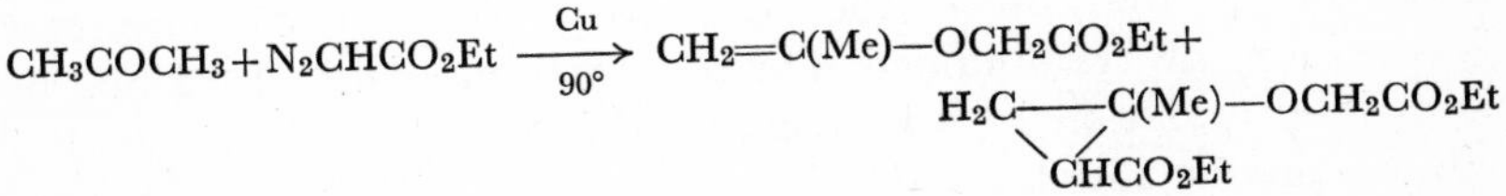

$$\underset{\substack{| \\ CHCO_2Et}}{H_2C\text{————}C(Me)}\text{—OCH}_2CO_2Et$$

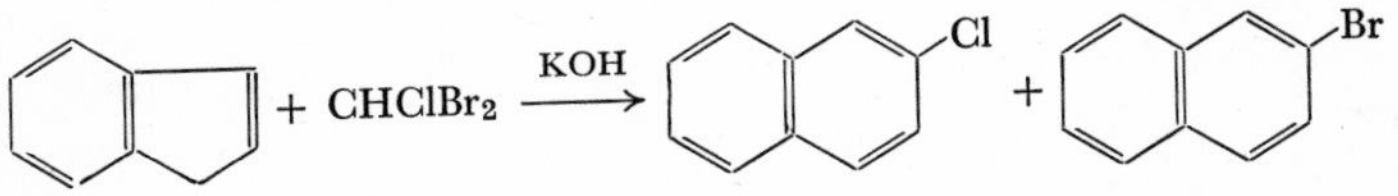

(k) + CHClBr$_2$ $\xrightarrow{\text{KOH}}$ +

CHAPTER 10

RADICALS IN SYNTHESIS

Many of the reactions that have been discussed so far have obvious synthetic potentiality. In this final chapter, certain reactions which have been developed specifically because of their synthetic usefulness are collected together.

Aromatic Arylation. *Intermolecular Reactions.* Theoretical aspects of this topic were discussed in Chapter 3. A reaction by which aryl groups can be introduced into aromatic nuclei has obvious utility for the synthesis of biaryls. The only effective rival is the Ullmann reaction which requires severer conditions and is not well suited to synthesis of unsymmetrical compounds. Homolytic arylation, however, suffers from the disadvantage that unless the substrate is symmetrical, mixtures of isomers are always obtained. On this account, synthesis of biaryls by homolytic arylation is often conducted by placing the required substituent in the radical and using a symmetrical substrate. Some 400 examples of homolytic arylation are given in the reviews listed at the end of the section and, in general, the reaction can be performed with groups such as halogeno-, cyano-, nitro-, alkoxycarbonyl-, alkoxy-, aryl-, and acyl- present in either the aryl radical or the component to be arylated. The variety of possible substrates is wide, and in addition to benzenoid compounds, thiophen, furan, pyridine, quinoline, and ferrocene are all suitable. Examples are given in Table 10.1.

The 'nitrite' method refers to a method of arylation (Cadogan, 1962) which involves direct treatment of a primary aromatic amine with pentyl nitrite in a solution of the aromatic substrate. The reaction is very simple to carry out and yields are relatively good.

Intramolecular Reactions. When the aryl radical is connected to another aromatic nucleus, the possibility of intramolecular reaction arises:

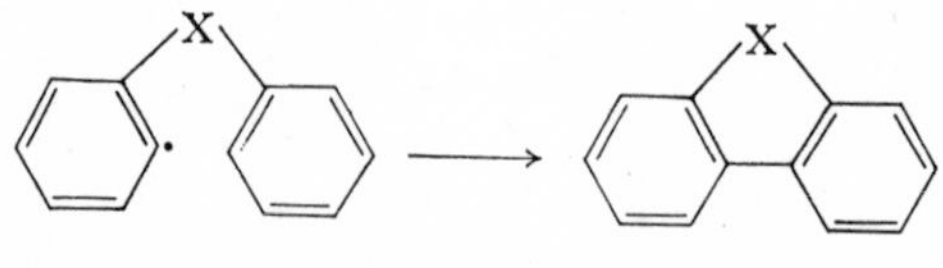

This type of reaction is best known in connection with the synthesis of phenanthrenes developed by Pschorr. Diazotization of *trans*-2-amino-α-phenylcinnamic acid (*10.1*) and treatment of the diazonium solution

144

Table 10.1. Synthesis of Biaryls

Substituents in phenyl radical	Substrate	Method	Biphenyl product	Yield (%)
2-NO$_2$	Benzene	G	2-NO$_2$	45
3-Cl	Benzene	G	3-Cl	25
4-MeO	Benzene	N	4-MeO	33
2-CN,5-Me	p-Dimethoxybenzene	NA	2-CN,5-Me,2′,5′-Di-MeO	41
3,4-Di-MeOCO	Benzene	G	3,4-Di-MeOCO	37
None	Mesitylene	NA	2,4,6-Tri-Me	42
p-Ph	Benzene	NA	p-Ph	50
None	s-Trichlorobenzene	P	2,4,6-Trichloro	42
2-OH	Benzene	I	2-OH	60
α-Naphthyl	Nitrobenzene	NA	α-(4′-nitrophenyl)naphthalene	39
3-Pyridyl	Benzene	N	3-phenylpyridine	52
3-Quinolyl	Benzene	N	3-phenylquinoline	35
3-CN	Thiophen	G	3-cyanophenylthiophens	15
4-Me	Ferrocene	G	p-tolylferrocene	57

G = Gomberg reaction; N = nitrite method; NA = nitrosoacylarylamine; P = peroxide; I = iodide photolysis. For formulation of these reactions, see p. 28–29.

with aqueous sodium hydroxide, yields phenanthrene-9-carboxylic acid (*10.2*) in 55% yield:

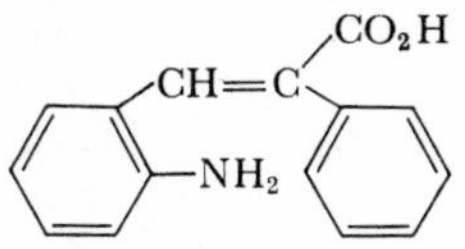

(*10.1*) 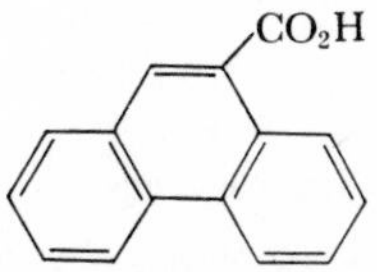   (*10.2*)

Cyclization of the diazonium salt is generally carried out in one of three ways: (i) thermal decomposition in acid solution, (ii) treatment with copper powder either in acid solution or in an organic solvent, and (iii) by the addition of alkali to the diazonium solution. Under the conditions of (i), there is good evidence that cyclization is *heterolytic* and involves aryl carbonium ions. Homolysis occurs under the other conditions. Cyclization of amino-derivatives can also be performed using nitrosoacylarylamines or triazens (cf. p. 29), and these reactions also involve radicals.

The link between the aryl nuclei may vary widely so that systhesis of a range of different polynuclear systems may be achieved by this process. Examples given in Table 10.2 are restricted to those in which homolytic cyclization is probable.

145

Table 10.2. Internuclear Cyclization

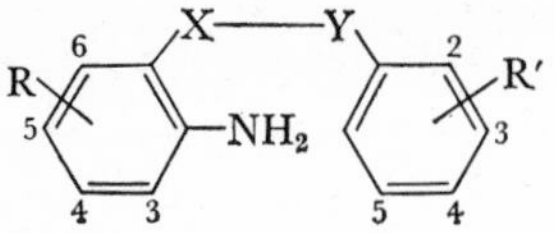

	Product	Yield (%)
R = H; X = CH; Y = CH; R′ = H	Phenanthrene	65
R = 3-Me; X = CH; Y = C−CO₂H; R′ = 4-Me	4,6-Dimethylphenanthrene-9-carboxylic acid	71
R = H; X = NMe; Y = −; R′ = 2-NO₂	9-Methyl-1-nitrocarbazole	38
R = H; X = S; Y = −; R′ = H	Dibenzothiophen	25
R = H; X = CO; Y = −; R′ = 4-NO₂	3-Nitrofluorenone	95
R = H; X = CO; Y = NMe; R′ = 4-Cl	5-Methyl-2-chloro-6(5)-phenanthridone	44

This type of reaction has also been applied in numerous syntheses of the ring system characteristic of the aporphine alkaloids. The starting materials are 1-benzyl-tetrahydroisoquinolines:

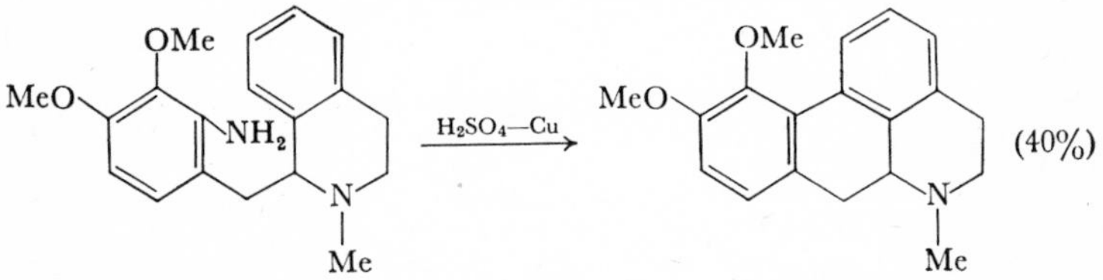

Suggestions for further reading

BACHMANN and HOFMANN, *Org. React.*, 1944, **2**, 224.
DERMER and EDMISON, *Chem. Rev.*, 1957, **57**, 77.
DE TAR, *Org. React.*, 1957, **9**, 409.
WILLIAMS, *Homolytic Aromatic Substitution*. Pergamon, London, 1960.

Arylation of Olefins—The Meerwein Reaction. Meerwein (1939) found that negatively substituted olefins reacted with diazonium salts in the presence of copper salts. The products were derived from replacement, by an aryl group, of hydrogen situated β- to the negative substituent (for example, Ph,CN or COOH), the overall reaction being:

$$Ar\overset{\oplus}{N_2}\;\overset{\ominus}{X} + R{-}CH{=}CH{-}Y \xrightarrow{Cu^{++}} ArC(R){=}CHY$$

The replacement of vinyl hydrogen recalls the replacement of nuclear aromatic hydrogen (Chapter 3 and the preceding section). Yields are dependent both on solvent and pH.

Heterolytic and homolytic mechanisms have both been suggested for the reaction, and while the latter are currently favoured, the true situation is rather uncertain. In the postulated radical mechanism, the diazonium salt is considered to be in equilibrium with a covalent diazo compound (e.g. a diazoacetate). Dissociation of the covalent diazo-compound occurs readily (Chapter 3) and addition of the resulting aryl radical occurs at the β-position, giving a stabilized intermediate radical (cf. Chapter 6).

$$\overset{\oplus}{Ar}\overset{\ominus}{N_2}\,X \rightleftharpoons Ar—N{=}N—X \longrightarrow Ar\cdot + N_2 + [\cdot X]$$

$$Ar\cdot + RCH{=}CHY \longrightarrow ArCH(R)\overset{\bullet}{C}HY$$

The final stages are considered to involve electron transfer to cupric ion by the intermediate radical and subsequent loss of a proton or capture of the counter ion:

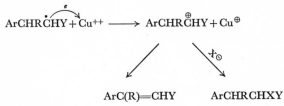

$$ArCHR\overset{\bullet}{C}HY + Cu^{++} \longrightarrow ArCHR\overset{\oplus}{C}HY + Cu^{\oplus}$$

$$ArC(R){=}CHY \qquad ArCHRCHXY$$

The electron transfer step is postulated to account for the fact that the Meerwein reaction goes well with olefins, such as acrylonitrile and styrene that polymerize in the presence of radicals. This step recalls the chain termination of polymerization caused by salts such as ferric chloride (p. 97). The simple mechanism given is certainly an over-simplification. The actual route probably depends upon the components and reaction conditions.

Examples of the reaction are given in Table 10.3.

Although yields, particularly with unsubstituted diazonium salts, are often poor, the ready availability of the starting materials favours this method.

Reactivities of the unsaturated components have only been qualitatively studied, but the trends observed are in accord with those found in quantitative studies (Chapters 6 and 7). With a particular activating group present, terminal olefins are more reactive than non-terminal olefins (cf. Table 6.5, Chapter 6). Addition occurs more readily β- to the aryl group than to other groups. This is shown, for example, by the product obtained in the p-nitrophenylation of methyl styryl ketone. We know from copolymerization (Table 7.8, Chapter 7) that styrene is more reactive than monomers such as methyl methacrylate towards radicals.

147

Table 10.3. Arylation of Olefins

Olefin	Product	Yield (%)
$CH_2\!=\!CH\!-\!CH\!=\!CH_2$	$PhCH_2CH\!=\!CHCH_2Cl$	70
Ferrocene	Phenylferrocene	66
$CH_2\!=\!CHPh$	$PhCH\!=\!CHPh$	23
$CH_2\!=\!CHCHO$	$p\text{-}ClC_6H_4CH_2CHClCHO$	38
$MeCOCH\!=\!CHPh$	$p\text{-}NO_2C_6H_4C(COMe)\!=\!CHPh$	39
$CH_2\!=\!CHCO_2H$	$p\text{-}NO_2C_6H_4CH\!=\!CHCO_2H$	60
$CH_2\!=\!CHCN$	$PhCH_2CHClCN$	81

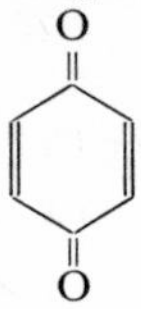

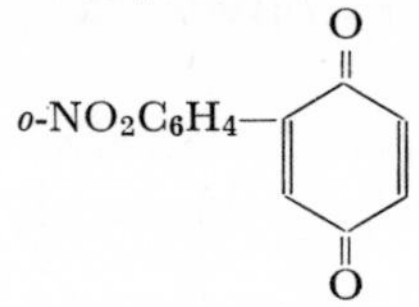

76

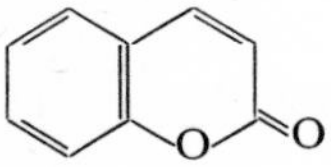

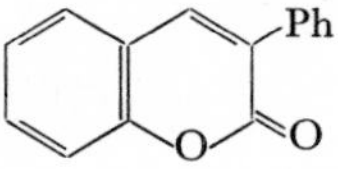

60

For further reading

RONDESTVEDT, *Org. React.*, 1960, **11**, 189.

Hypophosphorous Deamination. Treatment of diazonium salts with hypophosphorous acid causes replacement of the diazonium group by hydrogen. Although other methods for this conversion are available, this procedure is preferred because of its simplicity, good yields with a wide variety of compounds, and frequent success where other methods fail. An interesting example of its use is the introduction of deuterium at specific positions by treatment of diazonium salts with deuterohypophosphorous acid (Ingold, 1962).

The overall reaction is given by:

$$Ar\overset{\oplus}{N_2}\overset{\ominus}{X} + H_3PO_2 + H_2O \longrightarrow ArH + N_2 + H_3PO_3 + \overset{\oplus}{H} + \overset{\ominus}{X}$$

but a fairly large excess of the reagent (5–15 moles) is normally used.

The mechanism of the reaction has chiefly been investigated by Kornblum. The following observations are relevant to the mechanism.

(i) The reaction is catalysed by oxidizing agents, but with powerful oxidisers a short period of acceleration is often followed by complete inhibition. (ii) The reaction is retarded or even stopped by small amounts of benzoquinone. (iii) Nuclear substituents give the order of increasing reactivity: $p\text{-}OMe < p\text{-}Me < p\text{-}NO_2 < Brs$. (iv) A readily reducible salt such as pentabromobenzenediazonium hydrogen sulphate catalyses the reduction of a slowly reduced salt such as the *p*-tolyl analogue. (v) Deuterium is only slowly incorporated when deuterium oxide is the solvent.

Kornblum has suggested a radical chain mechanism with the following steps:

Initiation.

$$\overset{\oplus}{Ar N_2} + Y^{\ominus} \rightleftharpoons Ar-N=N-Y \longrightarrow Ar\cdot + N_2 + [\cdot Y]$$
$$(Y = \text{any counter ion, e.g. } H_2PO_2{}^{\ominus}, Cl^{\ominus}, \text{etc.})$$

Polarographic behaviour of diazonium salts provides evidence for the equilibrium between ionic and covalent forms of the diazonium compound, and decomposition of the covalent form is postulated as for the Gomberg reaction.

Propagation.

$$Ar\cdot + H-P\overset{OH}{\underset{OH}{\diagdown}} \longrightarrow ArH + \cdot P\overset{OH}{\underset{OH}{\diagdown}}$$

$$H_2PO_2\cdot \overset{e}{\frown} + \overset{\oplus}{N_2Ar} \longrightarrow H_2PO_2{}^{\oplus} + \cdot N_2Ar \longrightarrow Ar\cdot + N_2$$
$$H_2PO_2{}^{\oplus} + H_2O \longrightarrow H_3PO_3 + H^{\oplus}$$

The fact that deuterium incorporation is slower than reduction supports the suggestion that P—H fission occurs in the first propagation step. The hydroxyl hydrogens are known to exchange rapidly, but P—H exchange is slow. The P—H bond is, in any case, 32 kcal/mole weaker than the O—H bond.

The more rapid rate of reduction found with negatively substituted diazonium salts is evidence for the second propagation step, as electron transfer is assisted. Diazonium salts with electron-withdrawing substituents also have a greater tendency towards formation of the covalent form in the initiation stage.

Inhibition by benzoquinone is strongly suggestive of a radical *chain* mechanism, and the weak oxidizing agents that promote reaction doubtless do so by participating in one-electron transfer with hypophosphite ion:

e.g. $$Cu^{++} \overset{e}{\frown} + H_2PO_2{}^{\ominus} \longrightarrow Cu^{\oplus} + H_2PO_2\cdot$$

Strong oxidizing agents, however, while also oxidizing hypophosphorous acid or its anion, probably convert diazonium salts to quinonoid compounds which subsequently inhibit the chain process.

The practical aspects of the reaction have been discussed by Kornblum and do not require further elaboration or tabulation here.

For further reading

KORNBLUM, *J. Amer. chem. Soc.*, 1950, **72**, 3013; *Org. React.*, 1944, **2**, 262.

Electrolytic Synthesis. Electrolysis of solutions of carboxylate ions constitutes an important method for carbon–carbon coupling. The reaction, discovered by Kolbe (1849), allows the conversion of a carboxylic acid containing n carbon atoms into a molecule containing $2n-2$ carbons:

$$2RCO_2^{\ominus} \xrightarrow{-2e} R\!-\!R + 2CO_2$$

A single acid may be used, in which case a symmetrical molecule results, or two different acids may be employed, when a statistical mixture of coupling products is obtained.

It seems clear that the reaction is homolytic, and involves three stages:

(i) Discharge of the carboxylate ion at the anode with formation of the acyloxy radical:

$$RCO_2^{\ominus} \xrightarrow{-e} RCO_2\cdot$$

(ii) Decarboxylation of the acyloxy radical produced:

$$RCO_2\cdot \longrightarrow R\cdot + CO_2$$

(iii) Combination of two (like or unlike) alkyl radicals:

$$R\cdot + R'\cdot \longrightarrow R\!-\!R'(+R\!-\!R+R'\!-\!R')$$

Several lines of evidence support the intervention of radicals in the reaction. By-products obtained under certain conditions are very similar to those obtained when radical sources such as acyl peroxides are used. Thus the yields of trinitro-xylenes produced by the electrolysis of sodium acetate in the presence of trinitro-toluene are comparable with those obtained when acetyl peroxide and other sources of methyl radicals are used. Electrolysis of sodium benzoate in pyridine gives phenylpyridines with the same isomer distribution as that obtained with benzoyl peroxide (Table 3.3, Chapter 3). In addition, alcohols, olefins, and esters frequently accompany the coupling products. These are readily accounted for by the alternative reactions of acyl and alkyl radicals:

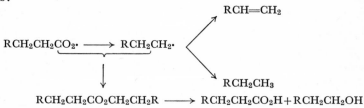

Electrolysis of carboxylic acids in the presence of monomers such as styrene causes polymer formation and the kinetics of electrode processes further confirm the participation of radicals.

An interesting feature of the Kolbe synthesis is that relatively high yields (Table 10.4) of dimeric products can be obtained. Combination of unstabilized and highly reactive radicals is rather unusual when we consider their behaviour in other systems. Two factors, however, favour combination in electrosynthesis. First, radicals are produced in high local concentrations adjacent to the anode. 'Solvent cages' of surrounding molecules restrict diffusion and encourage the radical–radical reactions which account for the products obtained. Secondly, the solvent used is frequently water or methanol. Transfer reactions with these compounds are difficult (Chapter 6) because of the high bond strengths involved; the less probable radical–radical interactions are thus favoured.

Studies of the Kolbe reaction have, incidentally, thrown light on the mechanism of radical disproportionation. Electrolysis of $\beta\beta\beta$-tri-deuteropropionic acid and of $\alpha\alpha$-dideuteropropionic acid gives 1,1-dideuteroethylene, showing that one propyl radical (produced by decarboxylation) abstracts a β-hydrogen from the other:

$$2CD_3CH_2CO_2\cdot \longrightarrow 2CD_3CH_2\cdot \longrightarrow CD_2{=}CH_2 + CD_3CH_2D$$

$$2CH_3CD_2CO_2\cdot \longrightarrow 2CH_3CD_2\cdot \longrightarrow CH_2{=}CD_2 + CH_3CHD_2$$

Disproportionation, being a radical–radical reaction, is usually poorly favoured on statistical grounds. On the other hand, C—H bonds adjacent to carbon bearing an unpaired electron are very weak (cf. Bond Energy Table, p. 167) so that the process is energetically well disposed.

A short selection of simple anodic couplings is given in Table 10.4. A wide variety of substituents in the acid can be tolerated and the electrolysis of half esters of dibasic acids is of particular value. Table 10.4 lists only successes. Failure to couple attends the electrolysis of aryl acids, α,β and β,γ-unsaturated acids, and many halogeno acids particularly those containing β-bromo or -iodo substituents.

Failure of the reaction with aryl acids is understandable; benzoyloxy radicals are much longer lived than, for example, acetyloxy radicals, and consequently diffuse away from the vicinity of the electrode. On decarboxylation, the aryl radicals produced quickly attack the solvent. Failures with α,β and β,γ-unsaturated acids are due, at least in part, to polymerization, and with β-bromo and iodo acids, elimination of a halogen atom from the radical is an important competing reaction (cf. Chapters 4 and 6).

$$RCHBrCH_2\cdot \longrightarrow RCH{=}CH_2 + Br\cdot$$

Acids which are asymmetric about the carbon atom bearing the carboxyl group give inactive coupling products:

$$\text{EtCH(Me)CO}_2\text{H} \longrightarrow [\text{EtCH(Me)}]_2$$
$$(-)$$

This observation fits well with the proposed mechanism, as racemization of the derived alkyl radical would be rapid. When the asymmetric centre is remote from the carboxyl group, optical activity is preserved.

Table 10.4. Anodic Coupling of Acids $[(X—CH_2(CH_2)_nCO_2H]$ to give Symmetrical Products

n	X	Solvent	Yield (%)
1	H	H_2O	40
4	H	H_2O	89
12	H	H_2O-EtOH	73
0	EtOCO	H_2O	60
3	MeOCO	MeOH	90
9	MeOCO	MeOH	43
16	EtOCO	H_2O-EtOH	60
1	$(EtO)_2CH$	H_2O	35
3	Cl	MeOH	51
7	F	MeOH	65
9	Br	MeOH	54
1	Ac	H_2O	50
0	Ph	MeOH/Pyridine	50
2	EtO	H_2O	30
2	CN	MeOH	40
4	AcNH	MeOH	40
1	EtOCOCH=C(Me)	MeOH	55

'Crossed coupling' with a mixture of acids is an important variation in the procedure because it allows the synthesis of molecules which are not bilaterally symmetrical. Mixtures of symmetrical and unsymmetrical products are always obtained, but by using excess of one component, the relative yield of unsymmetrical product can be increased. The two acids may be of similar or different types and monocarboxylic acids, for example, are readily obtained by cross-coupling a monocarboxylic acid with the half ester of a dibasic acid. Stearic acid has been obtained by coupling C_5+C_{13}, C_9+C_9, and $C_{17}+C_1$ units in yields of 28, 18 and 25% respectively.

The potentialities and usefulness of anodic coupling are nicely illustrated by the synthesis of $(-)$-tuberculostearic acid (*10.3*) in which an optically active, branched-chain, half ester component is used:

$$CH_3(CH_2)_6CO_2H + HO_2CCH_2\overset{*}{C}HMeCH_2CO_2Me \longrightarrow$$

$$CH_3(CH_2)_7\overset{*}{C}HMeCH_2CO_2H + HO_2C(CH_2)_7CO_2Me \longrightarrow$$
$$(48\%)$$

$$CH_3(CH_2)_7\overset{*}{C}HMe(CH_2)_8CO_2H$$
$$(31\%)$$
$$(10.3)$$

Radicals, other than acyloxy radicals, have also frequently been produced in both anodic (electron removal) or cathodic (electron capture) processes.

Anodic:

$$Me_2\overset{\ominus}{C} \overset{-e}{\longrightarrow} Me_2\overset{\bullet}{C} \longrightarrow Me_2C\text{——}CMe_2$$
$$\underset{NO_2}{|} \qquad \underset{NO_2}{|} \qquad \underset{NO_2}{|}\ \underset{NO_2}{|}$$

$$H\overset{\ominus}{C}(CO_2Me)_2 \overset{-e}{\longrightarrow} H\overset{\bullet}{C}(CO_2Me)_2 \longrightarrow (MeO_2C)_2CHCH(CO_2Me)_2$$

Cathodic:

$$PhCH{=}CHPh \underset{+H^{\oplus}}{\overset{+e}{\longrightarrow}} Ph\overset{\bullet}{C}HCH_2Ph \longrightarrow PhCH_2CH(Ph)CH(Ph)CH_2Ph$$

$$PhCHO \underset{+H^{\oplus}}{\overset{+e}{\longrightarrow}} Ph\overset{\bullet}{C}HOH \longrightarrow PhCHOHCHOHPh$$

As in these examples, the electron donors are usually stabilized anions, and the electron acceptors are carbon–carbon double bonds and carbonyl groups.

For further reading

SVADKOVSKAYA and VOITKEVICH, *Russian Chem. Rev.*, 1960, 161.
TOMILOV and FIOSHIN, *Russian Chem. Rev.*, 1963, 30.
WEEDON, *Advances in Organic Chemistry: Methods and Results* (ed. Raphael, Taylor and Wynberg). Interscience, New York, 1960, Vol. I.

Abstraction–Combination and Addition–Combination Reactions.

Previous chapters have exemplified the numerous reaction pathways available to radicals. Radicals can usually be obtained only in fairly low concentrations so that combination is consequently unfavourable on statistical grounds. As we saw in the preceding section, combination is favoured when the radical is weakly reactive, when it is generated in high local concentrations, or when its environment is

11

poorly susceptible to radical attack. This section briefly reviews combination reactions that have actual or potential synthetic value.

Abstraction–Combination Reactions. This heading embraces the following type of reaction:

$$RH + R'\cdot \longrightarrow R'H + R\cdot \longrightarrow R{-}R$$

This is not, of course, a chain reaction; a pair of radicals must be generated for each molecule of dimer produced.

Three sources of radicals have commonly been used to provide the radicals that perform the abstraction step. Acetyl peroxide was used by Kharasch in the earlier work on this type of reaction and while good yields are often obtained, the reagent suffers from the disadvantage of being dangerous to handle. In later work it has been prepared and decomposed *in situ*. The radical responsible for abstraction with this reagent is methyl; the acetyloxy radicals produced quickly decarboxylate. t-Butyl peroxide has been used chiefly with aromatic substrates containing benzylic hydrogens. It is not always clear whether t-butoxy or methyl radicals are responsible for hydrogen abstraction as t-butanol/acetone ratios (Chapter 8) have not usually been determined. A third radical source, Fenton's reagent (p. 7), generates hydroxyl radicals and requires aqueous media for operation. A large number of substrates have been subjected to this reagent by Coffmann and his collaborators (1958). Table 10.5 gives examples of the type of dimerizations that can be effected.

In most abstraction–combination reactions in non-aqueous media, the substrates give stabilized radicals containing the unpaired electron on carbon adjacent to an aryl or carbonyl group. The ready dimerization of α-halogeno and α-amino radicals suggests stabilization in the following way (cf. p. 102):

$$Cl{-}\overset{\cdot}{C}HR \longleftrightarrow \overset{\cdot}{\overset{\oplus}{Cl}}{=}CHR \qquad {>}\overset{\cdot\cdot}{N}{-}\overset{\cdot}{C}HR \longleftrightarrow {>}\overset{\cdot}{\overset{\oplus}{N}}{=}CHR$$

Fenton's reagent, however, gives good dimer yields when the hydrogen atom is hard to remove and the resulting radical is reactive. Aqueous conditions favour radical–radical reactions, and with t-butyl compounds, disproportionation is impossible, making dimer yields good. Hydroxyl radicals are so reactive and unselective that in substrates with alternative abstraction sites, hydrogen removal from each is observed. The products from propionitrile illustrate this point. The intermediate radical, $\cdot CH_2C(Me)_2OH$, obtained in the t-butyl alcohol–titanous–hydrogen peroxide system has been observed by ESR techniques using a flow

154

Table 10.5. Products of Abstraction–Combination Reactions

Substrate	Radical source	Radical	Dimer		Yield (%)
CH_3CO_2H	A	Me·	$HO_2CCH_2CH_2CO_2H$		50
CH_3CO_2H	F	·OH	$HO_2CCH_2CH_2CO_2H$		4
$(Me)_2CHCO_2H$	A	Me·	Me_2CCO_2H $\mid$ Me_2CCO_2H		40
Me_3CCO_2H	F	·OH	$[HO_2CC(Me)_2CH_2-]_2$		37
$ClCH_2CO_2Me$	A	Me·	$ClCHCO_2Me$ $\mid$ $ClCHCO_2Me$		41
CH_3CH_2CN	F	·OH	$NCCH_2CH_2CH_2CH_2CN$ $NCCH(Me)CH(Me)CN$ $NCCH(Me)CH_2CH_2CN$	}	60
$PhCH_2CO_2Me$	A	Me·	$PhCHCO_2Me$ $\mid$ $PhCHCO_2Me$	(meso) (racemic)	15 17
CH_2CO_2Me $\mid$ CH_2CO_2Me	A	Me·	$\begin{bmatrix} -CHCO_2Me \\ CH_2CO_2Me \end{bmatrix}_2$		43
$Me_2CHCOMe$	A	Me·	Me_2CCOMe $\mid$ Me_2CCOMe		43
$CH_3(CH_2)_2CH_2Cl$	A	Me·	$CH_3(CH_2)_2CHCl$ $\mid$ $CH_3(CH_2)_2CHCl$		32
Me_3COH	F	·OH	$[HOC(Me)_2CH_2-]_2$		36
Ph_2CH_2	A	Me·	$Ph_2CHCHPh_2$		70
$PhNMe_2$	B	$Me_3CO·$	$PhN(Me)CH_2CH_2N(Me)Ph$		50
Me_3CNH_2	F	·OH	$[NH_2C(Me)_2CH_2-]_2$		10
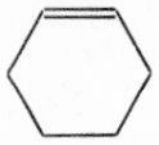 ⬡	B	$Me_3CO·$ or Me·	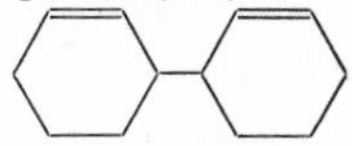 ⬡–⬡		52
$PhCHMe_2$	B	$Me_3CO·$ or Me·	$PhC(Me)_2C(Me)_2Ph$		86
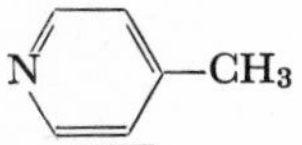 N◯–CH_3	B	$Me_3CO·$ or Me·	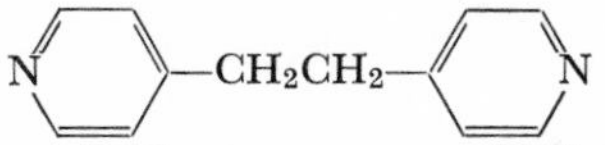 N◯–CH_2CH_2–◯N		42
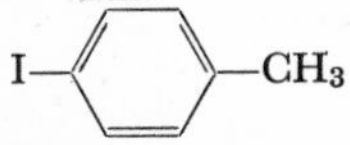 I–◯–CH_3	B	$Me_3CO·$ or Me·	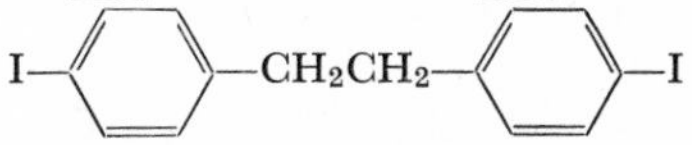 I–◯–CH_2CH_2–◯–I		34

(A = acetyl peroxide; F = Fenton's reagent; B = t-Butyl peroxide)

system. The absorption shows a widely spaced triplet (strong CH_2 splitting) which is weakly split into septets [$(CH_3)_2$].

$$H_2O_2 + Ti^{3+} \xrightarrow{e} HO· + \overset{\ominus}{O}H + Ti^{4+}$$

$$Me_3COH + ·OH \longrightarrow ·CH_2C(Me)_2OH + H_2O$$

Addition–Combination Reactions. We saw earlier that addition of a radical to a simple olefin gives a new radical which either removes hydrogen from a suitable substrate, or adds to a new molecule of olefin. When the radical produced by addition is unreactive, however, combination of the radical can compete effectively with its other reactions. Additions to butadiene are of this type, the overall reaction being:

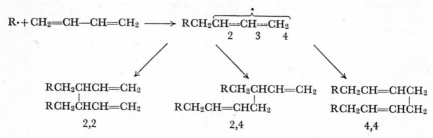

In principle, all three types of combination product are possible, but the 4,4 dimer is normally formed in greatest amount. Examples of the

Table 10.6. Addition–Combination Reactions with Butadiene

Radical X	Source	Yield of $X-C_4H_6-C_4H_6-X$ (%)
$CH_3COCH_2\cdot$	$CH_3COCH_3 + \cdot OH$	51
⬡—$\cdot$H (cyclopentanone with $\cdot$H)	⬡ + $\cdot OH$	70
$HOC(CH_3)_2CH_2\cdot$	$(CH_3)_3COH + \cdot OH$	64
$CH_3\dot{C}HOH$	$CH_3CH_2OH + \cdot OH$	77
$\cdot CH_2CO_2CH_3$ $CH_3CO_2CH_2\cdot$	$CH_3CO_2CH_3 + \cdot OH$	27
$CH_3CO\cdot$ $\cdot CH_2CHO$	$CH_3CHO + \cdot OH$	7
Me⬡O (radical)	Me⬡OOH + Fe^{++}	90
$Br\cdot$	$Ce^{4+} + Br^{\ominus}$	50
$NH_2\cdot$	$\overset{\oplus}{N}H_3OH + Ti^{3+}$	42
$CH_3\cdot$	Electrolysis of $CH_3CO_2^{\ominus}K^{\oplus}$	58
$EtO_2C\cdot$	Electrolysis of $EtO_2CCO_2^{\ominus}K^{\oplus}$	40
$(CH_3)_3CO\cdot$	$(CH_3)_3COOH + Fe^{++}$	70
HO⬡O (radical)	HO⬡OOH + Fe^{++}	75
$PhC(CH_3)_2O\cdot$	$PhC(CH_3)_2OOH + Fe^{++}$	25

reaction are given in Table 10.6. A significant feature of the reactions is that stabilized radicals such as those derived from ketones, and reactive ones such as t-butoxy, can both partake in addition–combination.

The production, by electron transfer reactions, of amino radicals, bromine atoms, and carbethoxy radicals in aqueous solution was developed by Coffmann (1959). The decomposition of 'ketone hydro-peroxides' in the presence of butadiene constitutes a potentially valuable method for the synthesis of ω-dicarboxylic acids.

Combination of aryloxy radicals has been increasingly investigated because of its biogenetic and synthetic importance. For these reasons a separate section (p. 161) has been devoted to this topic.

For further reading

COFFMANN *et al.*, *J. Amer. chem. Soc.*, 1958, **80**, 2864, 2872, 2877; 1959, **81**, 1489, 2073; 1960, **82**, 1395.

Intramolecular Abstraction in Synthesis. Specific introduction of a functional group at a position in a molecule remote from another functional group is a chronic problem in synthetic organic chemistry. Particular attention has recently been paid to this problem in connection with reactions of the angular methyl groups of steroids. A number of naturally occurring steroids, for example (*10.6*), possess functional groups attached to C_{18} or C_{19}. The objective of partial synthesis of such compounds has produced a number of approaches to the achievement of specific reaction at these centres. Synthetic routes for other structures have been developed as a result of these investigations.

Azide Photolysis. Formation of 'nitrenes', R—N̈:, analogous to carbenes, was discussed at the end of the preceding chapter. One of their character-istic reactions, intramolecular hydrogen abstraction, is followed by intramolecular combination. These processes result in the formation (usually) of a pyrrolidine derivative.

This reaction of nitrenes has been applied by Barton and his collab-orators to the synthesis of the steroidal alkaloid, conessine (*10.6*) in which C_{18} is part of a pyrrolidine ring. Photolysis of the bis-azide (*10.4*), with an intact C_{18} methyl group, gave the cyclized imino-amine (*10.5*) by the abstraction–combination mechanism outlined previously. Completion of the synthesis by saturation of the imino-group and *N*-methylation gave the alkaloid, albeit in low yield.

($\pm$)-Proline (*10.8*) was obtained similarly in 15% overall yield from azido-ester (*10.7*).

Photolysis of Nitrites and Hypochlorites. Irradiation of both types of

$$\left. \begin{array}{l} RONO \\ ROCl \end{array} \right\} \xrightarrow{h\nu} RO\cdot + \left\{ \begin{array}{l} NO \\ Cl\cdot \end{array} \right.$$

157

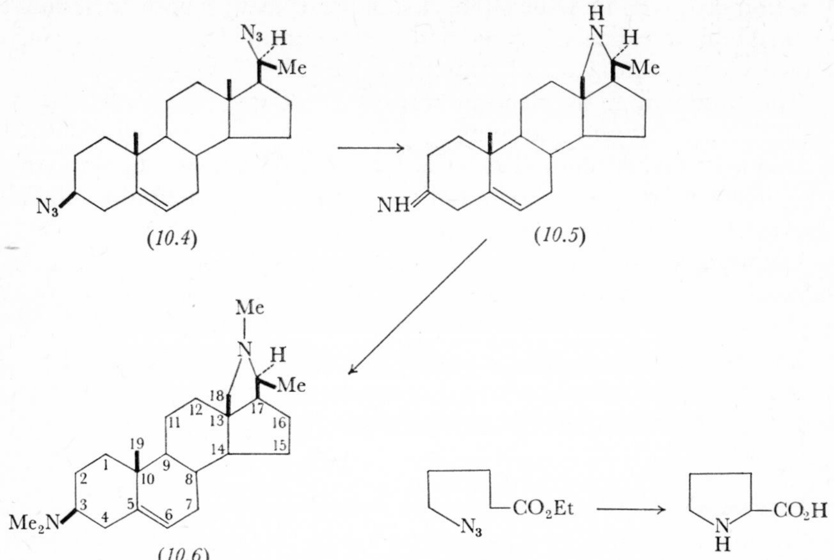

(*10.4*)

(*10.5*)

(*10.6*)

(*10.7*)

(*10.8*)

compound involves the formation of alkoxy radicals which have two main alternative reactions open to them:

(i) Fragmentation (discussed in Chapter 8).

(ii) Abstraction of hydrogen either intermolecularly (cf. the use of t-butyl peroxide above) or intramolecularly. The latter reaction forms the basis of another recent method for the introduction of substituents into the angular methyl groups of steroids. The synthesis of aldosterone

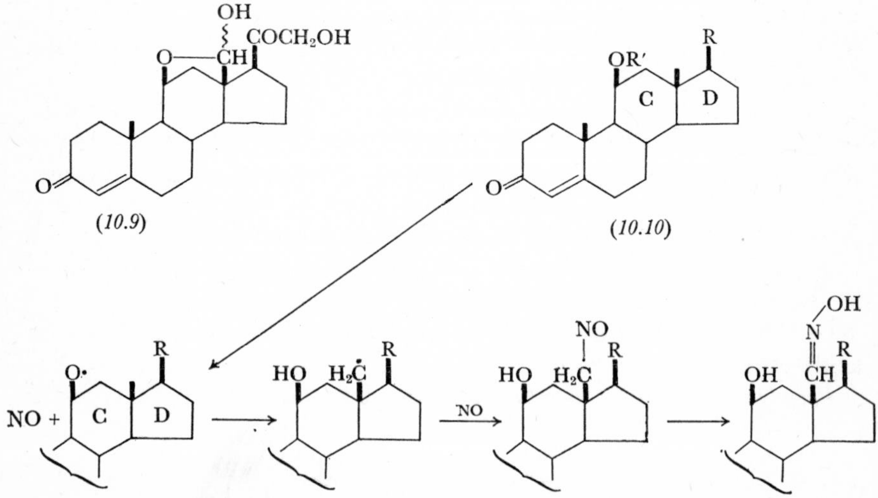

(*10.9*)

(*10.10*)

(*10.9*) (Barton *et al.*, 1960) is a notable example. The starting material, corticosterone acetate (*10.10*; R=COCH₂OAc; R′=H), was converted into the nitrite (*10.10*; R=COCH₂OAc; R′=NO) which, on irradiation, gave aldosterone acetate oxime by the sequence of reactions given in the scheme. Many other examples of the preparative uses of nitrite photolysis have been given by Nussbaum and Robinson. Note that these reactions do not have chain mechanisms; the nitric oxide produced in the photolysis step subsequently captures the alkyl radical produced by internal hydrogen transfer.

Photolysis of hypochlorites proceeds similarly but the reactions involve a chain mechanism (cf. p. 52):

(i) *Introduction of Chlorine at* C_{18}:

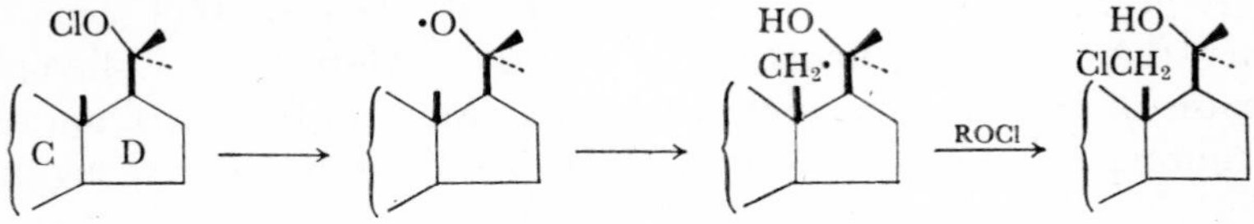

(ROCl represents the steroid hypochlorite)

(ii) *Reaction at* C_{19}:

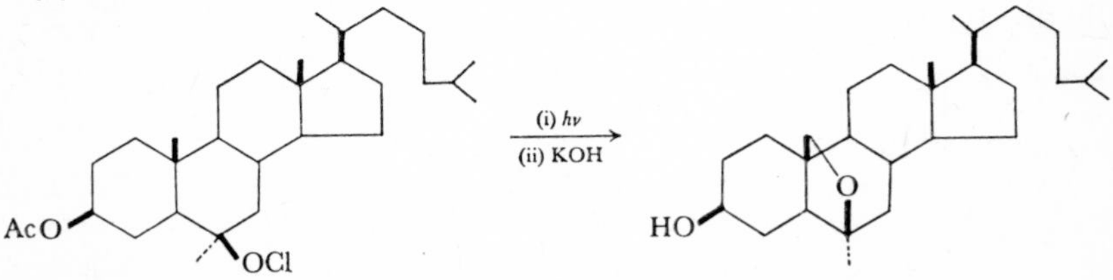

Cyclization of N-Haloamines—The Hofmann-Löffler Reaction. This reaction, originally developed more than sixty years ago, involves the formation of pyrrolidines by the cyclization of *N*-haloamines. A notable early example of its use is the synthesis of nicotine (10.11) by Loffler:

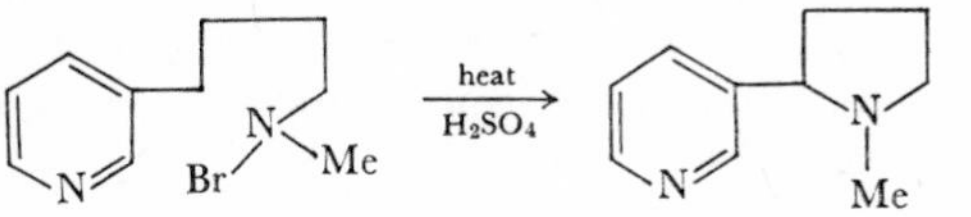

(*10.11*)

Careful study of the reaction established that cyclization proceeded with racemization at the carbon terminus:

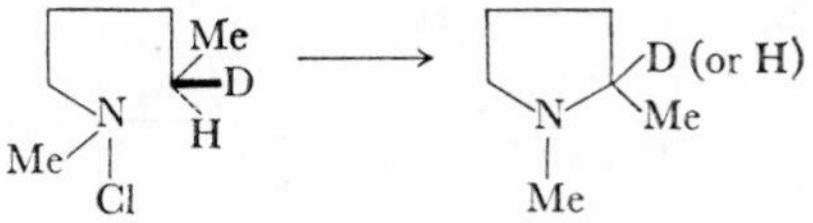

(active)   (racemic)

159

The isotope effect k_H/k_D was 3·5 and the reaction went rapidly on irradiation but not in the dark. Oxygen present caused induction periods and ferrous ion acted as a catalyst. It was further shown that δ-chloroamines are the primary products and that these are converted into pyrrolidines on basification.

The following mechanism fits these findings:

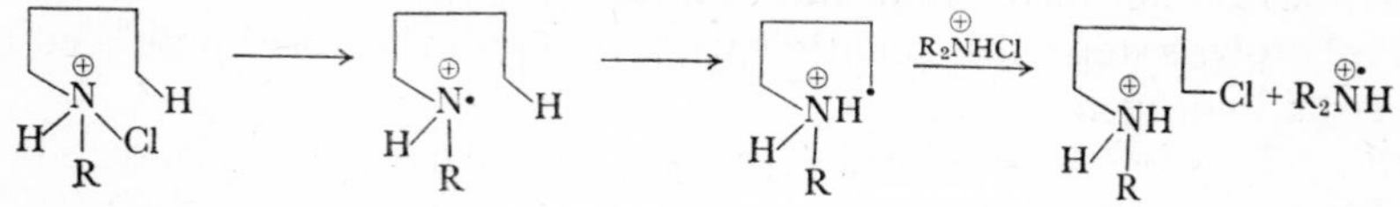

The selectivity of δ-hydrogen transfer indicates the intramolecular nature of the reaction, and the preference for abstraction of secondary rather than primary hydrogen is strong. δ-Abstraction is favoured because angle strain and non-bonded repulsions in the transition state are minimized and there is a preference for a linear N...H...C, arrangement.

The reaction constitutes a method for introducing a functional group at an unactivated δ-position. Corey has applied it to the synthesis of dihydroconessine (*10.12*).

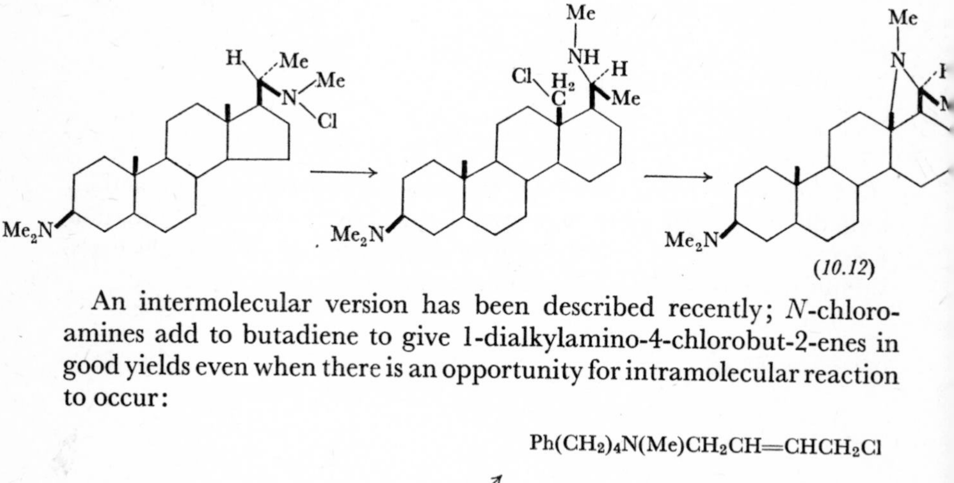

(*10.12*)

An intermolecular version has been described recently; *N*-chloroamines add to butadiene to give 1-dialkylamino-4-chlorobut-2-enes in good yields even when there is an opportunity for intramolecular reaction to occur:

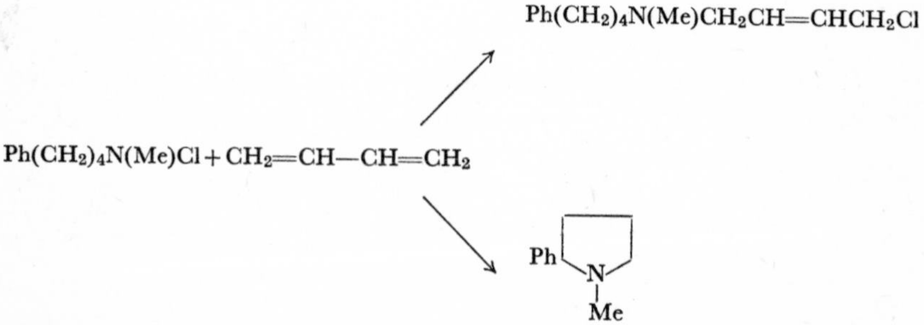

$Ph(CH_2)_4N(Me)CH_2CH=CHCH_2Cl$

$Ph(CH_2)_4N(Me)Cl + CH_2=CH-CH=CH_2$

For further reading
Azide Photolysis: Barton and Morgan, *J.*, 1962, 622.
Nitrite Photolysis: Nussbaum and Robinson, *Tetrahedron*, 1962, **17**, 35.
The Hoffmann–Löffler reaction: Wolff, *Chem. Rev.*, 1963, **63**, 55.

Phenol Dehydrogenation. Hydrogen is readily removed from the hydroxyl group of phenols and this dehydrogenation is particularly easily effected by 'one-electron transfer' oxidizing agents such as Fe^{3+}. Stabilized phenoxy radicals are produced:

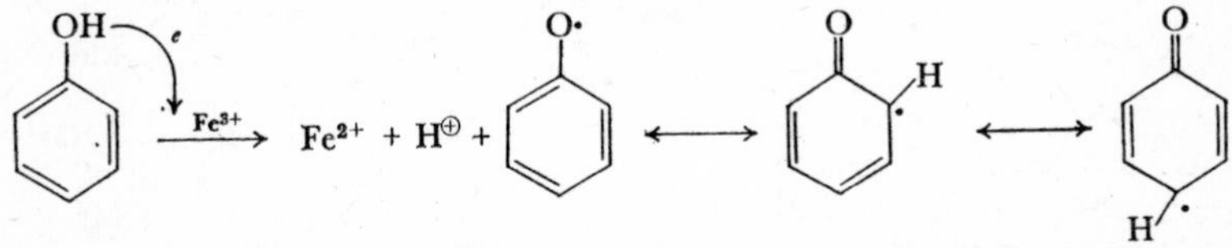

Simple phenoxy radicals disappear, chiefly by coupling, quite rapidly after formation. These combination reactions are the subject of this section and they have great synthetic and biosynthetic significance.

When a phenoxy radical, such as 2,4,6-tri-t-butylphenoxy (*10.13*), is very hindered, coupling is sterically prevented. Combination only with small radicals such as oxygen is then observed:

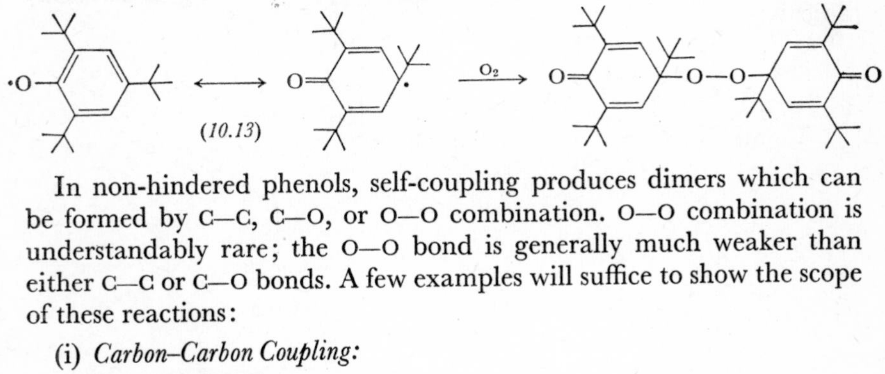

(*10.13*)

In non-hindered phenols, self-coupling produces dimers which can be formed by C—C, C—O, or O—O combination. O—O combination is understandably rare; the O—O bond is generally much weaker than either C—C or C—O bonds. A few examples will suffice to show the scope of these reactions:

(i) *Carbon–Carbon Coupling:*

ortho-ortho-Coupling:

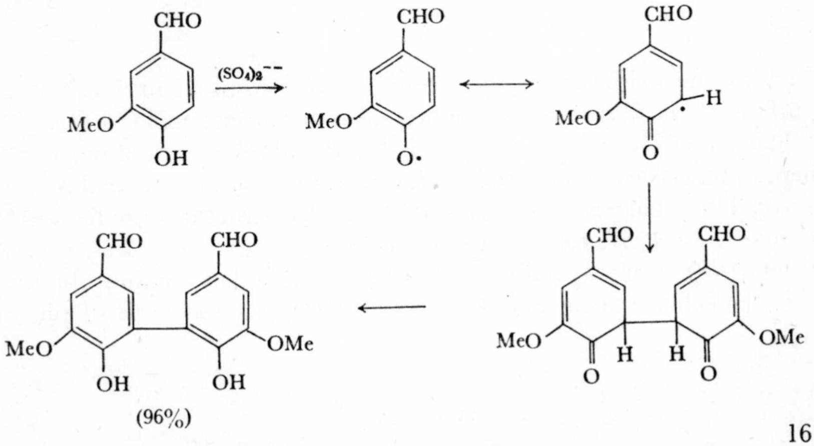

(96%)

Radicals in Synthesis

para-para-Coupling:

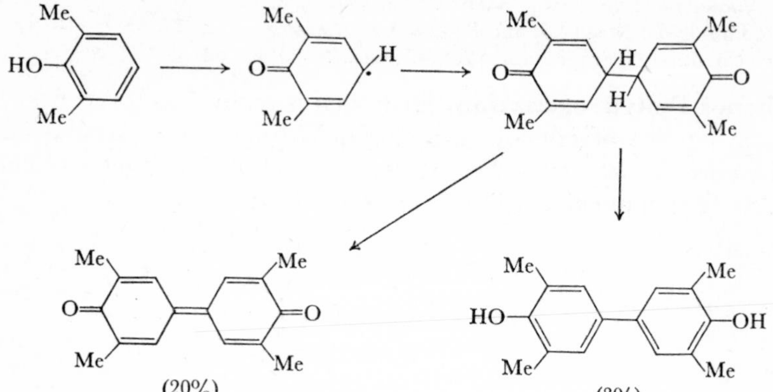

(20%)

(3%)

ortho-para-Coupling:

Barton and his collaborators have shown that 'Pummerer's ketone', obtained by oxidation of *p*-cresol, has structure (*10.14*). Its formation is accounted for by a scheme involving *ortho-para*-coupling of *p*-cresoxy radicals:

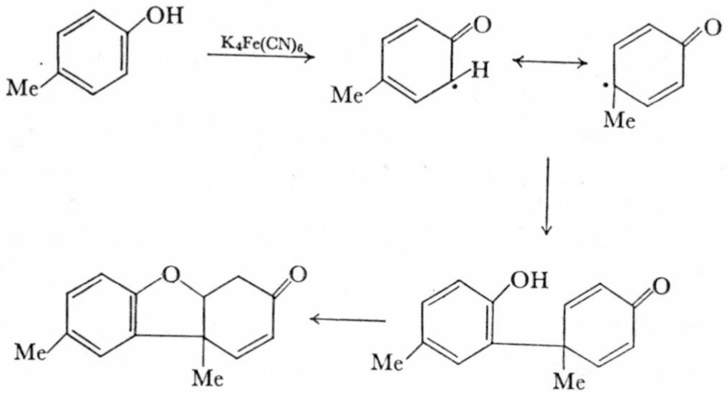

(*10.14*)

Ferricyanide oxidation of the phenol (*10.15*) resulted in a two stage synthesis of the closely related lichen substance, usnic acid (*10.16*).

This type of reaction *in vitro* has led to the development of biogenetic theories based on one-electron oxidation and subsequent radical pairing *in vivo*. These biogenetic theories have enabled structural predictions to be made. In 1957, for example, two possible part-structures, (*10.17*) and (*10.18*), were available for the alkaloid galanthamine obtained from daffodils. Barton and Cohen predicted, on the basis of phenol

162

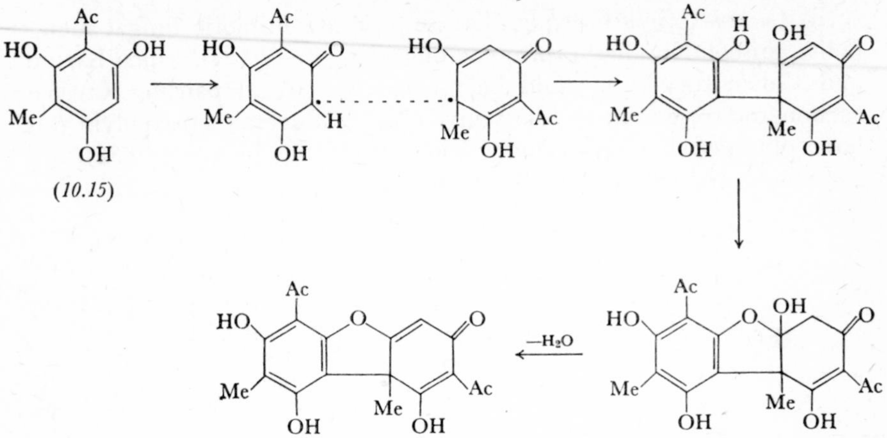

(10.15)

(10.16)

coupling, that structure (*10.19*) was the correct one for the alkaloid. This was later confirmed by degradative studies and subsequently

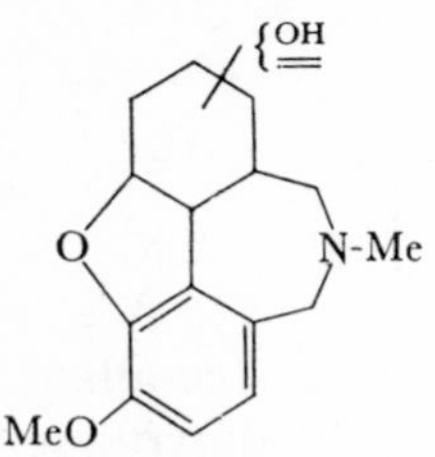

(10.17) 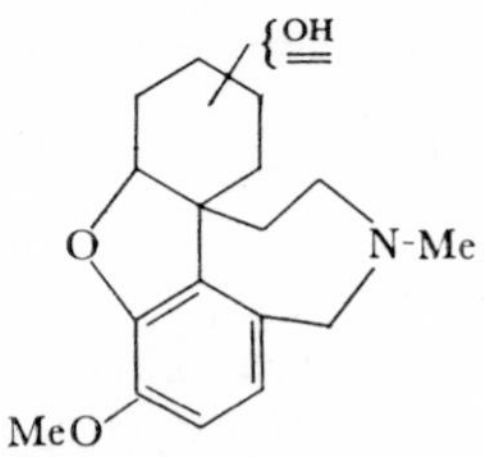   (10.18) 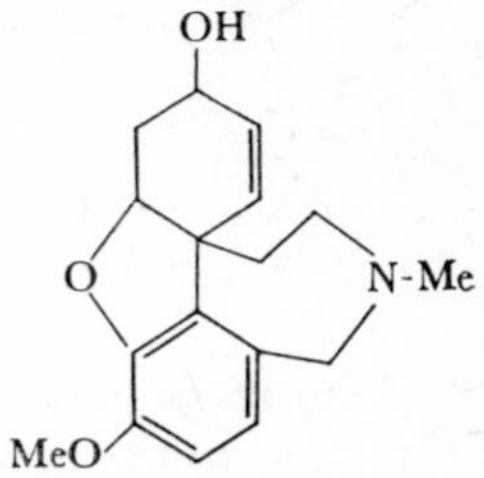   (10.19)

Barton obtained the dehydro-alkaloid narwedine (*10.21*) by oxidation of the phenol (*10.20*). *ortho-para*-Coupling is involved:

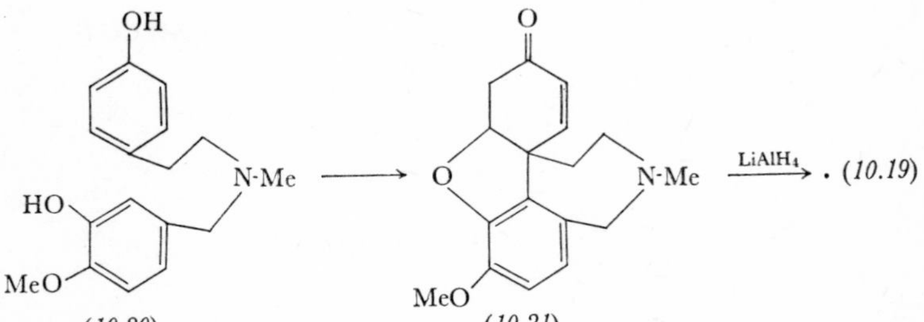

(10.20)   (10.21)

When the phenol (*10.20*), labelled with ^{14}C, was fed to daffodils, radio-active galanthamine was obtained.

163

(ii) *Carbon–Oxygen Coupling*. The important antibiotic fungal metabolite, griseofulvin, has a spiro-ene-one structure (*10.24*), which Barton and Cohen suggested could be formed by radical pairing between carbon and oxygen in the derivative (*10.23*). Racemic griseofulvin was later obtained by ferricyanide oxidation of the phenol (*10.22*) and subsequent reduction of the coupled product.

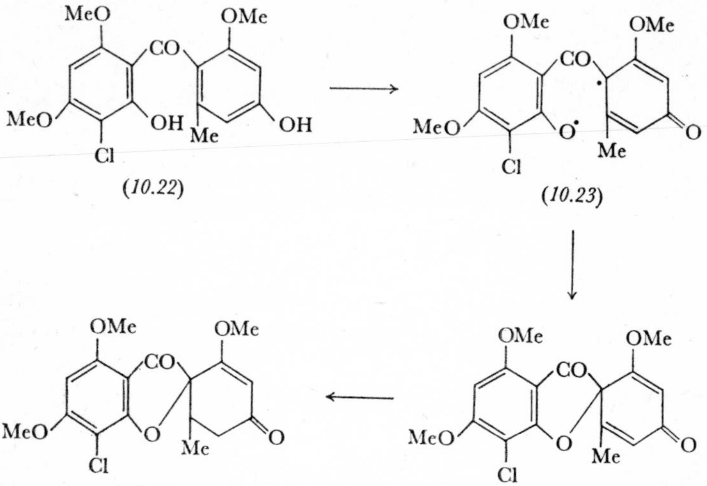

(*10.22*)   (*10.23*)

(*10.24*)

A synthesis of thyroxine (*10.26*) by oxidative carbon–oxygen coupling is related to the above sequence; the starting material is diiodotyrosine (*10.25*):

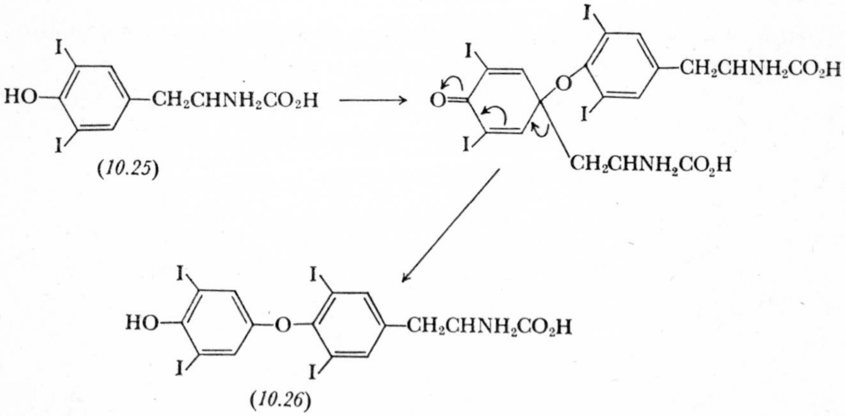

(*10.25*)

(*10.26*)

(iii) *Side-chain Coupling*. Oxidative coupling of phenols is by no means restricted to direct bond formation with aromatic nuclei. A widely

164

distributed group of natural compounds, the lignans, contain the general structure (*10.27*)

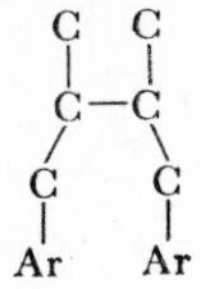

C   C
| |
C—C
| |
C   C
| |
Ar Ar

(*10.27*)

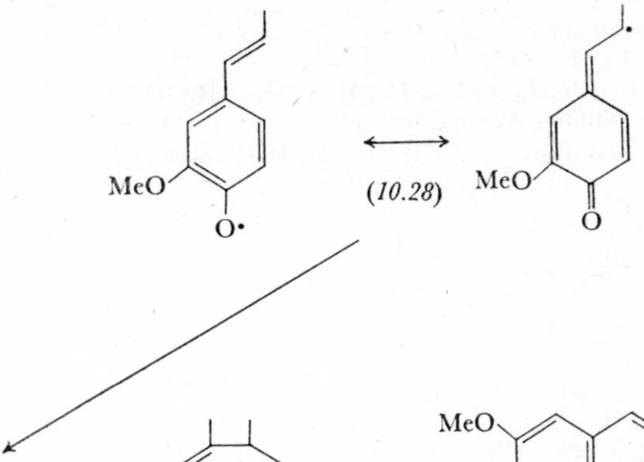

MeO

O·

(*10.28*)   MeO

O

MeO   OMe

O   O

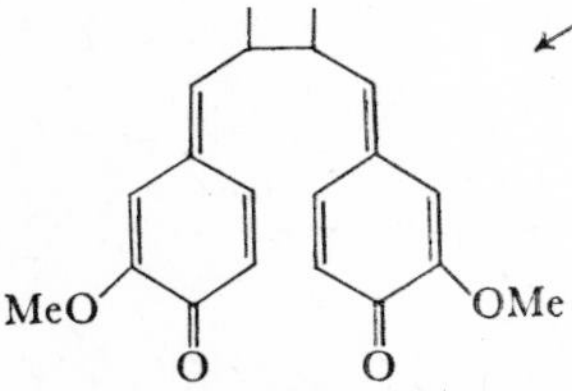

(*10.29*)

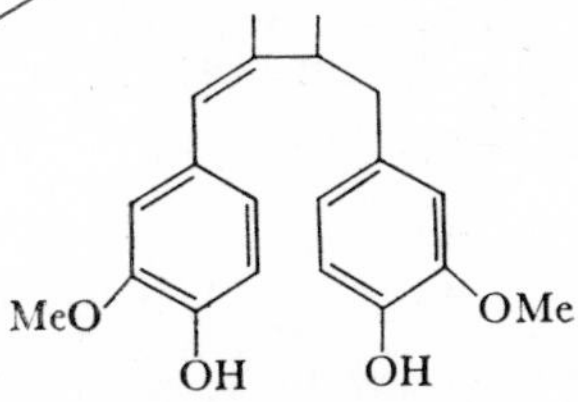

MeO   OMe

OH   OH

(*10.30*)

MeO

HO

MeO

OH

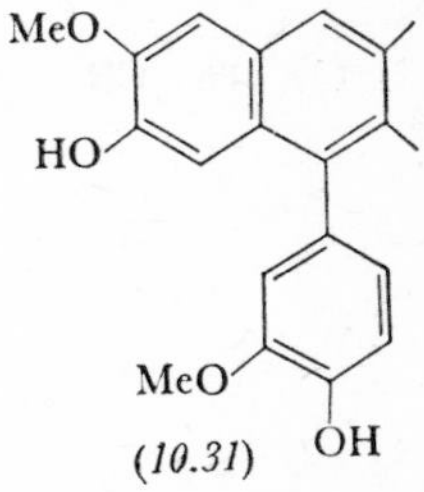

(*10.31*)

An example is guaiaretic acid (*10.30*) which can be derived, in principle, from the oxidation of isoeugenol (cf. *10.28*) *via* (*10.29*). In this case, the unpaired electron may be delocalized in the unsaturated side chain, and radical pairing can occur at side-chain carbon atoms. *In vitro*, the reaction (oxidation with ferric chloride) is more complex, and cyclization of the intermediate follows, with formation of dehydroguaiaretic acid (*10.31*).

Even in this brief survey, the parallelism of biogenetic theory and *in vitro* synthesis will be clear. Many relatively complex biological compounds now appear to be formed by radical pairing, and in many recent instances have been susceptible to a simple synthesis involving dehydrogenation of an appropriate phenol.

For further reading

Numerous references will be found in BARTON, 'The Biogenesis of Phenolic Alkaloids' *Proc. chem. Soc.*, 1963, 293, and LEWIS, *Chem. & Ind.*, 1962, 159.

PROBLEMS

Devise syntheses of the following:

(a) $p\text{-ClC}_6\text{H}_4\text{C}\equiv\text{CPh}$

(b) $\text{Ph(CH}_2)_5\text{NH}_2$

(c) $\text{PhCO(CH}_2)_6\text{CH}=\text{CH(CH}_2)_2\text{CH}=\text{CH(CH}_2)_6\text{COPh}$

(d) 4,6-dimethylphenanthrene

(e) $meso\text{-HO}_2\text{C}-\text{CH}_2\text{CHMeCH}_2\text{CH}_2\text{CHMeCH}_2\text{CO}_2\text{H}$

(f)

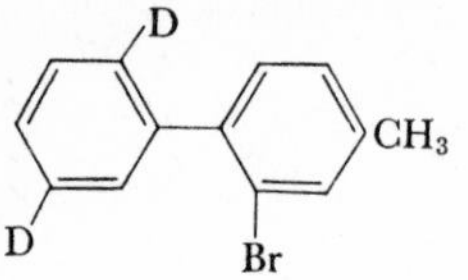

(g)

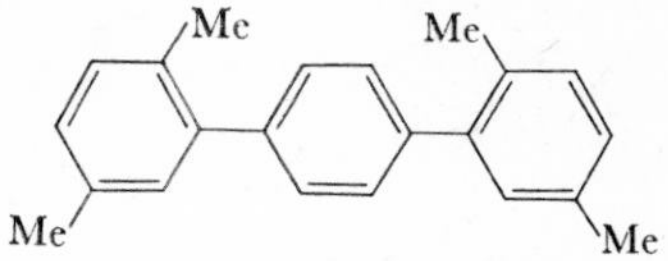

(h) $\text{Ph}-\text{CH}=\text{CH}-$
$-\text{CH}=\text{CH}-\text{Ph}$

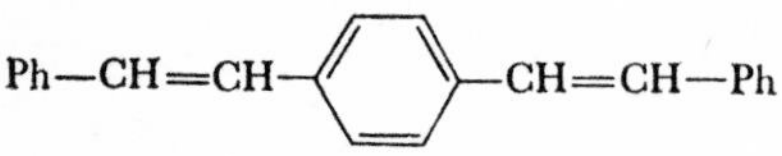

(i)

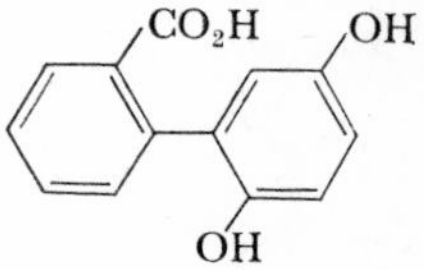

(j)

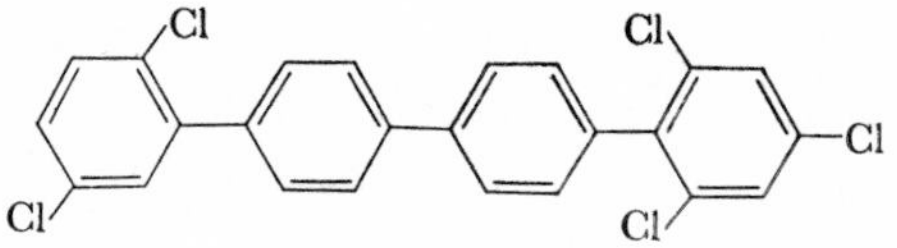

Bond Energy Table

(values of D are given in kcal/mole†)

Carbon–Hydrogen Bonds

CH_3—H	101	$HC{\equiv}C$—H	121
C_2H_5—H	98	$H_2C{=}CH$—H	121
$(CH_3)_2CH$—H	94	$\cdot CH_2$—H	88
$(CH_3)_3C$—H	89	$\cdot CH_2CH_2$—H	40
Ph—H	102	NC—H	114
$PhCH_2$—H	78	OCH—H	76
$PhCH(Me)$—H	75	F_3C—H	103
$PhC(Me)_2$—H	74	Cl_3C—H	90
		$BrCH_2$—H	99

Carbon–Carbon Bonds

CH_3—CH_3	83	CH_3—$\overset{\bullet}{C}O$	17
CH_3—CH_2CH_3	85	F_3C—CF_3	69
CH_3CH_2—CH_2CH_3	78	$PhCH_2$—CH_2Ph	47
CH_3—$CH_2CH{=}CH_2$	62	$PhCH_2$—CH_3	63
CH_3—CHO	75	CH_3—CN	103
CH_3—$COCH_3$	72	$H_2C{=}CH_2$	125

Other Bonds to Carbon

CH_3—F	107	$CH_2{=}CHCH_2$—Br	46
CH_3—Cl	80	$PhCH_2$—Br	51
CH_3—Br	67	CH_3CO—Cl	73
CH_3—I	53	PhCO—Cl	73
Cl_2CH—Cl	72	CH_3—OH	90
F_3C—F	121	CH_3—SH	70
F_3C—Cl	83	CH_3S—CH_3	73
Cl_3C—Cl	68	$PhCH_2$—NH_2	59
Cl_3C—Br	49	$CH_3N{=}N$—CH_3	46
Br_3C—Br	50	CH_3Hg—CH_3	51

Other Bonds

H—H	103	F—F	36		
H—OH	120	Cl—Cl	57		
H—OOH	90	Br—Br	46		
H—SH	90	I—I	36	HO—OH	51
H—F	134			CH_3O—OCH_3	37
H—Cl	103	$N{\equiv}N$	225	t-BuO—Ot-Bu	37
H—Br	87	H_2N—NH_2	60	CH_3COO—$OCOCH_3$	30
H—I	71	O_2N—NO	10	CH_3S—SCH_3	73
H—NH_2	102	CH_3O—NO	36		

---

† Some values are uncertain.

SOURCES

In addition to the sources cited at the end of each chapter, the following books contain valuable information on radical chemistry:

WALLING, *Free Radicals in Solution.* Wiley, 1957.
WATERS, *The Chemistry of Free Radicals.* Oxford, 1948.
LEFFLER, *The Reactive Intermediates of Organic Chemistry.* Interscience, 1956.
HINE, *Physical Organic Chemistry,* 2nd edition. McGraw Hill, 1962.
GOULD, *Mechanism and Structure in Organic Chemistry.* Holt, 1959.
WHELAND, *Advanced Organic Chemistry,* 2nd edition. Wiley, 1949.
STEACIE, *Atomic and Free Radical Reactions.* Reinhold, 1946.

Tabulated data

The information given in tables throughout the book is taken, with the exceptions listed below, from the sources quoted at the end of each chapter and above. In these the original references will be found. In certain tables, the data are taken from several sources and rough corrections for temperature differences between determinations have sometimes been applied. The tables are intended to illustrate points made in the text and should not be treated as collections of precise data; for the latter the original sources should be consulted.

The following tables contain data which may not be readily found in the works already referred to:

Chapter 3, Tables 2 and 4. Data on aromatic nitration:

DE LA MARE and RIDD, *Aromatic Substitution: Nitration and Halogenation.* Butterworths, 1959.

Chapter 4, Table 5:

RUSSELL, *J. Org. Chem.,* 1958, **23**, 1407; HUYSER, *J. Amer. Chem. Soc.,* 1960, **82**, 394.

Chapter 4, Table 6:

RUSSELL, *J. Amer. Chem. Soc.,* 1958, **80**, 4987.

Chapter 4, Table 7:

NEWMAN, *Steric Effects in Organic Chemistry,* p. 145. Wiley, 1956.

Chapter 9, Table 3:

DOERING, BUTTERY, LAUGHLIN and CHAUDHURI, *J. Amer. Chem. Soc.,* 1956, **78**, 3224.

Chapter 9, Table 4:

HEACOCK and EDMISON, *J. Amer. Chem. Soc.,* 1960, **82**, 3460.

Bond Energy Table:

COTTRELL, *The Strengths of Chemical Bonds,* 2nd edition. Butterworths, 1958.

INDEX

Page numbers in **bold** *type indicate principal references.*

169